OPTICAL
INTERFEROMETRY

OPTICAL
INTERFEROMETRY

M. FRANÇON

INSTITUT D'OPTIQUE
PARIS, FRANCE

1966

ACADEMIC PRESS   New York and London

PHYSICS

ACADEMIC PRESS INC.
111 Fifth Avenue, New York, New York 10003

United Kingdom Edition published by
ACADEMIC PRESS INC. (LONDON) LTD.
Berkeley Square House, London W.1

LIBRARY OF CONGRESS CATALOG CARD NUMBER: 66-28312

PRINTED IN THE UNITED STATES OF AMERICA

Preface

The concept of coherence has developed over the years in a way which permits the presentation of interference phenomena in a highly theoretical and fundamental manner. Thus this book begins with a chapter devoted to coherence. The reader will find in this first chapter the necessary background for understanding Chapter VIII on interference and partial coherence, Chapter IX on intensity interferometers, and Chapter X on interference phenomena produced by lasers.

All other chapters have been presented with a rather experimental approach and can be tackled without necessarily going through the first chapter. However, Chapter XII on the interferometric measurement of transfer function and Chapter XIV on interference spectroscopy require some knowledge of Fourier transformations.

The reader who is particularly interested in the experimental aspects of interference phenomena should concentrate on Chapters II–V on two-beam interference, Chapter VI on multiple-beam interference, Chapter VII on polarization interferometers, Chapter XI on the study of wave surfaces, Chapter XIII on thin films, and Chapters XV and XVI which treat the various applications of interferometry. The other chapters can be taken up in a second reading.

I have endeavored to present the material clearly, occasionally sacrificing brevity.

The notation used in Chapters I, VIII, IX, and X is that generally employed by Wolf and Mandel, two important contributors in this subject area.

The manuscript was translated from the French by Dr. I. Wilmanns.

I am thankful to Dr. S. Mallick who has kindly read the proofs.

September 1966
Paris

M. FRANÇON

Contents

Chapter I. Coherence Produced by Thermal Luminous Sources

Chapter II. Interferences of Two Waves by Wavefront Division

Chapter III. Interferences of Two Waves by Amplitude Division

Chapter IV. Two-Beam Interferometers

Chapter V. Standing Waves

Chapter VI. Multiple Beam Interferences

Chapter X. **Interferences with Lasers**

Chapter XI. **Interferential Study of Wavefronts**

Chapter XII. **Interferometric Measurement of the Transfer Function of an Optical Instrument—Noncoherent Illumination**

Chapter XIII. **Thin Films**

Chapter XIV. Interference Spectroscopy

Chapter XV. Application of Interferences for the Measurement of Length

Chapter XVI. Diverse Applications of Interference

Chapter I

Coherence Produced by Thermal Luminous Sources

1.1 Complex Representation of Monochromatic Light Waves

In electromagnetic theory light appears to be the result of the simultaneous propagation of an electric and a magnetic field; vibrations of the electric field represent light vibration in the space in which the light is propagated.

Let us consider an isotropic dielectric medium in which the velocity of propagation of the electric field is equal to v. To simplify, we assume that the light is linearly polarized so that the light waves may be represented by a scalar E. Let x be the abscissa of the vibration at a time t; starting with Maxwell's equations, the equation for the propagation of a plane wave can be derived as

$$\frac{\partial^2 E}{\partial x^2} = \frac{1}{v^2} \frac{\partial^2 E}{\partial t^2}. \tag{1.1}$$

Then, if

$$u = t - \frac{x}{v}, \qquad w = t + \frac{x}{v}, \tag{1.2}$$

(1.1) gives

$$\frac{\partial^2 E}{\partial u \, \partial w} = 0. \tag{1.3}$$

The general solution of (1.3) is

$$E = G(u) + H(w), \tag{1.4}$$

in which G and H are two arbitrary functions. We retain only the function $G(u)$ which represents a vibration propagated toward positive values of x. Maxwell's theory shows in this way that a variable electromagnetic field does not stay localized in a region of space: there is propagation of the electric and the magnetic field. Because the function $G(u)$ is arbitrary, (1.1) does not depend on the law of the variation of the vibration as a function

1

of time. Let us take as the function G a sinusoidal function of time. According to (1.2) and (1.4), the vibration at any given point of the abscissa x is only a function of time which can be written

$$E = a \cos\left[2\pi v\left(t - \frac{x}{v}\right) + \theta\right],$$

(1.5)

where a is the amplitude, θ the phase, and v the frequency of the vibration. In a spherical wave we obtain

$$E = \frac{a}{x} \cos\left[2\pi v\left(t - \frac{x}{v}\right) + \theta\right],$$

where x is the distance of the point under consideration from the wave-center. If T is the period of the vibrations, ω, the angular frequency, and $\lambda_n = vT$, the wavelength of the vibrations, we have

$$v = \frac{\omega}{2\pi} = \frac{1}{T}.$$

(1.6)

If

$$\varphi = \frac{\omega x}{v} = \frac{2\pi x}{vT} = \frac{2\pi x}{\lambda_n},$$

(1.7)

the wavelength λ_n is characteristic of a given radiation in a certain medium. If a given radiation changes its medium, its frequency stays fixed, but its wavelength changes. Radiation can be characterized by its wavelength in vacuo: $\lambda = c/v$, where

$$c = 3.10^8 \text{ meters/sec.}$$

In a medium of index of refraction n, in which the radiation of frequency v is propagated, its wavelength is

$$\lambda_n = \frac{v}{v} = \frac{\lambda v}{c} = \frac{\lambda}{n},$$

(1.8)

and we can write (1.7) as

$$\varphi = \frac{2\pi n x}{\lambda} = \frac{2\pi \delta}{\lambda},$$

(1.9)

where the product $\delta = nx$ is the optical path between the origin and the point on the abscissa x; δ is also called the path difference between these two points and φ is their phase difference. These calculations are simplified by use of complex notation. By neglecting θ in (1.5) we find

$$E = \mathcal{R}\left\{a\exp\left[j2\pi v\left(t - \frac{x}{v}\right)\right]\right\}, \qquad j = \sqrt{-1}, \tag{1.10}$$

in which $\mathcal{R}$ represents the real part of the expression in braces. We may write

$$A = a\exp\left(-j2\pi v\frac{x}{v}\right) = ae^{-j\varphi} \tag{1.11}$$

so that

$$E = \mathcal{R}(Ae^{j2\pi vt}). \tag{1.12}$$

If the operations on E are linear, we can drop the symbol $\mathcal{R}$ and operate directly with the complex function

$$E = Ae^{j2\pi vt}, \tag{1.13}$$

the physical quantity will be the real part of the final expression resulting from the calculation. The complex function

$$A = ae^{-j\varphi} \tag{1.14}$$

is the *complex amplitude* of the vibration.

1.2   Complex Representation of a Nonmonochromatic Vibration: Analytic Signal

In Section 1.1 we discussed a monochromatic vibration, that is, an unlimited vibration $\cos(2\pi vt - \varphi)$. In reality, the electromagnetic waves emitted by the atoms are not unlimited. They are discharged as wavetrains. Because of the finite length of the wavetrains, the radiation emitted by the atoms is not monochromatic but forms a frequency spectrum. A nonmonochromatic vibration can be represented by a complex function, which is a generalization of (1.13).

Let us assume a real, nonmonochromatic vibration

$$V^{(r)}(t) = \int_0^\infty b(v)\cos[2\pi vt - \Phi(v)]\,dv, \tag{1.15}$$

where $b(v)$ and $\Phi(v)$ are real and give the amplitude and phase, respectively, of each monochromatic component of the frequency v. With the real vibration $V^{(r)}(t)$, we associate a second vibration, also real:

$$V^{(i)}(t) = \int_0^\infty b(v)\sin[2\pi vt - \Phi(v)]\,dv, \tag{1.16}$$

4   I   COHERENCE PRODUCED BY THERMAL LUMINOUS SOURCES

and by using Euler's formulas we find

$$V(t) = V^{(r)}(t) + j\,V^{(i)}(t) = \int_0^\infty b(v)e^{j[2\pi vt - \Phi(v)]}\,dv. \qquad (1.17)$$

The complex function $V(t)$ is called the *analytic signal* associated with the real function $V^{(r)}(t)$. This signal contains only positive frequencies, which is advantageous for the representation of a real vibration. The complex representation is used whenever the vibration is not monochromatic. Calculations are performed with (1.17) rather than with (1.15). Equation (1.17) may be expressed in a different way and calculated as follows.

At first, we consider $V^{(r)}(t)$ as given by (1.15). Let $v(v)$ be the Fourier transform of $V^{(r)}(t)$. We then have

$$V^{(r)}(t) = \int_{-\infty}^{+\infty} v(v)e^{j2\pi vt}\,dv. \qquad (1.18)$$

If we split the integral on the right-hand side of (1.18) into two integrals with limits of $-\infty$ to 0 and 0 to $+\infty$ and then replace v with $-v$ in the integral with the limits $-\infty$ to 0, we can write

$$V^{(r)}(t) = \int_0^\infty v(-v)e^{-j2\pi vt}\,dv + \int_0^\infty v(v)e^{j2\pi vt}\,dv. \qquad (1.19)$$

Let Z be a complex number:

$$Z + Z^* = 2\mathscr{R}[Z]. \qquad (1.20)$$

Then

$$v(-v)e^{-j2\pi vt} \quad \text{and} \quad v(v)e^{j2\pi vt}$$

must be conjugate because $V^{(r)}(t)$ is real. We have therefore

$$v(-v) = v^*(v), \qquad (1.21)$$

from which

$$V^{(r)}(t) = \int_0^\infty v^*(v)e^{-j2\pi vt}\,dv + \int_0^\infty v(v)e^{j2\pi vt}\,dv \qquad (1.22)$$

and, according to (1.20),

$$V^{(r)}(t) = 2\mathscr{R}\!\left[\int_0^\infty v(v)e^{j2\pi vt}\,dv\right]. \qquad (1.23)$$

By comparing (1.15) and (1.23) we can see that

$$v(v) = \tfrac{1}{2}b(v)e^{-j\Phi(v)}, \qquad v \geqslant 0. \qquad (1.24)$$

According to (1.24), the analytic signal (1.17) then takes the form

$$V(t) = \int_0^\infty b(v)e^{j[2\pi vt - \Phi(v)]}\,dv = 2\int_0^\infty v(v)e^{j2\pi vt}\,dv. \qquad (1.25)$$

If the operations on $V^{(r)}(t)$ are linear, we can work directly with $V(t)$ and take the real part at the end of the calculation. This real part gives the real vibration according to (1.23).

For nonmonochromatic light we therefore use the expression

$$V(t) = 2\int_0^\infty v(v)e^{j2\pi vt}\,dv. \tag{1.26}$$

1.3 Some Useful Relations

Let $V_1(t)$ and $V_2(t)$ be the analytic signals associated with the real vibrations $V_1^{(r)}(t)$ and $V_2^{(r)}(t)$. We have

$$\int_{-\infty}^{+\infty} V_1(t+\theta)\,V_2{}^*(t)\,dt = \int_{-\infty}^{+\infty} V_2{}^*(t)\left[2\int_0^{+\infty} v_1(v)e^{j2\pi v(t+\theta)}\,dv\right]dt, \tag{1.27}$$

where $V_1(t+\theta)$ has been replaced by its value taken from (1.26). By reversing the order of the integrations we find

$$\int_{-\infty}^{+\infty} V_1(t+\theta)\,V_2{}^*(t)\,dt = 2\int_0^{+\infty} v_1(v)e^{j2\pi v\theta}\left[\int_{-\infty}^{+\infty} V_2{}^*(t)e^{j2\pi vt}\,dt\right]dv. \tag{1.28}$$

Then, according to (1.26),

$$2v_2(v) = \int_{-\infty}^{+\infty} V_2(t)e^{-j2\pi vt}\,dt.$$

It follows that

$$2v_2{}^*(v) = \int_{-\infty}^{+\infty} V_2{}^*(t)e^{j2\pi vt}\,dt, \tag{1.29}$$

so that (1.28) becomes

$$\int_{-\infty}^{+\infty} V_1(t+\theta)\,V_2{}^*(t)\,dt = 4\int_0^{+\infty} v_1(v)\,v_2{}^*(v)e^{j2\pi v\theta}\,dv, \tag{1.30}$$

a relation that will be useful subsequently. We may calculate the convolution of the two functions $V_1^{(i)}(t)$ and $V_2^{(i)}(t)$ as well as the convolution of the functions $V_1^{(r)}(t)$ and $V_2^{(i)}(t)$ or $V_1^{(i)}(t)$ and $V_2^{(r)}(t)$. For the calculation of the convolutions of $V_1^{(i)}(t)$ and $V_2^{(i)}(t)$ it suffices to note that we may pass from $V^{(r)}(t)$ to $V^{(i)}(t)$ by introducing the factor $\exp[j(\pi/2)]$ in the second term of (1.18) because of a phase difference of $\pi/2$ between each component of $V^{(r)}(t)$ and $V^{(i)}(t)$. We now have

$$\int_{-\infty}^{+\infty} V_1^{(r)}(t+\theta)\,V_2^{(r)}(t)\,dt = \int_{-\infty}^{+\infty} V_1^{(i)}(t+\theta)\,V_2^{(i)}(t)\,dt \tag{1.31}$$

and

$$\int_{-\infty}^{+\infty} V_1^{(r)}(t + \theta)\, V_2^{(i)}(t)\, dt = -\int_{-\infty}^{+\infty} V_1^{(i)}(t + \theta)\, V_2^{(r)}(t)\, dt \qquad (1.32)$$

and can calculate the integral

$$\int_{-\infty}^{+\infty} V_1(t + \theta)\, V_2{}^*(t)\, dt. \qquad (1.33)$$

According to (1.17),

$$\int_{-\infty}^{+\infty} V_1(t + \theta)\, V_2{}^*(t)\, dt = \int_{-\infty}^{+\infty} [V_1^{(r)}(t + \theta) + j\, V_1^{(i)}(t + \theta)]$$

$$\times\, [V_2^{(r)}(t) - j\, V_2^{(i)}(t)]\, dt, \qquad (1.34)$$

and by using (1.31) and (1.32) we obtain

$$\int_{-\infty}^{+\infty} V_1(t + \theta)\, V_2{}^*(t)\, dt = 2\int_{-\infty}^{+\infty} V_1^{(r)}(t + \theta)\, V_2^{(r)}(t)\, dt$$

$$-2j\int_{-\infty}^{+\infty} V_1^{(r)}(t + \theta)\, V_2^{(i)}(t)\, dt. \qquad (1.35)$$

This important relation shows that the real part of the convolution of two analytic signals equals, up to a factor of 2, the convolution of the real functions associated with the analytic signals. Let us now set $V_1(t) = V_2(t)$. According to (1.35), we have

$$\int_{-\infty}^{+\infty} V_1(t + \theta)\, V_1{}^*(t)\, dt = 2\int_{-\infty}^{+\infty} V_1^{(r)}(t + \theta)\, V_1^{(r)}(t)\, dt$$

$$-2j\int_{-\infty}^{+\infty} V_1^{(r)}(t + \theta) V_1^{(i)}(t)\, dt. \qquad (1.36)$$

Now (1.32) gives

$$\int_{-\infty}^{+\infty} V_1^{(r)}(t + \theta)\, V_1^{(i)}(t)\, dt = -\int_{-\infty}^{+\infty} V_1^{(i)}(t + \theta)\, V_1^{(r)}(t)\, dt, \qquad (1.37)$$

and for $\theta = 0$

$$\int_{-\infty}^{+\infty} V_1^{(r)}(t)\, V_1^{(i)}(t)\, dt = 0. \qquad (1.38)$$

This relation shows that the functions $V^{(r)}(t)$ and $V^{(i)}(t)$ are orthogonal. We now set $\theta = 0$ in (1.36).

$$\int_{-\infty}^{+\infty} V_1(t)\, V_1{}^*(t)\, dt = 2\int_{-\infty}^{+\infty} V_1^{(r)2}(t)\, dt\,; \qquad (1.39)$$

hence the time integral of the square of the modulus of the analytic signal is equal to twice the time integral of the real function with which the analytic signal is associated. If we add $\theta = 0$ to (1.30), we obtain the relations

$$\int_{-\infty}^{+\infty} V(t)\, V^*(t)\, dt = 2\int_{-\infty}^{+\infty} |v(v)|^2\, dv = 4\int_{0}^{\infty} |v(v)|^2\, dv$$

$$= 2\int_{-\infty}^{+\infty} V^{(r)2}(t)\, dt = 2\int_{-\infty}^{+\infty} V^{(i)2}(t)\, dt. \quad (1.40)$$

1.4 Case of Quasi-monochromatic Light

We now consider the analytic signal associated with a real vibration (1.26).

$$V(t) = 2\int_{0}^{\infty} v(v)e^{j2\pi vt}\, dv. \quad (1.41)$$

Introducing a mean frequency v_0 around which the frequencies v are distributed, we have

$$V(t) = 2e^{j2\pi v_0 t}\int_{0}^{\infty} v(v)e^{j2\pi(v - v_0)t}\, dv. \quad (1.42)$$

We define a new function $a(t)$ such that

$$a(t) = 2\int_{0}^{\infty} v(v)e^{j2\pi(v - v_0)t}\, dv. \quad (1.43)$$

Because $a(t)$ is normally complex, we may write it in the form

$$a(t) = A(t)e^{-j\Phi(t)}. \quad (1.44)$$

The analytic signal (1.42) is written

$$V(t) = a(t)e^{j2\pi v_0 t}. \quad (1.45)$$

If the Fourier transform $v(v)$ of $V^{(r)}(t)$ differs from zero only for the values of v near v_0, the integral (1.43) represents a superposition of harmonic components of the frequencies $v - v_0$, that is, of low frequencies. Moreover, if the interval $\Delta v = v - v_0$ over which $v(v)$ differs from zero is small with respect to the mean frequency v_0, the term $\exp[j2\pi(v - v_0)t]$ varies slowly in comparison to $\exp(j2\pi v_0 t)$ in the course of time. In this case we say that the light being emitted by the source is quasi-monochromatic light. In (1.45) the variations of $a(t)$ in time are slow with respect to the oscillatory term $\exp(j2\pi v_0 t)$. The function $a(t)$ is the instantaneous complex amplitude of the vibration. We can consider (1.45) as a monochromatic vibration with variable amplitude $a(t)$ and a frequency equal to the mean frequency v_0. Obviously, for thermal sources $a(t)$ varies extremely fast in comparison with our means of observation. If we replace the value of $a(t)$ given by (1.44) in (1.45), we have

$$V(t) = A(t)e^{-j\Phi(t)}e^{j2\pi v_0 t} ; \qquad (1.46)$$

hence the real vibration

$$V^{(r)}(t) = A(t)\cos[2\pi v_0 t - \Phi(t)], \qquad (1.47)$$

and we see that $A(t)$ is the envelope of the real vibration.

1.5   Relation between the Length of the Wavetrains and the Bandwidth of the Emitted Radiations: Coherence Length and Coherence Time

We know that the waves emitted by the atoms are not infinite waves. They are discharged as wavetrains. Experiments show that the coherence of two light beams which may interfere is linked with the duration and consequently with the length of the wavetrains; but the length of the wavetrains determines the bandwidth of the radiations emitted by the atoms. A wavetrain that is very weakly damped is almost a sinusoidal oscillation and therefore monochromatic. A highly damped wavetrain corresponds to a simple nonharmonic oscillation and as a consequence to a nonmonochromatic radiation.

Let $V^{(r)}(t)$ be a vibration at a given point at a time t, caused by a single wavetrain.

The real vibration can be represented by the integral (1.18).

$$V^{(r)}(t) = \int_{-\infty}^{+\infty} v(v)e^{j2\pi vt} \, dv. \qquad (1.48)$$

The Fourier transform $v(v)$ of $V^{(r)}(t)$ is given by

$$v(v) = \int_{-\infty}^{+\infty} V^{(r)}(t)e^{-j2\pi vt} \, dt. \qquad (1.49)$$

In general, a large number of wavetrains arrive at the detector during the time necessary for an observation. In a first example let us assume that all the wavetrains have the same duration τ during which $V^{(r)}(t)$ is a simple harmonic of the frequency v_0:

$$V^{(r)}(t) = \cos 2\pi v_0 t, \qquad |t| \leqslant \frac{\tau}{2},$$

$$V^{(r)}(t) = 0, \qquad |t| > \frac{\tau}{2}. \qquad (1.50)$$

According to (1.49), the Fourier transform of $V^{(r)}(t)$ is given by

$$v(v) = \tfrac{1}{2}\int_{-\tau/2}^{+\tau/2} (e^{j2\pi v_0 t} + e^{-j2\pi v_0 t})e^{-j2\pi v t}\, dt$$

or

$$v(v) = \frac{\tau}{2}\frac{\sin \pi(v_0 - v)\tau}{\pi(v_0 - v)\tau} + \frac{\tau}{2}\frac{\sin \pi(v_0 + v)\tau}{\pi(v_0 + v)\tau}. \qquad (1.51)$$

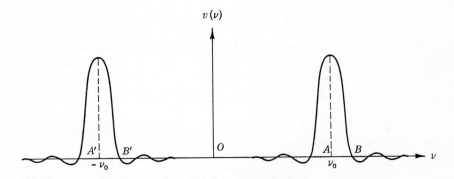

FIG. 1.1   Fourier transform of a finite sinusoidal vibration.

Figure 1.1 shows the curve representing the variations of $v(v)$ as a function of v. The interval Δv of the frequencies between A and B is given by

$$\Delta v = v_0 - v = \frac{1}{\tau}. \qquad (1.52)$$

If the light is quasi-monochromatic, $OA \gg AB$; that is, $\Delta v \ll v_0$. The spectrum therefore is narrow enough to prevent the two terms on the right-hand side of (1.51) from overlapping.

Starting with (1.51) and using (1.48), we can re-establish the form of the vibration $V^{(r)}(t)$. We set

$$v(v_0 - v) = \frac{\sin \pi(v_0 - v)\tau}{\pi(v_0 - v)\tau}, \qquad v(v_0 + v) = \frac{\sin \pi(v_0 + v)\tau}{\pi(v_0 + v)\tau},$$

and have

$$V^{(r)}(t) = \frac{\tau}{2}\int_{-\infty}^{+\infty} v(v_0 - v)e^{j2\pi v t}\, dv + \frac{\tau}{2}\int_{-\infty}^{+\infty} v(v_0 + v)e^{j2\pi v t}\, dv.$$

We can write

$$V^{(r)}(t) = \frac{\tau}{2}\int_{-\infty}^{0} v(v_0 - v)e^{j2\pi vt}\, dv + \frac{\tau}{2}\int_{0}^{\infty} v(v_0 - v)e^{j2\pi vt}\, dv$$

$$+ \frac{\tau}{2}\int_{-\infty}^{0} v(v_0 + v)e^{j2\pi vt}\, dv + \frac{\tau}{2}\int_{0}^{\infty} v(v_0 + v)e^{j2\pi vt}\, dv.$$

In the first and the third integrals we change v into $-v$ and also the order of the integration to obtain

$$V^{(r)}(t) = \tau\int_{0}^{\infty} [v(v_0 + v) + v(v_0 - v)]\cos 2\pi vt\, dv.$$

If the spectrum is sufficiently narrow so that $v(v_0 + v)$ and $v(v_0 - v)$ do not overlap, we can write

$$V^{(r)}(t) \simeq \tau\int_{0}^{\infty} v(v_0 - v)\cos 2\pi vt\, dv. \qquad (1.53)$$

By comparison with (1.15) the distribution of energy in the spectrum of the vibration $V^{(r)}(t)$ is given by

$$b^2(v) = \tau^2\left[\frac{\sin \pi(v_0 - v)\tau}{\pi(v_0 - v)\tau}\right]^2. \qquad (1.54)$$

The width of the spectral band can be characterized by the interval $AB = \Delta v$. According to (1.52), we see that the spectral bandwidth is of the order of the inverse of the duration of a wavetrain. The time τ is called *coherence time*. For the best monochromatic thermal sources the coherence time is of the order of 10^{-8} sec, whereas for lasers it can be of the order of 10^{-2} sec. Let

$$l = c\tau, \qquad (1.55)$$

where c is the speed of light. With $\lambda = c/v$, we have

$$\Delta\lambda = \frac{c\,\Delta v}{v^2} = \Delta v\frac{\lambda^2}{c},$$

and if λ_0 is the mean wavelength, which corresponds to v_0,

$$l = \frac{c}{\Delta v} = \frac{\lambda_0^2}{\Delta\lambda}, \qquad (1.56)$$

in which l is the coherence length. We shall see later (Section 1.12) why l and τ are called coherence length and coherence time.

As a second example we take a damped harmonic vibration with the damping constant τ. The vibration is of the form

$$V^{(r)}(t) = e^{-t/\tau} \cos 2\pi v_0 t, \qquad t > 0. \tag{1.57}$$

According to (1.49), the Fourier transform is given by

$$v(v) = \int_0^\infty e^{-t/\tau} \cos 2\pi v_0 t e^{-j2\pi vt}\, dt . \tag{1.58}$$

We have

$$v(v) = \tfrac{1}{2}\int_0^\infty e^{-t/\tau} e^{j2\pi(v_0 - v)t}\, dt + \tfrac{1}{2}\int_0^\infty e^{-t/\tau} e^{-j2\pi(v_0 + v)t}\, dt. \tag{1.59}$$

It follows that

$$v(v) = \frac{1}{2}\left[\frac{1}{\tau} - j2\pi(v_0 - v)\right]^{-1} + \frac{1}{2}\left[\frac{1}{\tau} + j2\pi(v_0 + v)\right]^{-1}. \tag{1.60}$$

As in the preceding calculations, we can re-establish the vibration by using (1.48) and (1.60):

$$V^{(r)}(t) = \frac{1}{2}\int_{-\infty}^{+\infty}\frac{e^{j2\pi vt}\, dv}{1/\tau - j2\pi(v_0 - v)} + \frac{1}{2}\int_{-\infty}^{+\infty}\frac{e^{j2\pi vt}\, dv}{1/\tau + j2\pi(v_0 + v)}.$$

We set

$$\rho e^{j\theta} = \frac{1}{\tau} - j2\pi(v_0 - v), \qquad \rho' e^{j\theta'} = \frac{1}{\tau} + j2\pi(v_0 + v).$$

We split each integral into two integrals with the limits 0 and $+\infty$. In the first and third integrals we change v into $-v$. Since we have

$$\frac{1}{\tau} - j2\pi(v_0 + v) = \rho' e^{-j\theta'}, \qquad \frac{1}{\tau} + j2\pi(v_0 - v) = \rho e^{-j\theta},$$

we obtain

$$V^{(r)}(t) = \int_0^\infty \left[\frac{\cos(2\pi vt - \theta')}{\rho'} + \frac{\cos(2\pi vt - \theta)}{\rho}\right] dv; \tag{1.61}$$

if the spectrum is narrow, the first term is almost negligible compared with the second (in the neighborhood of $v = v_0$), and we have

$$V^{(r)}(t) \simeq \int_0^\infty \frac{\cos(2\pi vt - \theta)}{\rho}\, dv.$$

The spectral distribution of the energy is therefore given by

$$b^2(v) = \frac{1}{\rho^2} = \left[\frac{1}{\tau^2} + 4\pi^2(v_0 - v)^2\right]^{-1}. \qquad (1.62)$$

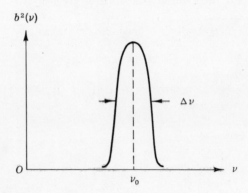

FIG. 1.2   Spectrum of a decaying sinusoidal vibration.

Figure 1.2 shows the variations of $b^2(v)$ as a function of v. If we characterize the spectral bandwidth Δv by the width that corresponds to one half the maximum ordinate τ^2,

$$\left[\frac{1}{\tau^2} + 4\pi^2(v_0 - v)^2\right]^{-1} = \frac{\tau^2}{2},$$

from which

$$(v_0 - v)^2 = \left(\frac{\Delta v}{2}\right)^2 = \frac{1}{4\pi^2\tau^2}$$

and

$$\Delta v = \frac{1}{\pi\tau}. \qquad (1.63)$$

Once again we obtain the same result: the spectral bandwidth is inversely proportional to the damping constant (coherence time), that is, to the average length of the wavetrain (coherence length).

Let us obtain an order of magnitude of the coherence length $l = c\tau$. According to (1.56) and (1.63), we have here

$$l = \frac{c}{\pi\,\Delta v} = \frac{\lambda_0^2}{\pi\,\Delta\lambda}; \qquad (1.64)$$

for a bandwidth $\Delta\lambda = 300$ Å we find

$$l = \frac{(0.546)^2}{3.14 \times 0.03} = 3.2 \, \mu.$$

For the most monochromatic thermal sources the coherence length is of the order of magnitude of 1 meter. In lasers it may reach and even surpass hundreds of kilometers.

In the two preceding examples we have assumed that all the wavetrains emitted by the source were identical, which is not the case in reality. The atoms disturb one another and the wavetrains are irregularly modified. In addition, the spectral lines are widened by other phenomena (e.g., the Doppler effect). We can therefore define only the mean values of the duration of the wavetrains and the spectral width Δv.

Nevertheless, those mean values satisfy relations of the type (1.52) and (1.63).

1.6   Variation of the Complex Amplitude of the Vibration during the Duration of a Wavetrain

A monochromatic vibration characterized by the frequency v_0 can be written in complex form (1.5):

$$V(t) = \exp j \left[2\pi v_0 \left(t - \frac{x}{v} \right) + \theta \right]. \tag{1.65}$$

If once again we use the notation in (1.45), we shall see that in monochromatic vibration the complex amplitude $a(t)$ is constant and that it

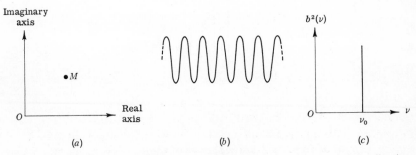

FIG. 1.3   Complex amplitude of an infinite sinusoidal vibration. Spectrum of the vibration.

can be represented in the complex plane by a point M (Fig. 1.3a). Figure 1.3b shows the spatial or time representation of the real vibration $V^{(r)}(t)$; Fig. 1.3c is the spectrum.

The vibrations emitted by atoms cannot be sinusoidal (or eternal), for they are, in reality, interrupted or disturbed by shocks or damped by the loss of energy by radiation. Let us assume that the vibration emitted by an atom has the form (1.65) but that it is interrupted after a certain time τ. In the complex plane the amplitude is still represented by M during the vibration (Fig. 1.4a). Figures 1.4b and 1.4c represent the real vibration and the corresponding spectrum.

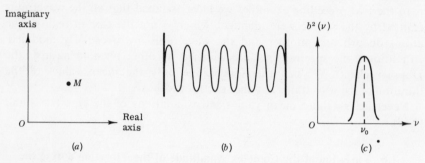

FIG. 1.4   Complex amplitude of a finite sinusoidal vibration. Spectrum of the vibration.

Let us consider a vibration of the complex form (1.57)

$$V(t) = e^{-t/\tau}e^{j(2\pi v_0 t + \theta)}.\tag{1.66}$$

By comparison with (1.45) we see that

$$a(t) = e^{-t/\tau}e^{j\theta}.\tag{1.67}$$

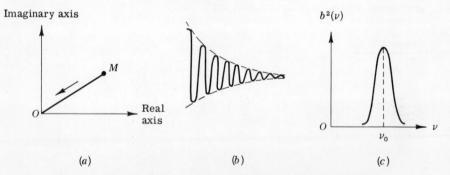

FIG. 1.5   Complex amplitude of a decaying sinusoidal vibration. Spectrum of the vibration.

In the complex plane (Fig. 1.5a) the complex amplitude $a(t)$ approaches zero by following the straight line OM without rotation (θ has a determined value for each wavetrain). Figures 1.5b and 1.5c illustrate the vibration and its spectrum.

Let us show by numerical example that in quasi-monochromatic light the variations of the complex amplitude $a(t)$ are slow in relation to the oscillatory term $\exp(j2\pi v_0 t)$.

By taking a radiation of wavelength $\lambda = 0.5\,\mu$ and of spectral bandwidth $\Delta\lambda = 0.5 \times 10^{-2}$ Å, which correspond to a very fine line, we have according to (1.64)

$$\tau = \frac{\lambda^2}{\pi c\,\Delta\lambda} = 0.5 \cdot 10^{-9}\,\text{sec}.$$

Since the period T of the vibrations is

$$T = \frac{\lambda}{c} = 1.6 \cdot 10^{-15}\,\text{sec},$$

we have

$$\frac{\tau}{T} \simeq 300{,}000.$$

Therefore during the time $\tau = 0.5 \times 10^{-9}$ sec the complex amplitude $a(t)$ given by (1.67) varies little but $3 \cdot 10^5$ periods of the vibration will have taken place.

Let us now consider the Doppler effect. An apparent variation of the frequency δv is due to the speed v_0 of the atom in relation to the observer. This fractional change in frequency is given by

$$\frac{\delta v}{v} = \frac{v_0}{C}. \tag{1.68}$$

According to (1.45), the atom seems to emit the vibration

$$V(t) = a(t)e^{j2\pi(v_0 + \delta v)t}, \tag{1.69}$$

in which $a(t)$ is a complex amplitude whose variations are relatively slow

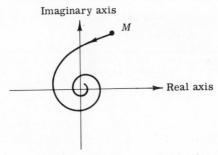

FIG. 1.6   Variation of the complex amplitude of a vibration in presence of the Doppler effect.

in comparison to the variations of the oscillatory term of the frequency v_0. In a damped vibration (1.67) we have

$$V(t) = e^{-t/\tau}e^{j\theta}e^{j2\pi(v_0 + \delta v)t} = a_0(t)e^{j2\pi v_0 t} \tag{1.70}$$

with

$$a_0(t) = e^{-t/\tau}e^{j(\theta + 2\pi\delta vt)}. \tag{1.71}$$

The phase of the complex amplitude $a_0(t)$ varies in time, and on the complex plane we have the curve of Fig. 1.6. Finally, in the general case, in which the vibration is disturbed by the neighboring atoms, the complex amplitude may vary in a very complicated manner, and we have a curve analogous to that of Fig. 1.7.

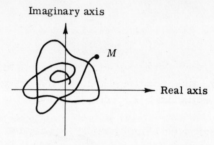

FIG. 1.7   Variation of the complex amplitude of a vibration in the general case.

1.7   Successive Wavetrains Emitted by an Atom

For thermal light sources the times τ are in general very small in relation to the time necessary to make an observation. During the time of one observation, therefore, the complex amplitude $a(t)$ will assume a large number of values which are distributed at random. In limited sinusoidal vibration (Fig. 1.4) we have a large number of points distributed at random (Fig. 1.8). In damped harmonic vibrations segments of straight lines,

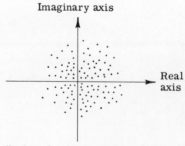

FIG. 1.8   Complex amplitudes of a large number of sinusoidal wavetrains emitted at random.

which are distributed at random (Fig. 1.9), pass through the origin. Finally, for vibrations in general we have a large number of curves of a type analogous to those of Fig. 1.7, but none of which bears any relation to the other.

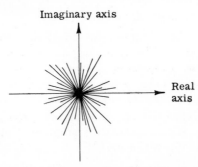

Imaginary axis

Real axis

FIG. 1.9 Complex amplitudes of a large number of decaying sinusoidal wavetrains emitted at random.

In general the detector will receive only an average of the effects produced by the different values of $a(t)$. (We consider here a detector with a resolution time that is large compared to τ.)

We assume that the atom emits complex vibrations $V_1(t), V_2(t),\ldots$ at times $t_1, t_2,\ldots$ distributed at random. The expressions $V_1(t), V_2(t),\ldots$ are analytic signals associated with real vibrations. The vibration emitted at time t_1 is represented by $V_1(t - t_1)$ at time t. In the same way for other wavetrains and the complex vibration that leaves the atom at time t we can write

$$V(t) = V_1(t - t_1) + V_2(t - t_2). \tag{1.72}$$

The phase of each wavetrain is variable and there is no phase relation between the different wavetrains. According to (1.26), for each wavetrain we have

$$v(v) = v_1(v)e^{-j2\pi vt_1} + v_2(v)e^{-j2\pi vt_2} + \cdots \tag{1.73}$$

from which

$$V(t) = 2\int_0^\infty [v_1(v)e^{-j2\pi vt_1} + v_2(v)e^{-j2\pi vt_2} + \cdots]e^{j2\pi vt}\, dv. \tag{1.74}$$

If we set

$$V_1(t - t_1) = 2\int_0^\infty v_1(v)e^{j2\pi v(t - t_1)}\, dv, \tag{1.75}$$

we find

$$V(t) = 2\int_0^\infty v(v)e^{j2\pi vt}\, dv. \tag{1.76}$$

The two expressions (1.76) and (1.26) are identical. The complex vibration $V(t)$, given by one or the other of these expressions can represent a succession of wavetrains emitted by an atom. Because all of these wavetrains are incoherent, it makes little difference whether they are emitted by one atom or by a number of atoms. The complex vibration $V(t)$, given by (1.26) or (1.76), can represent the vibration emitted at the time t by an extended incoherent source. Besides, $V(t)$ represents a nonmonochromatic vibration. Consequently, we can characterize the vibration emitted by an extended incoherent and nonmonochromatic source by the complex vibration $V(t)$. If the light is quasi-monochromatic, we can use the expressions (1.44) and (1.45). The detector, the eye or a photoelectric cell, for example, is sensitive only for the square of $V^{(2)}(t)$. The intensity of the phenomenon is therefore characterized by the mean

$$\overline{V^{(r)2}(t)} = \lim_{T \to \infty} \frac{1}{2T} \int_{-T}^{+T} V^{(r)2}(t) \, dt, \qquad (1.77)$$

where T is the time necessary to make one observation. Now T is in general very large in comparison to the coherence time. Therefore we can write

$$\overline{V^{(r)2}(t)} \simeq \frac{1}{2T} \int_{-\infty}^{+\infty} V^{(r)2}(t) \, dt, \qquad (1.78)$$

but if the integral (1.77) tends toward a finite limit when $T \to \infty$ the integral $\int_{-\infty}^{+\infty} V^{(r)2}(t) \, dt$ is divergent. The difficulty is removed by considering the truncated function $V_T^{(r)}(t)$ equal to $V^{(r)}(t)$ in the interval $-T, T$ and identically zero outside this interval. In the following we assume this by keeping the notation $V^{(r)}(t)$. According to (1.40), we have

$$\overline{V^{(r)2}(t)} = \tfrac{1}{2} \overline{V(t)V^*(t)} = \overline{V^{(i)2}(t)}. \qquad (1.79)$$

As we stated earlier, if the operations on $V^{(r)}(t)$ are linear, we can perform the calculations with $V(t)$ and take the real part at the end of the calculation. The relations (1.79) are important. They show that we can calculate the mean of the square of the real vibration (the light intensity) by means of the complex vibration associated with it.

1.8   Coherence of the Vibrations

We consider the complex vibrations $V_1(t)$ and $V_2(t)$ emitted by two point sources, M_1 and M_2 (Fig. 1.10). These vibrations are superposed at P and we calculate the luminous intensity at this point. For the moment we will not specify the nature of these two sources. It is possible that there is a relation between the vibrations emitted by these two sources; for example, because they are two images of the same source. In the opposite case the two sources can be independent. The vibrations $V_1(t)$ and $V_2(t)$ are considered at the time they leave the two sources. If θ_1 and θ_2 are the times taken by the vibrations to travel the distances M_1P and M_2P (for one frequency),

$$\theta_1 = \frac{M_1P}{v}, \qquad \theta_2 = \frac{M_2P}{v}, \tag{1.80}$$

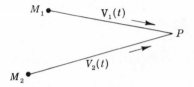

FIG. 1.10   Coherence of two vibrations, $V_1(t)$ and $V_2(t)$ at P.

where v is the speed of the light. If $v(M_1, v)$ is the Fourier transformation of the vibration at M_1, we can write the vibration at M_1 in the form (1.76):

$$V_1(t) = 2\int_0^\infty v(M_1, v)e^{j2\pi vt}\,dv.$$

When the vibration $V_1(t)$ emitted by M_1 arrives at P it has traveled along a path M_1P which can be characterized for each frequency by a complex number

$$g(v)e^{-j2\pi v\theta_1},$$

where $g(v)$ determines the ratio of the amplitudes at M_1 and P for the frequency v. The Fourier transformation of the vibration at P is given by

$$v(M_1, v)\,g(v)e^{-j2\pi v\theta_1},$$

according to which the vibration at P at time t is

$$V_P(t) = 2\int_0^\infty v(M_1, v)\,g(v)e^{j2\pi v(t-\theta_1)}\,dv.$$

In order to simplify, we assume a homogeneous transparent medium with an index of refraction equal to 1. If I_1 and I_2 are the intensities of M_1 and M_2, the intensities in P due to the two sources which act independently are $I_1/(M_1P)^2$ and $I_2/(M_2P)^2$. Therefore we may consider these two quantities as constants in the phenomena that we shall study later on. It should be noted that the variations of M_1P and M_2P play a fundamental role. However, because we are interested only in the relative values, we shall assume for the time being that $g(v) = 1$ for the two paths M_1P and M_2P. Thus we have

$$V_P(t) = 2\int_0^\infty v(M_1, v)e^{j2\pi v(t-\theta_1)}\, dv = V_1(t - \theta_1),$$

which states simply that the vibration at P at the time t is the same as at M_1 at the time $t - \theta_1$. The time θ_1 does not depend on v, for there is no dispersion. We still do the same for the vibration $V_2(t)$ emitted by M_2. Under these conditions we can write the complex vibration at P at time t:

$$V(t) = V_1(t - \theta_1) + V_2(t - \theta_2). \tag{1.81}$$

According to (1.79), the observable intensity I at P is given as

$$I = \overline{V(t)\, V^*(t)} = 2\overline{V^{(r)2}(t)}, \tag{1.82}$$

from which

$$I = \overline{[V_1(t - \theta_1) + V_2(t - \theta_2)][V_1^*(t - \theta_1) + V_2^*(t - \theta_2)]} \tag{1.83}$$

or

$$I = \overline{V_1(t - \theta_1)\, V_1^*(t - \theta_1)} + \overline{V_2(t - \theta_2)\, V_2^*(t - \theta_2)}$$

$$+ \overline{V_1(t - \theta_1)\, V_2^*(t - \theta_2)} + \overline{V_2(t - \theta_2)\, V_1^*(t - \theta_1)}.$$

Since the light waves are considered stationary, we can change the time origin in all the terms:

$$\overline{V_1(t - \theta_1)\, V_1^*(t - \theta_1)} = \overline{V_1(t)\, V_1^*(t)},$$

$$\overline{V_2(t - \theta_2)\, V_2^*(t - \theta_2)} = \overline{V_2(t)\, V_2^*(t)}.$$

If we set

$$\theta = \theta_2 - \theta_1, \tag{1.84}$$

we find

$$\overline{V_1(t - \theta_1)\, V_2^*(t - \theta_2)} = \overline{V_1(t + \theta)\, V_2^*(t)},$$

$$\overline{V_1^*(t - \theta_1)\, V_2(t - \theta_2)} = \overline{V_1^*(t + \theta)\, V_2(t)}.$$

The two expressions $V_1(t + \theta)\, V_2^*(t)$ and $V_1^*(t + \theta)\, V_2(t)$ are conjugate; therefore

$$V_1(t + \theta)\, V_2^*(t) + V_1^*(t + \theta)\, V_2(t) = 2\mathscr{R}[V_1(t + \theta)\, V_2^*(t)].$$

Hence the intensity at P is

$$I = \overline{V_1 V_1^*} + \overline{V_2 V_2^*} + 2\mathscr{R}\left[\overline{V_1(t+\theta)\,V_2^*(t)}\right]. \tag{1.85}$$

The quantities $\overline{V_1 V_1^*}$ and $\overline{V_2 V_2^*}$ are the energies emitted by M_1 and M_2. With the hypotheses made, these quantities are the intensities in P if M_1 and M_2 act separately. Let

$$I_1 = \overline{V_1 V_1^*}, \quad I_2 = \overline{V_2 V_2^*}. \tag{1.86}$$

We then have

$$I = I_1 + I_2 + 2\mathscr{R}\left[\overline{V_1(t+\theta)\,V_2^*(t)}\right]. \tag{1.87}$$

The quantity

$$\Gamma_{12}(\theta) = \overline{V_1(t+\theta)\,V_2^*(t)} \tag{1.88}$$

is called *mutual coherence* of the vibrations emitted by M_1 and M_2; the vibrations at M_1 are considered a moment later than at M_2. We normalize $\Gamma_{12}(\theta)$; the quantity

$$\gamma_{12}(\theta) = \frac{\Gamma_{12}(\theta)}{\sqrt{I_1}\,\sqrt{I_2}} = \frac{\overline{V_1(t+\theta)\,V_2^*(t)}}{\sqrt{(V_1 V_1^*)}\,\sqrt{(V_2 V_2^*)}}$$

$$\gamma_{12}(\theta) = \frac{\overline{V_1(t+\theta)\,V_2^*(t)}}{\sqrt{I_1}\,\sqrt{I_2}} \tag{1.89}$$

is called the *complex degree of coherence* of the vibrations. Equation (1.87) then becomes

$$I = I_1 + I_2 + 2\sqrt{I_1}\,\sqrt{I_2}\,\mathscr{R}[\gamma_{12}(\theta)]. \tag{1.90}$$

This fundamental expression shows that in order to determine the light intensity at P when two light waves are superposed at this point we must determine the intensity due to each source acting separately and the real part of the complex degree of coherence. If $\Phi'(\theta)$ is the argument of the complex quantity $\gamma_{12}(\theta)$, we can write

$$\gamma_{12}(\theta) = |\gamma_{12}(\theta)|e^{j\Phi'(\theta)}. \tag{1.91}$$

Let us consider a mean frequency ν_0: we can set

$$\Phi'(\theta) = \alpha(\theta) + 2\pi\nu_0\theta,$$

from which

$$\mathscr{R}[\gamma_{12}(\theta)] = |\gamma_{12}(\theta)| \cos[\alpha(\theta) + 2\pi\nu_0\theta]. \tag{1.92}$$

The relations (1.80) and (1.84) give

$$\theta = \frac{M_1P - M_2P}{c}.$$

To this value of θ corresponds a phase difference

$$\varphi(\nu_0) = 2\pi\nu_0\theta.$$

By inserting (1.92) in (1.90) we have

$$I = I_1 + I_2 + 2\sqrt{I_1}\sqrt{I_2}|\gamma_{12}(\theta)| \cos[\alpha(\theta) + 2\pi\nu_0\theta]. \tag{1.93}$$

The quantity $|\gamma_{12}(\theta)|$ is called the degree of coherence of the vibrations. According to an inequality, after Schwarz,

$$|\gamma_{12}(\theta)| \leqslant 1,$$

the degree of coherence may vary between 0 and 1. If $|\gamma_{12}(\theta)| = 0$, (1.93) becomes

$$I = I_1 + I_2. \tag{1.94}$$

The vibrations add up in intensity at P, and we say that the vibrations are incoherent. If $|\gamma_{12}(\theta)| = 1$, we have

$$I = I_1 + I_2 + 2\sqrt{I_1}\sqrt{I_2} \cos[\alpha(\theta) + 2\pi\nu_0\theta]. \tag{1.95}$$

The variations of the intensity I are a function of θ only. When $\cos[\alpha(\theta) + 2\pi\nu_0\theta] = 1$ we have

$$I = (\sqrt{I_1} + \sqrt{I_2})^2, \tag{1.96}$$

and if $\cos[\alpha(\theta) + 2\pi\nu_0\theta] = -1$

$$I = (\sqrt{I_1} - \sqrt{I_2})^2. \tag{1.97}$$

Hence in certain cases the resulting amplitude at P equals the sum of the amplitudes (vibration in phase); in others it can be equal to the difference of the amplitudes (vibrations in phase opposition). When $|\gamma_{12}(\theta)| = 1$, we say that the vibrations are coherent. If $0 < |\gamma_{12}(\theta)| < 1$, the vibrations are partially coherent and $|\gamma_{12}(\theta)|$ is their degree of coherence. In summing up, we call

(1) $\Gamma_{12}(\theta) = \overline{V_1(t + \theta) V_2{}^*(t)}$ the mutual coherence of the vibrations,

(2) $\gamma_{12}(\theta) = \dfrac{\Gamma_{12}(\theta)}{\sqrt{(V_1 V_1{}^*)}\sqrt{(V_2 V_2{}^*)}} = \dfrac{\Gamma_{12}(\theta)}{\sqrt{I_1}\sqrt{I_2}}$ the complex degree of coherence of the vibrations,

(3) $0 \leqslant |\gamma_{12}(\theta)| \leqslant 1$ the degree of coherence of the vibrations.

When the two vibrations V_1 and V_2 are superposed at P, the intensity I is given by any one of the expressions (1.87), (1.90), or (1.93). Let us return now to (1.85) and give it another form. According to (1.40),

$$\overline{V_1 V_1{}^*} = \frac{1}{T}\int_{-\infty}^{+\infty} |v(M_1, v)|^2 \, dv, \tag{1.98}$$

$$\overline{V_2 V_2{}^*} = \frac{1}{T}\int_{-\infty}^{+\infty} |v(M_2, v)|^2 \, dv. \tag{1.99}$$

Hence from (1.30) and (1.88)

$$\Gamma_{12}(\theta) = \overline{V_1(t + \theta) V_2{}^*(t)} = \frac{2}{T}\int_{0}^{+\infty} v(M_1, v)v^*(M_2, v)e^{j2\pi v\theta} \, dv. \tag{1.100}$$

By substituting (1.98), (1.99) and (1.100) into (1.85) we obtain, up to a constant factor,

$$I = \int_{0}^{+\infty} |v(M_1, v)|^2 \, dv + \int_{0}^{+\infty} |v(M_2, v)|^2 \, dv$$

$$+ 2\mathscr{R}\left[\int_{0}^{+\infty} v(M_1, v)\, v^*(M_2, v)e^{j2\pi v\theta} \, dv\right]. \tag{1.101}$$

According to (1.100), we see that if the vibrations V_1 and V_2 are incoherent we have

$$I = \int_{0}^{+\infty} |v(M_1, v)|^2 \, dv + \int_{0}^{+\infty} |v(M_2, v)|^2 \, dv. \tag{1.102}$$

1.9   Coherence of Vibrations Originating from Two Atoms

We assume that the two sources M_1 and M_2 are two atoms. In this case series of wavetrains are emitted by two independent sources. According to (1.75), if N and N' are the numbers of wavetrains emitted by the two sources and arriving on the detector during the time of one observation, we have

$$v(M_1, v) = \sum_{n=1}^{N} v_n(v)e^{-j2\pi vt_n},$$

$$v(M_2, v) = \sum_{m=1}^{N'} v_m'(v)e^{-j2\pi vt_m'}.$$

(1.103)

We use (1.103) to evaluate the third term on the right-hand side of (1.101). If J_n and J_m' are the moduli of $v_n(v)$ and $v_m'^*(v)$ and α_{nm} is the argument of the product $v_n(v) v_m'^*(v)$ we obtain

$$v(M_1, v) v^*(M_2, v) = \sum_{n=1}^{N} \sum_{m=1}^{N'} v_n(v) v_m'^*(v)e^{-j2\pi v(t_n - t_m')}$$

(1.104)

$$v(M_1, v) v^*(M_2, v) = \sum_{n=1}^{N} \sum_{m=1}^{N'} J_n J_m'\{\cos[2\pi v(t_n - t_m') - \alpha_{nm}]$$

$$+ j \sin[2\pi v(t_n - t_m') - \alpha_{nm}]\}.$$

(1.105)

Because we are dealing with two independent sources, the angles $2\pi v(t_n - t_m') - \alpha_{nm}$ which appear in (1.105) take on all the possible values, and the sums of the sines and the cosines are separately equal to zero. Thus we have

$$v(M_1, v)v^*(M_2, v) = 0,$$

and, according to (1.100) and (1.89),

$$\Gamma_{12}(\theta) = \overline{V_1(t + \theta) V_2^*(t)} = 0$$

and

$$\gamma_{12}(\theta) = 0.$$

(1.106)

Therefore the vibrations emitted by two atoms are incoherent. The expressions (1.87) and (1.90) are reduced to

$$I = I_1 + I_2$$

and, according to (1.101),

$$I = \int_0^{+\infty} |v(M_1, v)|^2 \, dv + \int_0^{+\infty} |v(M_2, v)|^2 \, dv.$$

(1.107)

The monochromatic components that originate from two atoms are incoherent and add their intensities. The vibrations that originate from two atoms are incoherent even if the two atoms emit on the same frequency.

A monochromatic filter that transmits only the frequency v_0 would give

$$I = |v(M_1, v_0)|^2 + |v(M_2, v_0)|^2. \tag{1.108}$$

1.10   Coherence of the Vibrations of Different Frequencies Originating from One Atom

We now assume that the two vibrations ending at P (Fig. 1.11) originate from the same atom M. Some instrument, not shown in Fig. 1.11, divides one incident wave into two waves, which follow two different paths (1) and (2). The two waves are then recombined so that they are superposed at P. If θ_1 and θ_2 are the times taken by the vibrations to traverse the two paths, the vibration at P at time t is written

$$V(t - \theta_1) + V(t - \theta_2).$$

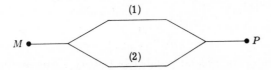

FIG. 1.11   Coherence of vibrations at P when emitted by an atom M.

The wavetrains that follow path (1) are displaced only with respect to the wavetrains that follow path (2). We now consider two monochromatic filters; one placed in path (1) transmits the frequency v; the other in path (2) transmits the frequency v'. We have

$$v(M, v) = v_1(v)e^{-j2\pi v t_1} + \cdots,$$
$$v(M, v') = v_1(v')e^{-j2\pi v' t_1} + \cdots. \tag{1.109}$$

The times $t_1, t_2, \ldots$ are the same for these two expressions because they are the instants at which the wavetrains are being emitted by the atom. The expression (1.104) becomes

$$v(M, v)\, v^*(M, v') = \sum_{n=1}^{N} \sum_{m=1}^{N} v_n(v)\, v_m{}^*(v')e^{-j2\pi(v t_n - v' t_m)}. \tag{1.110}$$

The angles $v t_n$ and $v' t_m$ are still arbitrary, and thus the sums of the sines and the cosines are equal to zero. We have

$$v(M, v)\, v^*(M, v') = 0.$$

The expression (1.101) is written

$$I = |v(M, v)|^2 + |v(M, v')|^2. \tag{1.111}$$

This expression shows that for observations for which the time is very long compared to the duration of the wavetrains the different frequencies originating from the same atom are incoherent and add their intensities.

1.11   Coherence of the Vibrations of the Same Frequency Emitted by One Atom: Interferences

If we consider the vibrations of the same frequency emitted by one atom, which traveled along different paths, the two expressions (1.109) are identical. We have

$$v(M, v) \, v^*(M, v) = \sum_{n=1}^{N} \sum_{m=1}^{N} v_n(v) \, v_m^*(v) e^{-j2\pi v(t_n - t_m)}, \qquad (1.112)$$

in which the times t_n and t_m are still arbitrary and the sums of sines and cosines are equal to zero, but the terms $m = n$ remain:

$$v(M, v) \, v^*(M, v) = \sum_{n=1}^{N} v_n(v) \, v_n^*(v) = \sum_{n=1}^{N} |v_n(v)|^2 = I_0(v). \qquad (1.113)$$

The third term of the second number of (1.101) is now written ($v_1 = v_2$):

$$2\mathscr{R}\left[\int_0^{+\infty} v(v) \, v^*(v) e^{j2\pi v\theta} \, dv\right] = 2\mathscr{R}\left[\int_0^{+\infty} I_0(v) e^{j2\pi v\theta} \, dv\right]$$

$$= 2\int_0^{+\infty} I_0(v) \cos 2\pi v\theta \, dv. \qquad (1.114)$$

If δ represents the path difference of two vibrations, one having traveled along path (1) and the other along path (2) (both vibrations having originated from one initial vibration), we have

$$2\pi v\theta = \frac{2\pi v\delta}{c} = \frac{2\pi \delta}{\lambda} = \varphi(v, \theta), \qquad (1.115)$$

where λ is the wavelength and c, the speed of light in vacuo. The expression (1.114) is written

$$2\int_0^{+\infty} I_0(v) \cos \varphi(v, \theta) \, dv,$$

from which, by substituting in (1.101), we obtain

$$I(\theta) = 2\int_0^{+\infty} I_0(v)[1 + \cos \varphi(v, \theta)] \, dv. \qquad (1.116)$$

In monochromatic light we would have, up to a constant factor,

$$I = \cos^2 \frac{\varphi}{2}. \qquad (1.117)$$

The expressions (1.116) and (1.117) show that vibrations of the same frequency, emitted by the same atom, are coherent. The intensity at an arbitrary point P, at which the vibrations are superposed, is a function of the phase difference φ, and we say that there is interference of the vibrations in P.

1.12   Time Coherence and Spatial Coherence

Let us consider an atom M which emits wavetrains (Fig. 1.12). At A a device divides the incident wave into two waves which follow paths (1) and (2) and are superposed on each other at P. We allow that during the time of observation a large number of wavetrains will pass through P at arbitrary time intervals. Each incident wavetrain arriving at A is divided into two wavetrains. Let us assume that the difference between the two paths (1) and (2) is larger than the length of the wavetrains. At the moment when the wavetrain following path (1) arrives at P the other is between B and P. These two wavetrains do not meet. The wavetrains that meet at P originate from two different incident wavetrains, which have no correlation, for the different wavetrains emitted by the atom have no phase relation. There is temporary incoherence, resulting here from the finite length of the wavetrains, which means from the emission not of a single frequency but of a spectrum of frequencies by the atom. If θ is the difference in travel time for paths (1) and (2), the mutual coherence of the vibrations emitted by M is given by (1.88), which is written

$$\Gamma(\theta) = \overline{V(t + \theta)\, V^*(t)}. \tag{1.118}$$

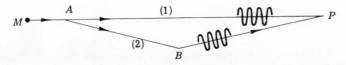

FIG. 1.12   Temporal coherence at P.

This is the autocorrelation function of $V(t)$. It has a maximum for $\theta = 0$ and represents the energy emitted by M. It decreases with θ, and for $\theta \gg \tau$ (coherence time) the two vibrations $V(t + \theta)$ and $V^*(t)$ no longer have any relation to one another. The mutual coherence $\Gamma(\theta)$ becomes equal to zero, because, for a given value of $V(t + \theta)$, the vibration $V^*(t)$ is represented by two opposite points on the complex plane. We have

$$\Gamma(\theta) = \overline{V(t + \theta)\, V^*(t)} = 0 \qquad \text{if} \quad \theta \gg \tau. \tag{1.119}$$

When θ is of the order of τ, the two wavetrains originating from the same initial wavetrain cover each other. The correlation between these two wavetrains remains the same for the other wavetrains arriving at P. There is temporary partial coherence.

We now turn from the atom that emits nonmonochromatic light (limited wavetrains) to consider instead an extended source that emits light in a narrow spectral region.

Let S be the source that illuminates two points T_1 and T_2 (Fig. 1.13). An atom A_1 of S' sends coherent vibrations to T_1 and T_2. Because these two points are not at the same distance from A, the vibrations arriving in T_1 and T_2 have a phase difference φ_1. For atom A_2 the vibrations arriving in T_1 and T_2 have a phase difference φ_2, and so on for all the other atoms. It should be noted that there is no relation between the phases $\varphi_1, \varphi_2, \ldots$. These phases are numerous because all sources, even a point source in the optical sense, contain a large number of atoms. In any case, if the differences $A_1T_2 - A_1T_1$ are smaller than the wavelength, the phase differences $\varphi_1, \varphi_2, \ldots$ will always be small and the points T_1 and T_2 will receive the vibrations from each atom practically in phase. The vibratory states in T_1 and T_2 will be the same, whether the two points are illuminated by one atom or by all atoms in S. The degree of coherence at the two points T_1 and T_2, which are illuminated by S', is equal to 1, and we say that there is spatial coherence.

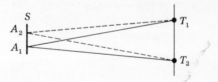

FIG. 1.13   Coherence of points T_1 and T_2 illuminated by source S.

We now enlarge the source so that the differences $A_2T_2 - A_1T_1$ take on arbitrary values, which are not small compared to the wavelength. The vibration $V_1(t)$ in T_1, produced by S at time t, is no longer the same as the vibration $V_2(t)$ in T_2, produced at the same time by S. Points T_1 and T_2 have a mutual coherence defined by

$$\Gamma_{12}(0) = \overline{V_1(t)\,V_2{}^*(t)},$$

which diminishes in comparison with the preceding case, and from the spatial viewpoint the coherence is partial. If we continue to increase the dimensions of the source, a stage is reached when $\Gamma_{12}(0) = 0$, and points T_1 and T_2 are incoherent.

Thus we see that temporal coherence is measured by the autocorrelation function $\Gamma(\theta)$ and spatial coherence by the mutual coherence function $\Gamma_{12}(0)$.

1.13   General Conditions for the Possibility of Interference among the Wavetrains. A Case in Which a Large Number of Wavetrains Arrives on the Detector during the Time Necessary for One Observation

In Section 1.12 we considered thermal sources that emit a large number of wavetrains during the time necessary to make one observation. Under these conditions we can observe interference phenomena only if the superposed vibrations originate from the same light source. We have seen that two vibrations are coherent if they originate from the same atom and have the same frequency (Section 1.11) and that with a single source each atom of the source will contribute to the vibrations under consideration. Spatial and temporal coherence may result.

An interference instrument then appears as a wave divider. It divides the incident wave into two or more waves which, after having traveled along different paths, are superposed and give rise to interference phenomena.

Furthermore, we know that two perpendicular vibrations result in an elliptical vibration, the energy of which is equal to the sum of the energies of the two composing rectangular vibrations and does not depend on their phase. Consequently, under the conditions formulated, we will have interference if (a) the vibrations originate from a single source and have a sufficient degree of coherence, and (b) the vibrations are parallel.

1.14   Interference Fringes of Two Waves. Contrast of Fringes in Quasi-monochromatic Light

Let us take a source S (Fig. 1.14) and consider two rays, A_1 and A_2, emitted by a point M of the source. These rays travel along different paths and recombine in P. Each vibration emitted by M gives rise to two vibrations which travel along the paths $(MA_1A_1'P)$ and $(MA_2A_2'P)$. In studying

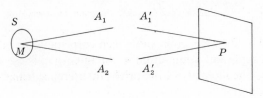

FIG. 1.14   Contrast of fringes produced by source S at P.

the interferences of these two vibrations in P, we say that we are considering the phenomena of the interference of two waves. According to (1.91), and by choosing a mean frequency v_0, we can write (1.100) in the form

$$\Gamma_{12}(\theta) = |\Gamma_{12}(\theta)|e^{j[\alpha(\theta) + 2\pi v_0\theta]} = \frac{2}{T} e^{j2\pi v_0\theta}\int_0^{+\infty} v(M_1, v)\, v^*(M_2, v)e^{j2\pi(v - v_0)\theta}\, dv.$$

(1.120)

Hence, if $v \simeq v_0$ (quasi-monochromatic light), the integral (1.120) contains only low-frequency terms; $|\Gamma_{12}(\theta)|$ and $|\gamma_{12}(\theta)|$ vary slowly with respect to the oscillatory term $e^{j2\pi v_0\theta}$, that is, with respect to $\cos 2\pi v_0\theta$ and $\sin 2\pi v_0\theta$. We concede that if point P is moved in the region of the plane in which the phenomenon is observed $|\gamma_{12}(\theta)|$ will remain almost constant. Furthermore, we can assume for many phenomena that in this region I_1 and I_2 (1.93) are constants. With these hypotheses, the variations of intensity I given by (1.93) depend only on the variations of $\alpha(\theta) + 2\pi v_0\theta$. Intensity I is a maximum if

$$\cos[\alpha(\theta) + 2\pi v_0\theta] = +1, \quad \alpha(\theta) + 2\pi v_0\theta = 2K\pi.$$

The curves $\alpha(\theta) + 2\pi v_0\theta = $ constant, which correspond to integer values of K: 0, 1, 2, 3,..., are curves along which the luminous intensity is at a maximum (Fig. 1.15). These are bright interference fringes, and the number K, which is attached to each curve, is the order of the fringe. The curves that correspond to a minimum of the intensity are given by

$$\cos[\alpha(\theta) + 2\pi v_0\theta] = -1, \quad \alpha(\theta) + 2\pi v_0\theta = (2K + 1)\pi.$$

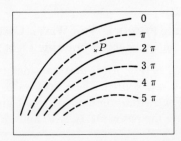

FIG. 1.15   Interference fringes in the plane of observation.

The curves $\alpha(\theta) + 2\pi v_0\theta = $ constant, which correspond to integer values of K: 0, 1, 2,..., represent a minimum of the intensity. These are dark interference fringes. The intensity of the bright interference fringes is given by

$$I_{max} = I_1 + I_2 + 2\sqrt{I_1}\,\sqrt{I_2}\,|\gamma_{12}(\theta)|,$$

(1.121)

and the intensity of the dark fringes by

$$I_{\min} = I_1 + I_2 - 2\sqrt{I_1}\sqrt{I_2}\,|\gamma_{12}(\theta)|. \qquad (1.122)$$

We define the contrast of the fringes by the ratio

$$\gamma = \frac{I_{\max} - I_{\min}}{I_{\max}} \qquad (1.123)$$

if $I_{\min} = 0$; that is, if the dark fringes are perfectly black, we have $\gamma = 1$ and the contrast of the phenomenon has a maximum. If $I_{\max} = I_{\min}$, $\gamma = 0$, the contrast is zero and the phenomenon disappears. According to (1.121) and (1.122), we see that the contrast is given by

$$\gamma = \frac{4\sqrt{I_1}\sqrt{I_2}|\gamma_{12}(\theta)|}{I_1 + I_2 + 2\sqrt{I_1}\sqrt{I_2}|\gamma_{12}(\theta)|}. \qquad (1.124)$$

Hence the contrast of the fringes, that is, the visibility of the phenomenon, is linked with the degree of coherence of the vibrations. If the vibrations are perfectly coherent,

$$|\gamma_{12}(\theta)| = 1$$

and (1.124) is written

$$\gamma = \frac{4\sqrt{I_1}\sqrt{I_2}}{(\sqrt{I_1} + \sqrt{I_2})^2}, \qquad (1.125)$$

which is equal to 1 if $I_1 = I_2$. If the degree of partial coherence equals 1, the relation (1.93) becomes

$$I = I_1 + I_2 + 2\sqrt{I_1}\sqrt{I_2}\cos[\alpha(\theta) + 2\pi\nu_0\theta]. \qquad (1.126)$$

We can then set $\alpha(\theta) = 0$ and, according to (1.115), we have

$$2\pi\nu_0\theta = \varphi(\theta),$$

from which

$$I = I_1 + I_2 + 2\sqrt{I_1}\sqrt{I_2}\cos\varphi. \qquad (1.127)$$

This is Fresnel's classical formula.

1.15 A Case in Which $\theta \ll \tau$. The Source Emits Quasi-monochromatic Light

Let us take θ much smaller than the coherence time τ. According to the definition of τ (Section 1.5) and θ (Section 1.11), this condition can now be written $\delta \ll l$. The path difference of the vibrations which interfere in P

must be much smaller than the coherence length l (length of the wavetrains). Therefore

$$|\gamma_{12}(\theta)| \simeq |\gamma_{12}(0)| \tag{1.128}$$

and the intensity I is given by

$$I = I_1 + I_2 + 2\sqrt{I_1}\sqrt{I_2}|\gamma_{12}(0)|\cos[\alpha(\theta) + 2\pi v_0 \theta]. \tag{1.129}$$

Equation 1.129 can be used if two conditions are fulfilled: (a) the light is quasi-monochromatic (which allows us to assume that $|\gamma_{12}(\theta)| = $ constant), and (b) the path difference δ is much smaller than the length of the wavetrains [which permits us to write $|\gamma_{12}(\theta)| \simeq |\gamma_{12}(0)|$]. According to (1.124), we can express the contrast of the fringes as

$$\gamma = \frac{4\sqrt{I_1}\sqrt{I_2}|\gamma_{12}(0)|}{I_1 + I_2 + 2\sqrt{I_1}\sqrt{I_2}|\gamma_{12}(0)|}, \tag{1.130}$$

and if $I_1 = I_2$ we have

$$\gamma = \frac{2|\gamma_{12}(0)|}{1 + |\gamma_{12}(0)|}. \tag{1.131}$$

1.16   Phenomena of Beats Obtained with Different Optical Frequencies

In Section 1.15 we stated that the vibrations of different frequencies are incoherent. Under certain conditions, however, we can produce observable beat frequencies. These are the phenomena we shall study now.

Let us consider a real vibration $V^{(r)}(t)$ which arrives on a detector (e.g., a photomultiplier). *The current $i(t)$ which we obtain is proportional to $V^{(r)2}(t)$.* Let $U(v)$ be the Fourier transform of $V^{(r)2}(t)$:

$$V^{(r)2}(t) = \int_{-\infty}^{+\infty} U(v)e^{j2\pi vt}\,dv. \tag{1.132}$$

We calculate the Fourier transform $U(v)$ by means of the Fourier transform $v(v)$ of $V^{(r)}(t)$, and, according to (1.18), we have

$$U(v) = \int_{-\infty}^{+\infty} V^{(r)2}(t)e^{-j2\pi vt}\,dt = \int_{-\infty}^{+\infty} V^{(r)}(t)\left[\int_{-\infty}^{+\infty} v(v')e^{j2\pi v't}\,dv'\right]e^{-j2\pi vt}\,dt$$

$$U(v) = \int_{-\infty}^{+\infty} v(v')\left[\int_{-\infty}^{+\infty} V^{(r)}(t)e^{-j2\pi(v-v')t}\,dt\right]dv',$$

from which

$$U(v) = \int_{-\infty}^{+\infty} v(v')\,v(v - v')\,dv'. \tag{1.133}$$

The Fourier transform $U(v)$ of $V^{(r)2}(t)$ is given by the convolution of the function $v(v)$ with itself. The spectral energy distribution of $i(t)$ is given by $|U(v)|^2$ up to a constant factor. Let us take a simple example in which the source emits limited sinusoidal wavetrains of a duration τ. We consider a source that emits two series of wavetrains: wavetrains of a frequency v_1 and wavetrains of a frequency v_2. According to (1.51), the emitted spectrum is

$$v(v) = \frac{\tau}{2} \frac{\sin \pi(v - v_1)\tau}{\pi(v - v_1)\tau} + \frac{\tau}{2} \frac{\sin \pi(v + v_1)\tau}{\pi(v + v_1)\tau}$$

$$+ \frac{\tau}{2} \frac{\sin \pi(v - v_2)\tau}{\pi(v - v_2)\tau} + \frac{\tau}{2} \frac{\sin \pi(v + v_2)\tau}{\pi(v + v_2)\tau}. \tag{1.134}$$

We assume that the spectrum is formed by two well-separated quasi-monochromatic spectral bands; that is, the four terms of the second member of (1.134) do not interact with one another. In order to simplify, we limit each term of the second member of (1.134) to $2/\tau$. Under these conditions we have four identical peaks (Fig. 1.16), two of which correspond to positive frequencies v_1 and v_2, and two to negative frequencies $-v_1$ and $-v_2$. Let us now determine the spectrum $U(v)$ of the current $i(t)$.

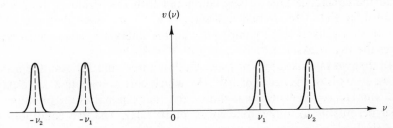

FIG. 1.16 Fourier transform when the source emits vibrations with frequencies v_1 and v_2.

According to (1.133), we must perform the convolution of the function $v(v)$ with itself. We outline Fig. 1.16 on tracing paper and then move the tracing to the right. For each position on the tracing we measure the area held in common by the two figures. The result is given by Fig. 1.17. By squaring this result we have the spectral distribution of the energy in the current $i(t)$, which consists of five peaks. The first peak (frequency zero) corresponds to the direct current furnished by the photomultiplier and which is the one always considered in experiments. The other four peaks correspond to oscillatory components of frequencies $v_2 - v_1$, $2v_1$, $v_1 + v_2$, and $2v_2$. In consideration of the order of magnitude of the luminous frequencies, it is not possible to observe the frequencies $2v_1$, $v_1 + v_2$, and $2v_2$. The frequency $v_2 - v_1$, however, may fall in the domain of radio-frequencies and consequently may be observable.

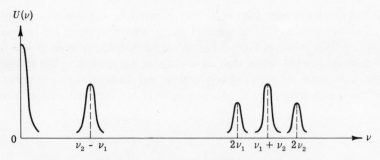

FIG. 1.17   Beats produced by two optical frequencies ν_1 and ν_2.

The phenomenon of beating, realized with optical frequencies, was observed for the first time by Forrester, Gudmundsen, and Johnson in 1955. In this experiment the two frequencies were obtained by Zeeman effect, starting from the mercury line at 5461 Å. According to the preceding discussion, beats are produced if (a) the coherence time is long compared with the period of the beats, and (b) the detector (photomultiplier) has a resolution time that is small compared with the period of the beats. That the coherence time is long compared with the period of the beats is verified in Fig. 1.16. Actually, $\tau \gg (\nu_2 - \nu_1)^{-1}$ indicates that the width $2/\tau$ of each peak is small compared with the interval $\nu_2 - \nu_1$ which separates the two peaks.

In the two rays used by Forrester, Gudmundsen, and Johnson the period of the beats is of the order of 10^{10} Hz, which corresponds to a wavelength of 3 cm. Hence the experiment shows that the response of the photomultiplier permits us to follow frequencies of 10^{10} Hz. The two conditions (a) and (b) lead us to the conclusion that the coherence time τ must be long enough, that is, the light of each line must be sufficiently monochromatic, to permit the time of resolution of the multiplier to be small in comparison to τ.

We show in a later chapter that the beats are much easier to observe with lasers.

Chapter II

Interferences of Two Waves by Wavefront Division

2.1 Introduction to the Interferences of Two Waves

The results in Chapter 1 show that to observe interferences with thermal sources under the usual conditions (a large number of wavetrains arrive at the detector during the time needed for one observation) it is necessary that the two waves originate from a single source. We can therefore classify the phenomena according to the method by which the interference apparatus divides the incident wave. There is division of the incident wavefront in the instruments which make use of the principle in Fig. 2.1.

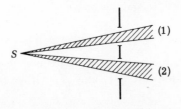

FIG. 2.1   Interference by division of a wavefront.

The source S emits in all directions, but only two separated parts (1) and (2) of the beam are used. These two beams are then superposed in the region in which the phenomenon is observed. Young's slits, Fresnel's mirrors, and other analogous instruments are based on this principle.

A second method of obtaining two coherent beams is by amplitude division, as shown in Fig. 2.2, in which the incident beam falls on a semi-transparent plate G. One part of the beam (1) is transmitted and one part (2) is reflected. The two beams are then superposed in the region in which the phenomena of interference are observed. The interferences produced by plane parallel plates or by the plates of variable thickness (Michelson's interferometer) are based on this principle. The division of the incident wave is not necessarily performed with a semireflecting plate, for the separation can be achieved, for example, by means of a double refracting plate or by diffusion.

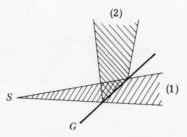

FIG. 2.2   Interference by division of amplitude.

For a description of the fundamental experiments it is suitable to consider first of all the purely hypothetical case of monochromatic light emitted by a point source. By adopting complex notation (Section 1.1) we can represent a monochromatic vibration by the expression $\exp[j(\omega t - \varphi)]$. If we consider the phenomena with two waves, we must study the super-position of two vibrations of the same frequency:

$$\sqrt{I_1}\,\exp[j(\omega t - \varphi_1)]$$

and

$$\sqrt{I_2}\,\exp[j(\omega t - \varphi_2)]$$

at a point P, in which their phase-difference is $\varphi = \varphi_1 - \varphi_2$. The ampli-tudes of the two vibrations are $\sqrt{I_1}$ and $\sqrt{I_2}$. If we neglect the factor $e^{j\omega t}$, the vibration at P is given by

$$x = \sqrt{I_1}\,e^{-j\varphi_1} + \sqrt{I_2}\,e^{-j\varphi_2}$$

and the intensity I at P is

$$I = xx^*,$$

from which we obtain

$$I = I_1 + I_2 + 2\sqrt{I_1^1}\sqrt{I_2^2}\cos\varphi. \tag{2.1}$$

These results were found in Section 1.14 (1.127). If δ is the path difference of the two vibrations at P, we set

$$p = \frac{\delta}{\lambda}; \tag{2.2}$$

p is the order of the interference. The bright fringes are given by

$$\varphi = 2K\pi, \qquad \delta = K\lambda, \qquad p = K, \tag{2.3}$$

and the dark fringes by

$$\varphi = (2K + 1)\pi, \qquad \delta = (2K + 1)(\lambda/2), \qquad p = K + \tfrac{1}{2}. \qquad (2.4)$$

According to the definition of the contrast γ (1.123), we have

$$\gamma = \frac{I_{max} - I_{min}}{I_{max}} = \frac{4\sqrt{I_1}\sqrt{I_2}}{(\sqrt{I_1} + \sqrt{I_2})^2}. \qquad (2.5)$$

In Chapters 2 to 7 we describe these phenomena in general by considering the hypothetical case of a monochromatic point source. In our study of the phenomena in nonmonochromatic light and with an extended source we approach the phenomena without calling on the theory of partial coherence developed in Chapter 1. This theory is applied to the phenomena of interference in Chapters 8, 9, and 10.

2.2   Young's Experiment

We now consider two identical pinholes T_1 and T_2 (Fig. 2.3) which are pierced into an opaque screen at the same distance from the point source S.

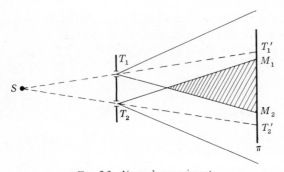

FIG. 2.3   Young's experiment.

If only geometrical optics were applied, we would have just two luminous spots in T_1' and T_2'. In reality, each small opening diffracts the light which is spread over the plane π. Everything proceeds as if T_1 and T_2 were real sources, but the vibrations they diffract originate from a single source S' and consequently are coherent. It is in the region M_1M_2, in which the diffracted beams are superposed and in which they have sufficient intensity, that we can observe the interference fringes. At an arbitrary point P of the screen π, the path difference δ is (Fig. 2.4)

$$\delta = T_2P - T_1P. \qquad (2.6)$$

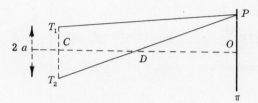

FIG. 2.4   Young's experiment and calculation of path difference at P.

Let

$$CO = D, \qquad OM = y, \qquad T_1 T_2 = 2a.$$

We then have

$$\delta = [D^2 + (y + a)^2]^{1/2} - [D^2 + (y - a)^2]^{1/2}. \tag{2.7}$$

As we observe the phenomena in the neighborhood of O, and $2a$ being very small compared to D, we can extract the roots by approximation. This gives us

$$\delta = \frac{2ay}{D}. \tag{2.8}$$

The fringes, to a first approximation, are parallel and equidistant straight lines. Their direction is perpendicular to the plane in Fig. 2.4.

The bright fringes are given by

$$p = \frac{\delta}{\lambda} = \frac{2ay}{\lambda D} = K, \qquad y = K \frac{\lambda D}{2a} \tag{2.9}$$

and the dark fringes by

$$p = \frac{\delta}{\lambda} = \frac{2ay}{\lambda D} = K + \frac{1}{2}, \qquad y = \left(K + \frac{1}{2}\right)\frac{\lambda D}{2a}. \tag{2.10}$$

Hence we have a bright fringe in O because $T_1 O = T_2 O$.

Because the openings T_1 and T_2 are identical, they diffract the same flux, and in (2.1) the amplitudes $\sqrt{I_1}$ and $\sqrt{I_2}$ are equal. In fact, we can assume that the distance between T_1 and T_2 and different points on the screen varies very little. The contrast between the fringes therefore has a maximum $\gamma = 1$. The variation of the luminous intensity in the plane P is given by

$$I = 4I_1 \cos^2 \frac{\varphi}{2} = 4I_1 \cos^2 \frac{2\pi a y}{\lambda D}. \tag{2.11}$$

The relations (2.9) and (2.10) permit us to calculate the distance that separates the fringes in the plane π. In passing from one fringe to the next,

K increases by one unit. For the bright fringes we have an interspace

$$l = \frac{\lambda D}{2a}. \tag{2.12}$$

This is the same for the dark fringes and the distance that separates a dark from a bright fringe is $\lambda D/4a$.

According to (2.4), the phase difference at P is

$$\varphi = \frac{2\pi(T_2 P - T_1 P)}{\lambda}, \tag{2.13}$$

where λ is the wavelength in the medium under consideration because $T_2 P - T_1 P$ represents the length. If n is the refractive index of the medium, we have

$$\varphi = \frac{2\pi n(T_2 P - T_1 P)}{\lambda_c}, \tag{2.14}$$

where λ_c is the wavelength in vacuo. If, however, the medium under consideration is air, we can write $n = 1$ and $\lambda = \lambda_c$.

Each source T_1 or T_2 produces on the screen π a light intensity that varies with distance. We have, however, considered these variations as negligible and $I_1 = I_2$. The lines of equal intensity coincide with the lines of equal path difference and are given by

$$T_2 P - T_1 P = \text{constant.}$$

These are hyperboloids, with T_1 and T_2 as foci. The fringes we observe in the plane π are therefore the intersections of the hyperboloids with the plane π. Because point P is always far from T_1 and T_2 we can approximate the hyperboloids by their asymptotical cones, and the fringes are hyperbolic arcs, the intersection of the asymptotic cones with the plane π.

As we observe the phenomena in a reduced region in the neighborhood of O in the plane π, every hyperbola coincides with its tangent on the apex and the fringes appear as straight lines. We can therefore use a fine slit parallel to the fringes as a source S. Every point of the slit is incoherent with respect to the others, but all the fringe systems due to all the points of the source are displaced parallel to the fringes. The phenomenon becomes brighter and the contrast does not change. The same is true if we replace the holes T_1 and T_2 by two slits parallel to the source slit.

Note   The energies of the two sources T_1 and T_2 are not additive in every point of the screen, and we may ask what becomes of the principle of conservation of energy.

In considering the curve $I = 4I_1 \cos^2 \varphi/2$, it is easy to see that the mean value of I is equal to $2I_1$ (Fig. 2.5). The crosshatched area is equal to that contained between the curve and the x-axis. The principle of the conservation of energy is respected if it is applied to the space contained between two fringes. The ensemble of the plane P receives as total energy the exact sum of the energies emitted by the two sources. The interference phenomena have no other effect than to modify the distribution of the energy.

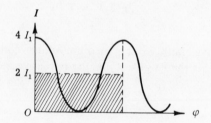

FIG. 2.5   Distribution of intensity in the two-beam interference fringes.

2.3   Fresnel's Mirrors and Lloyd's Device

The light emitted by the point source S (Fig. 2.6) is reflected in two plane mirrors R_1 and R_2 inclined toward each other at a small angle θ. The two mirrors give the two images, S_1 and S_2, of the source S which play the role of the two sources in phase in the preceding experiment. Following the reflection by R_1 and R_2 the two beams appear to come from S_1 and S_2. We must place the screen P in the part common to the two reflected

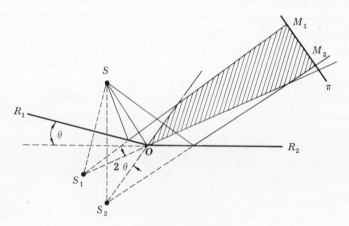

FIG. 2.6   Fresnel's mirrors.

beams to observe the interference fringes. S, S_1, and S_2 are on a circle with the center at O and in which the radius $d = SO$. We have

$$S_1 S_2 \simeq 2\theta d. \tag{2.15}$$

If D is the distance from O to P, the space between fringes is equal to $\lambda D / 2\theta d$.

It is possible to observe the fringes with a single mirror in Lloyd's device (Fig. 2.7) in which the source S is placed close to the extension of the surface of the mirror R.

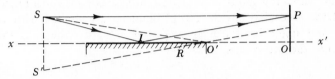

FIG. 2.7   Lloyd's experiment.

We observe the fringes produced by the two sources S and S' in which S' is the image of S in the mirror R. The interferences between the reflected and the incident beams (e.g., between SIP and P) produce these fringes. The central fringe is located on xx' in O if the observation plane is located in π ($SO = S'O$), hence outside of the field. By placing the screen π close to the end of the mirror we can observe the central fringe and find that it is dark. The vibrations coming from S and S' are not in phase at O'; they are in opposition. We explain this experiment by stating that the air–glass reflection introduces a phase change of π.

The phase change by reflection on a glass mirror has been observed by Fresnel in an experiment with three mirrors (Fig. 2.8). A source S sends light to the mirror R_1. The light reflected to the screen π appears to come from the image S_1. The same source S illuminates the two mirrors R_2 and R_3.

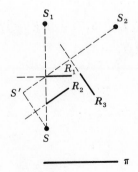

FIG. 2.8   Fresnel's explanation of the π-phase change in the air-glass reflection.

After reflection on these two mirrors, the reflected light appears to come from the source S_2. The fringes observed on the screen π are produced by interferences of the vibrations emitted by S_1 and S_2. We find that the central fringe is dark, which we can explain by assuming that each reflection introduces a phase difference equal to π.

This result, however, is of a general nature for dielectrics and is not limited to the air–glass reflection. There is a phase change equal to π each time reflection takes place from a high refracting medium into a medium with a lower index of refraction. There is no phase change for reflection from a medium with a low index of refraction into a medium with a higher index.

In all the preceding devices the phenomena are studied with very fine sources and unlocalized fringes are observed everywhere in the space common to the two beams.

2.4   Influence of the Size of the Source

Once again let us take up Young's experiment with pinholes (Fig. 2.9) and let us place a fine slit in S on the bisectrix of $T_1 T_2$. The bright central fringe is located at O on the straight line SC. At any point P of the plane π the path difference of the two interfering vibrations is (2.8)

$$\delta = \frac{2ay}{D}$$

and, up to a constant factor,

$$I = \cos^2 \frac{\pi\delta}{\lambda} = \cos^2 \frac{2\pi a y}{\lambda D}. \tag{2.16}$$

We move the fine slit to S_1. The central fringe moves to point O_1 so that the optical paths $(S_1 T_1 O_1)$ and $(S_1 T_2 O_1)$ are equal. At P the path difference is

$$\Delta = (S_1 T_2 + T_2 P) - (S_1 T_1 + T_1 P),$$

$$\Delta = S_1 T_2 - S_1 T_1 + T_2 P - T_1 P,$$

$$\Delta = S_1 T_2 - S_1 T_1 + \delta. \tag{2.17}$$

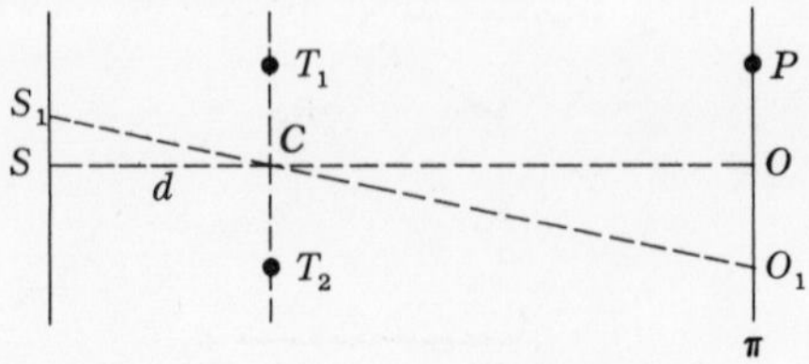

FIG. 2.9   Influence of the width of the source in Young's experiment.

This is an expression analogous to (2.6), to which has been added the constant $S_1T_2 - S_1T_1$. We therefore have the same phenomenon and the same distance between the fringes, but the fringe system has been moved as a whole on the screen π.

Let $SC = d$ and $SS_1 = x$. The path difference at P may be written

$$\Delta = \frac{2ay}{D} + \frac{2ax}{d}, \tag{2.18}$$

which is the same for all points of a fine slit of width dx placed at S_1. Because these points are incoherent, the intensity at P due to the fine slit is, up to a constant factor,

$$dI = \left(1 + \cos\frac{2\pi\Delta}{\lambda}\right)dx, \tag{2.19}$$

where Δ has the value given by (2.18). The intensity I at P due to a slit of width s is

$$I = \int_{-s/2}^{+s/2}\left[1 + \cos\frac{4\pi a}{\lambda}\left(\frac{x}{d} + \frac{y}{D}\right)\right]dx.$$

If

$$m = \frac{2\pi a}{\lambda d}, \tag{2.20}$$

we have

$$I = s\left(1 + \frac{\sin ms}{ms}\cos\frac{4\pi ay}{\lambda D}\right). \tag{2.21}$$

The position of the bright fringes is given by

$$\frac{4\pi ay}{\lambda D} = 2K\pi, \qquad y = K\frac{\lambda D}{2a}. \tag{2.22}$$

By comparison with the relations (2.9) we see that the bright as well as the dark fringes are at the same location as in a small source.

We compare the relation (2.21) with the point source (2.11), which up to a constant factor, can be written

$$I = 1 + \cos\frac{4\pi ay}{\lambda D}. \tag{2.23}$$

The two expressions (2.21) and (2.23) differ only by $\sin ms/ms$. The factor causes the disappearance of the null minima, and the contrast of the fringes decreases. We shall see that this factor is nothing but the degree of partial coherence. To calculate the contrast we have

$$I_{max} = s\left(1 + \frac{\sin ms}{ms}\right),$$

$$I_{min} = s\left(1 - \frac{\sin ms}{ms}\right),$$

from which

$$\gamma = \frac{I_{max} - I_{min}}{I_{max}} = \frac{2 \sin ms}{ms + \sin ms}. \tag{2.24}$$

Figure 2.10 shows the variations of the contrast γ as a function of s. If s is very small (fine slit), γ is equal to 1. If s increases, γ diminishes.

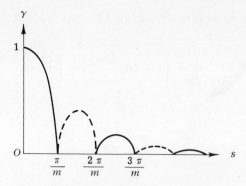

FIG. 2.10   Variation of fringe contrast as a function of source width.

The fringes disappear if $ms = \pi$

$$s = \frac{\lambda d}{2a}. \tag{2.25}$$

They reappear with reversed and weaker contrasts and disappear again for $s = \lambda d/a$, etc.

For each new reversal the contrast is weaker. To achieve a satisfactory contrast it is necessary, for example, that

$$s < \frac{\pi}{2m} \tag{2.26}$$

or

$$s < \frac{\lambda d}{4a};$$

s/d, however, represents the angle θ under which the slit is seen from point C. We must therefore have

$$\theta < \frac{\lambda}{4a}. \tag{2.27}$$

2.5   Phenomena in White Light

We now consider a point source of white light. A fringe system corresponds to each monochromatic radiation and each system adds its intensity in the observation plane. According to (2.3), the path difference is null at O (Fig. 2.4) for all radiations. At O we have a bright white fringe. Because the space between the fringes is equal to $\lambda D/2a$, it varies with the wavelength; the red fringes are larger than the blue.

Let us assume that all the radiations have the same energy and trace on a graph the variations of I as a function of $\sigma = 1/\lambda$, which is called *wavenumber* and measured in (centimeters)$^{-1}$. In order to trace the graph accurately, we should take the spectral sensitivity of the human eye into account. However, we shall simply assume that the usable portion is comprised of $\sigma = 13,000\ \mathrm{cm}^{-1}$ ($\lambda = 0.8\ \mu$; red) and $\sigma = 25,000\ \mathrm{cm}^{-1}$ ($\lambda = 0.4\ \mu$; blue). For each radiation the intensity up to a constant factor is given by (2.6).

$$I = \cos^2\frac{\pi\delta}{\lambda} = \cos^2\frac{2\pi a y}{\lambda D}; \tag{2.28}$$

δ is the path difference at point P of the plane π (Fig. 2.11), at which we observe the phenomenon.

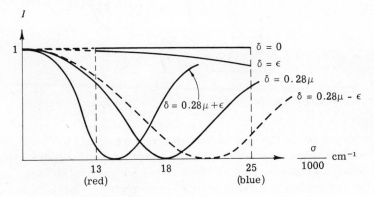

FIG. 2.11   Intensity as a function of the wave number σ.

At point O on the central fringe δ is zero for all radiations, and the curve $I = f(\sigma)$ (Fig. 2.11) is a straight line parallel to the x-axis. At O the central fringe is white. If we move out from the center and δ stays small ($\delta = \varepsilon$), the curve of intensity is a stretched sinusoid. The intensity is weaker for the short wavelengths than for the long. The resulting color is one in which the violet is more attenuated than the red, and is therefore reddish. Let us place ourselves at a point of the plane π such that $\delta = 0.28\,\mu$. According to (2.24), $I = 0$ if $\delta = \lambda/2$, that is, if $\lambda = 2\delta = 0.56\,\mu$. The sinusoid is tangent to the x-axis at point $\sigma = 18{,}000\,\mathrm{cm}^{-1}$ ($\lambda = 0.565\,\mu$), which corresponds to yellow-green. At the point under consideration we would have the first dark fringe if the source emitted only the radiation $\lambda = 0.565\,\mu$. The curve shows that the intensity remains weak almost everywhere. The exception is at the extremities of the visible spectrum, where the eye is quite insensitive. In the region under consideration of the plane π, the field is not very bright and presents a purple color, a mixture of red and violet.

Let us move very little from this position approaching O. The path difference becomes $\delta = 0.28\,\mu - \varepsilon$. The color is richer in red and less rich in violet, and the purple changes to red. At a point farther away from the central fringe $\delta = 0.28\,\mu + \varepsilon$ the color is bluer (indigo). A slight variation of δ causes the purple to change rapidly and the eye is very sensitive to this change in color. The color corresponding to $\delta = 0.28\,\mu$ is called purple of the first order.

For $\delta = 0.4\,\mu$ (Fig. 2.12) the curve presents a minimum of red ($\sigma = 13{,}000$ cm^{-1}; $\lambda = 0.8\,\mu$) and a maximum of violet ($\sigma = 250{,}000\,\mathrm{cm}^{-1}$; $\lambda = 0.4\,\mu$).

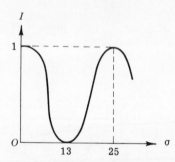

FIG. 2.12   Variation of intensity as a function of the wave number σ for the path difference $\delta = 0.4\,\mu$.

The result is blue. In this way we can observe a whole series of vivid colors if we do not move too far away from the central fringe. To each value of δ corresponds a determined color. These colors are given in Newton's color scale. In the preceding experiments (Young's pinholes, Fresnel's mirrors, etc.) the central fringe is white and the scale of the colors has a white center.

For other experiments, for example, Fresnel's experiment with the three mirrors, we have Newton's color scale with a dark center.

For increasing values of δ, the sinusoid of Fig. 2.11 continues to shrink, and we have a series of maxima and minima. The coloration is invisible when δ is larger than 3 or 4 μ. The impression received by the eye is called *white of higher order*.

2.6   Channeled Spectra

When δ increases, increasing amounts of radiation are extinguished in the visible spectrum (Fig. 2.13). For $\delta = 2\,\mu$ we have three minima ($I = 0$); for $\delta = 10\,\mu$, 12 minima ($I = 0$). If we inspect a white of higher order with a spectroscope, the spectrum will show black bands.

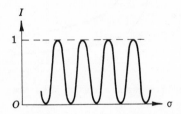

FIG. 2.13   Variation of intensity as a function of the wave number σ for a large path difference (channeled spectrum).

In the spectrum the order of the interference $p = \delta/\lambda$ varies according to the variation of λ. Whenever p is an integer K, we observe a maximum, and whenever it is equal to $K + \frac{1}{2}$ we observe a minimum. The dark bands are given by

$$p = \frac{\delta}{\lambda} = K + \frac{1}{2}, \qquad \lambda = \frac{\delta}{K + \frac{1}{2}}. \tag{2.29}$$

Let λ_1 and λ_2 be the wavelengths of the radiations that correspond to the extremes of the visible spectrum. The orders of interference related to these wavelengths are

$$p_1 = \frac{\delta}{\lambda_1}, \qquad p_2 = \frac{\delta}{\lambda_2}.$$

The difference $N = \delta(1/\lambda_1 - 1/\lambda_2)$ gives the number of bands. With $\lambda_1 = 0.4\,\mu$ and $\lambda_2 = 0.8\,\mu$ we have $N = 1.25\delta$. For $\delta = 1$ mm there will be 1250 bands in the visible spectrum. When δ increases progressively, the bands enter by the violet and leave by the red, but more enter than leave.

If the spectrum is normal (grating spectrum), the bands are not equidistant, for they are more numerous in the violet than in the red.

2.7 Achromatic Fringes

In the preceding section we have assumed that δ is independent of the wavelength. Because $p = \delta/\lambda$ if we trace a curve representing the variations of p as a function of λ for a given value of δ, we have an hyperbola (Fig. 2.14).

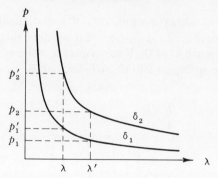

FIG. 2.14   Order of interference p as a function of wavelength λ for two path differences, δ_1 and δ_2.

We again take up Young's experiment as an example and consider a point at which the path difference is δ_2. If the visible spectrum is contained between the wavelength λ and λ', we see that p will take on all the values contained between p_2 and p_2'. If in the interval $p_2 p_2'$ the order of interference p takes six or seven integer values, we will have white of higher order. As we approach the central fringe, the path difference δ_2 diminishes and becomes δ_1. For the same interval $\lambda\lambda'$ the order of interference can take up only the values contained between p_1 and p_1', that is, in a smaller interval. The order of interference varies less with the wavelength and the colors appear. For $\delta = 0$, $p = 0$ for all wavelengths (the curve is coincident with the x-axis). We now have the white central fringe. The slope of the curve determines the phenomenon. The more the part of the curve located between λ and λ' approaches the horizontal, the less important are the variations of p with λ. If δ is independent of λ the part of the curve located between λ and λ' can be horizontal only for $\delta = 0$ (all the radiations are superimposed at the point under consideration). There is therefore only one white fringe in the center of the phenomenon.

If somewhere on the path of the rays we have a device that produces a variation of δ with λ (e.g., by placing a glass plate in front of one of the two slits of Young's experiment), the curves $p = \delta/\lambda$ are no longer hyperbolas.

In Fig. 2.15 the curves rise and it may happen that the slope will vanish for a wavelength λ_0 (Fig. 2.16). For all wavelengths between λ and λ' (visible spectrum) the order of interference varies very little.

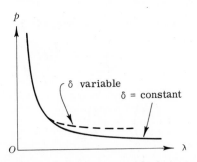

FIG. 2.15   Order of interference p as a function of wavelength λ in presence of dispersion.

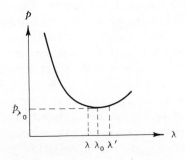

FIG. 2.16   Order of interference p as a function of wavelength λ (achromatic fringe).

In the region of the plane of observation in which the order of interference is p_{λ_0} there is very little variation of the order of interference with the wavelength (two wavelengths correspond to a given order of interference). We therefore obtain fringes that are almost white or black; that is, we have achromatism for wavelength $\lambda_0 = 0.565\,\mu$ (maximum of the sensitivity of the eye) if for this wavelength

$$\left(\frac{dp}{d\lambda}\right)_{\lambda_0} = 0.$$

Because $p = \delta/\lambda$, we have

$$\frac{dp}{d\lambda} = \frac{1}{\lambda}\frac{d\delta}{d\lambda} - \frac{\delta}{\lambda^2}, \qquad (2.30)$$

and chromatism occurs if

$$\frac{dp}{d\lambda} = \left(\frac{\delta}{\lambda}\right)_{\lambda_0} = p_a. \tag{2.31}$$

The yellow-green $\lambda_0 = 0.565\,\mu$ will be achromatic if

$$\left(\frac{dp}{d\lambda}\right)_{\lambda_0} = 0 \; ; \tag{2.32}$$

that is,

$$\left(\frac{d\delta}{d\lambda}\right)_{\lambda_0} = \left(\frac{\delta}{\lambda}\right)_{\lambda_0} = p_{\lambda_0} \; ; \tag{2.33}$$

$(d\delta/d\lambda)_{\lambda_0}$ is a characteristic property of the instrument and can be calculated.

In this way we obtain the order of interference p_{λ_0} (corresponding to yellow-green) for which there is achromatism. If we find that $p_{\lambda_0} = 10$, the achromatic fringe will appear where the tenth fringe of the wavelength $\lambda_0 = 0.565\,\mu$ is located. What happens to the fringes that are in the neighborhood of the achromatic fringe? The achromatic fringe is located in the region corresponding to p_{λ_0}, that is, at the point at which the path difference is δ for the wavelength λ_0. If we move away from the achromatic fringe, the order of interference is no longer p_{λ_0} for λ_0 and the variation of p as a function of λ is represented by another curve than that shown in Fig. 2.16. In Fig. 2.17 the first curve is labeled (1) and the new curve (2). The minimum occurs for the wavelength $\lambda_0{}'$ instead of the yellow-green λ_0, but the achromatism is not so good. In order to have an achromatism as good in the region of the observation plane corresponding to curve (2) as in the region corresponding to curve (1), it is necessary that the variation of the order of interference in passing from (1) to (2) cause no displacement of the abscissa of the minimum. It is therefore necessary that $d\lambda$ corresponding to dp be

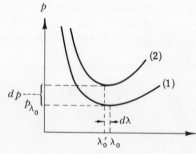

FIG. 2.17   Order of interference p as a function of wavelength λ (achromatic fringe and the neighboring fringes).

as small as possible, which means that $dp/d\lambda$ must be as large as possible (A as near as possible to the vertical passing through B). In the expression $dp/d\lambda$, p must have the value p_a corresponding to the achromatism in (2.31) because we pass from one minimum to another. The minima are given by (2.31). The calculation is done for each special case.

We take Young's experiment as an example (Fig. 2.18) and place a glass plate of thickness e and index of refraction n in front of one of the slits.

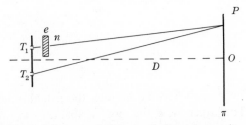

FIG. 2.18   Influences of dispersion in Young's experiment.

Without this plate the path difference is given by (2.8). With the plate we have

$$\delta = \frac{2ay}{D} - (n-1)e; \qquad (2.34)$$

according to (2.31),

$$p_a = \frac{d\delta}{d\lambda} = -e\frac{dn}{d\lambda}. \qquad (2.35)$$

The order in which we observe the achromatic fringe is

$$p_{\lambda_0} = \left(\frac{d\delta}{d\lambda}\right)_{\lambda_0} = \left(\frac{\delta}{\lambda}\right)_{\lambda_0} = -e\left(\frac{dn}{d\lambda}\right)_{\lambda_0}. \qquad (2.36)$$

The position of the achromatic fringe is given by

$$\frac{2ay}{\lambda_0 D} - (n_{\lambda_0} - 1)e = -e\left(\frac{dn}{d\lambda}\right)_{\lambda_0}$$

$$y = -\frac{\lambda_0 De}{2a}\left[\left(\frac{dn}{d\lambda}\right)_{\lambda_0} - \frac{n_{\lambda_0} - 1}{\lambda_0}\right].$$

If we consider a glass such that

$$p = A + \frac{B}{\lambda^2},$$

we will have

$$y = \frac{De}{2a}\left(\frac{3B}{\lambda_0{}^2} + A - 1\right). \tag{2.37}$$

In order that the neighboring fringes of the achromatic fringe may also be achromatic, it is necessary that $dp/d\lambda$ be infinite. We then have

$$p_a = -e\frac{dn}{d\lambda},$$

from which

$$\frac{dp_a}{d\lambda} = -e\frac{d^2n}{d\lambda^2}. \tag{2.38}$$

As this expression cannot become infinite, the neighboring fringes cannot be achromatic. The larger the e, the more visible they will be in white light.

Chapter III

Interferences of Two Waves by Amplitude Division

In the devices discussed in Chapter 2 the two sources S_1 and S_2, having as their origin a single source S, are obtained by division of the wavefront of the incident wave. In the interferences, which we shall study now, the incident wave is divided into two by a surface that is at the same time transparent and reflecting. The division produced by a double refracting system is treated separately (Chapter 7). The use of diffusion is described in Chapter 11.

3.1 Fringes of Equal Inclination Produced by a Plane Parallel Plate. Fringes by Reflection

We consider a plane parallel plate of thickness e and index of refraction n (Fig. 3.1), illuminated by an extended source S of monochromatic light. A ray $S_1 I_1$ is divided in I_1 on the plate and gives rise to one transmitted ray $I_1 J_1$ and one reflected ray $I_1 L_1$; $I_1 J_1$ is reflected in J_1 and emerges along $K_1 L_1'$ parallel to $I_1 L_1$. The two parallel rays $I_1 L_1$ and $L_1 L_1'$ meet each other in F in the focal plane π of the objective O at which they interfere.

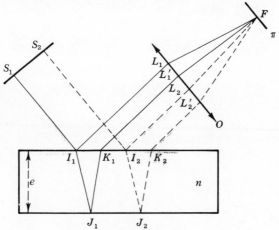

FIG. 3.1   Fringes at infinity of a plane parallel plate.

53

Let S_2 be another point of the source S. Let us consider among the rays emitted by S_2 the ray S_2I_2 parallel to the ray S_1I_1. The same phenomenon occurs again, and the two rays I_2L_2 and K_2L_2' end at the same point F at which they interfere. It can easily be seen that the path differences $(I_1J_1K_1L_1'F) - (I_1L_1F)$ and $(I_2J_2K_2L_2'F) - (I_2L_2F)$ are equal. The interference phenomena produced in F by S_1 and S_2 are incoherent but because they are identical the visibility of the phenomenon stays the same. This is true for all rays emitted from the different points of S which are parallel to S_1I_1. They give the same phenomenon in F. The parallel incident rays, corresponding to another inclination end at another point of the focal plane where they give a perfectly visible phenomenon.

If one observes the interference phenomena, produced by a plane parallel plate in the focal plane of an objective, these phenomena are perfectly clear, whatever the size of the source. In the foregoing, we have neglected the rays which are several times reflected because, due to the rapid decrease of their amplitudes, they produce only negligible contributions. We shall almost always study the phenomena near normal incidence. By taking the incident amplitude equal to unity, Fresnel's formulas give consequently for the amplitudes of the reflected and transmitted rays the values (Fig. 3.2) in Table 2.1.

TABLE 3.1

	(1)	(2)	(3)
Reflection	0.20	0.19	0.008
Transmission	0.96	0.038	0.001

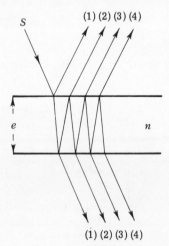

Fig. 3.2   Rays which have suffered several reflections.

We see that the amplitudes are almost negligible, beginning with the third ray, and for this reason we take into account only the rays (1) and (2).

We now calculate the path difference in F. Let an incident ray SI make an angle of incidence i (Fig. 3.3). After reflection on the two faces of the plate the incident ray SI gives rise to two rays IL and KL'. Their phase difference stays constant with respect to K and H, where H is the foot of the perpendicular from K to IL. Between I and KH the ray IL follows the path IH in air, and KL' the path IJK in the medium of the index of refraction n. Thus the path difference is $2nIJ - IH$, to which we must add the additional delay $\lambda/2$ caused by the advance in phase produced by the air-glass reflection at I. The path difference in F between the two rays IL and $IJKL'$ is

$$\delta = 2nIJ - IH + \frac{\lambda}{2}.$$ (3.1)

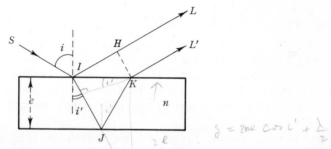

FIG. 3.3 Calculation of path difference in fringes at infinity.

Then

$$IJ = \frac{e}{\cos i'}, \qquad IH = IK \sin i, \qquad IK = 2e \tan i',$$

from which

$$\delta = \frac{2ne}{\cos i'} - 2e \sin i \tan i' + \frac{\lambda}{2},$$

$$\delta = 2ne \cos i' + \frac{\lambda}{2}.$$ (3.2)

Equation (3.2) shows that $\delta = $ constant for $i' = $ constant. The fringes therefore are rings, with the normal to the plane parallel plate forming an axis. In Fig. 3.4 the trace of the normal in the plane π is in C and the observed fringes are elliptic projections of the rings on the plane π.

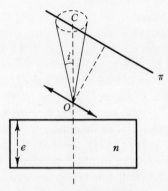

FIG. 3.4   Fringes at infinity given by a plane parallel plate are circles centered on the normal OC to the plate.

For the purpose of considering rays close to the normal we turn to the scheme of Fig. 3.5.

The source S is an extended source of monochromatic light, which sends rays under different angles to the plate l after reflection on the semitransparent plate G inclined at 45°. Letting the normal to l coincide with the optical axis of the objective O we observe that the fringes in the focal plane π are rings with the center at F. All points of a ring correspond to a particular direction of the incident rays. These rings are called fringes of equal inclination.

The rays parallel to the direction i, the angle of incidence on the plate, intersect the focal plane π on a circumference of a circle of radius FM.

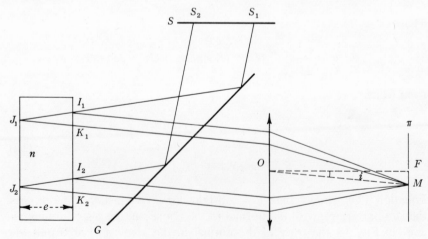

FIG. 3.5   Observation of fringes at infinity by reflection.

For all points of this circle the order of interference p is constant and equal to

$$p = \frac{\delta}{\lambda} = \frac{2ne \cos i'}{\lambda} + \frac{1}{2}. \qquad (3.3)$$

Now, the two reflected rays of which we have made use in these phenomena have almost the same amplitude equal to 0.20. Thus the variation of intensity along a diameter is given by (2.11):

$$I = \cos^2 \pi p. \qquad (3.4)$$

If $p = K$, we shall have a bright ring and if $p = K + \frac{1}{2}$, a black ring. In the center F the order of interference is

$$p_0 = \frac{\delta_0}{\lambda} = \frac{2ne}{\lambda} + \frac{1}{2}. \qquad (3.5)$$

If we move away from this point, the order of interference diminishes, and at the point M it becomes

$$p = p_0 - K, \qquad (3.6)$$

where K represents the number of fringes we see between F and M (K is an integer or a fraction). According to (3.3) and (3.5), the relation (3.6) can be written

$$\frac{2ne \cos i'}{\lambda} = \frac{2ne}{\lambda} - K. \qquad (3.7)$$

Assuming that the angles are small,

$$\frac{2ne}{\lambda} \left(1 - \frac{i'^2}{2}\right) = \frac{2ne}{\lambda} - K,$$

from which

$$i = \sqrt{\frac{n\lambda}{e}} \sqrt{K}. \qquad (3.8)$$

If we have a dark fringe at F, (3.8) will give the radius of the Kth dark ring. The radii of the rings, corresponding to the same state of interference as the center, vary like the square roots of consecutive integers. They become closer in proportion as we move out from the center F.

Remark 1 The thickness of the plate must be constant if we want to observe the phenomena. In fact, let us assume that one half the useful surface of the plate differs by $\lambda/4n$ from the thickness of the other half.

At point M one half gives an order of interference of

$$p = \frac{2ne\cos i'}{\lambda} + \frac{1}{2}$$

and the other

$$p' = \frac{2n(e + \lambda/4n)\cos i'}{\lambda} + \frac{1}{2}.$$

Near the center $p' - p \simeq \frac{1}{2}$, and the two systems of fringes given by the two halves of the plate destroy one another.

Remark 2   It is possible to observe fringes in other regions than in the focal plane of an objective. If we use a point source S (Fig. 3.6), point M at an arbitrary position always receives two beams such as $SI'M$ and $SIJKM$. There is interference at M and its position being arbitrary, we observe nonlocalized fringes which are everywhere in space. For reasons of symmetry these fringes are rings having as an axis the axis of revolution SH of the system.

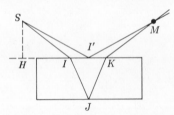

FIG. 3.6   Observation of fringes with a point source.

3.2   Fringes Produced by a Plane Parallel Plate: Fringes by Transmission

Phenomena in transmission may be observed according to the diagram in Fig. 3.7. No additional phase shift is caused by the reflections in J and K and the path difference is

$$\delta = 2ne\cos i'. \tag{3.9}$$

The phenomena are complementary to the phenomena by reflection. For each group of two beams that interfere, however, the amplitudes 0.96 and 0.038 are quite different. According to (2.5), we see that $\gamma \simeq 0.15$.

The fringes of equal inclination in transmission have a weak contrast.

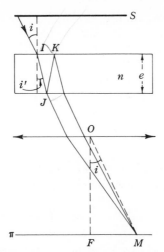

FIG. 3.7   Observation of fringes at infinity by transmission.

3.3   Fringes Produced by a Plate of Variable Thickness Illuminated by a Parallel Beam: Fringes by Reflection

We assume that the variations in thickness of the plate are small and that we have near normal incidence. The plate is illuminated with parallel light (Fig. 3.8). Let us consider two parallel incident rays (1) and (2): (1) travels along the path $SIJKL_1$; (2) arrives at K on the plate and follows the path SKL_2. Because we have almost normal incidence, points I and K are very close to each other. We can therefore assume that the plate has a well-defined thickness e in the region IJK. In the phenomena we are studying now we observe either the plate itself or its image formed by an objective. In Fig. 3.8 the objective O forms an image of the plate at K'. The objective O can be the eye of the observer who accommodates on the plate. The retina would then be at K'.

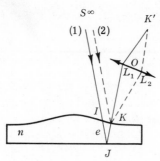

FIG. 3.8   Fringes of equal thickness by reflection.

Between K and K' the optical paths of the two rays are equal. It is sufficient to consider the path difference between K and the source S. By comparison with Fig. 3.2 it is easy to see that the path difference is $2ne$ for normal incidence. Ray (2) undergoes one air-glass reflection in K, and an additional phase shift equal to π must be added. The path difference at K (or at K') between rays (1) and (2) becomes

$$\delta = 2ne + \frac{\lambda}{2}. \tag{3.10}$$

The two rays (1) and (2) have almost the same amplitude. By observing the plate at K we have, up to a constant factor, an intensity

$$I = \cos^2 \frac{\pi\delta}{\lambda} = \cos^2 \frac{\pi}{\lambda}\left(2ne + \frac{\lambda}{2}\right). \tag{3.11}$$

If we consider K, another point on the plate, the thickness e is no longer the same and the intensity changes. The index of refraction n is assumed to be constant; hence the path difference δ is only a function of the thickness e. Observing the plate, we see fringes that indicate lines of equal thickness (Fizeau fringes). The bright fringes are given by

$$p = \frac{\delta}{\lambda} = \frac{2ne}{\lambda} + \frac{1}{2} = K \tag{3.12}$$

and the dark fringes by

$$p = \frac{\delta}{\lambda} = \frac{2ne}{\lambda} + \frac{1}{2} = K + \frac{1}{2}. \tag{3.13}$$

The dark fringes correspond to the thicknesses $e = K\lambda/2n$ (3.13), and whenever we pass from one fringe to the next the thickness of the plate changes by $\lambda/2n$. With an air plate contained between two glass plates, we find $\lambda/2n = 0.3\,\mu$ for $\lambda = 0.6\,\mu$. For oblique incidence (3.10) must be replaced by (3.2):

$$\delta = 2ne \cos i' + \frac{\lambda}{2}.$$

Furthermore, we observe fringes that are the loci of equal thickness in a thin film if the angle of incidence i and consequently the angle of refraction r are constant. The bright fringes are given by

$$p = \frac{\delta}{\lambda} = \frac{2ne \cos i'}{\lambda} + \frac{1}{2} = K \tag{3.14}$$

and the dark fringes by

$$p = \frac{\delta}{\lambda} = \frac{2ne\cos i'}{\lambda} + \frac{1}{2} = K + \frac{1}{2}. \qquad (3.15)$$

The dark fringes correspond to the thicknesses

$$e = \frac{K\lambda}{2n\cos i'}. \qquad (3.16)$$

3.4   Fringes Produced by a Plate of Variable Thickness Illuminated by Parallel Light: Fringes in Transmission

As in Section 3.3, we consider two parallel incident rays (1) and (2) (Fig. 3.9). Ray (1) travels along the path $SIJKL_1$. Ray (2) arrives at the plate at K and travels along SKL_2. We observe the plate in near normal incidence. Points I and K are very close to each other, and we can define the thickness e of the plate in the region IJK. The two reflections in J and in K are the same type (glass-air in Fig. 3.9), and the path difference in K (or in K') of the two rays (1) and (2) is

$$\delta = 2ne; \qquad (3.17)$$

for the bright fringes

$$p = \frac{\delta}{\lambda} = \frac{2ne}{\lambda} = K \qquad (3.18)$$

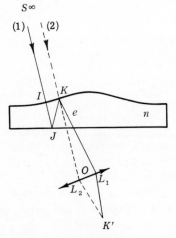

FIG. 3.9   Fringes of equal thickness by transmission.

and for the dark fringes

$$p = \frac{\delta}{\lambda} = \frac{2ne}{\lambda} = K + \frac{1}{2}.$$ (3.19)

Comparison of (3.12), (3.13) and (3.18), (3.19) shows that the fringes in transmission are complementary to the fringes in reflection. The amplitude of ray (1) is 0.038 and the amplitude of ray (2) is 0.96. According to (2.5), we can see that the contrast of fringes in transmission is weak ($\gamma \simeq 0.15$). For oblique incidence (3.17) must be replaced by the relation

$$\delta = 2ne \cos i'.$$ (3.20)

3.5   Localization and Visibility of the Fringes

Until now we have studied the phenomena under well-defined experimental conditions which permit us to arrive at a simpler explanation. However, it would be useful to review the general rules by which we can recognize the best conditions for the observation of the phenomena in each case. The fringes of equal inclination of a plane parallel plate are observed at infinity with an extended source. We can also observe fringes at any distance if we have a point source. Hence there is a relation between the size of the source and the localization of the fringes. It is this relation that we shall now discuss.

Let us consider a point source S and two rays SI_1 and SI_2 (Fig. 3.10).

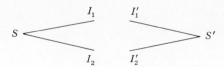

FIG. 3.10   Nonlocalized fringes with a point source.

After they have traveled along different paths, the two rays SI_1 and SI_2 reunite at S', where they interfere with each other. The path difference in S' is

$$\delta = (SI_2I_2'S') - (SI_1I_1'S').$$ (3.21)

The value of δ depends on the position of point S', but it is completely determined for any position. If a screen is placed so that the two beams are superposed, we obtain at all points a state of completely determined interference that varies from one point to another. By using a point source we obtain perfectly clear fringes for any position on the screen where the interfering beams are superposed. We say that the fringes are not localized.

Let us now consider an extended source which passes through S and let M be some point of this source (Fig. 3.11).

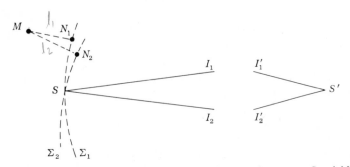

FIG. 3.11   Calculation of path difference at S' with two point sources S and M.

To begin with, we assume that we have placed a point source at S'. The two paths $S'I_1I_1S$ and $S'I_2'I_2S$ have corresponding waves in S and are represented by Σ_1 and Σ_2. These two wavefronts, which are two spheres with the radii R_1 and R_2, are normal to SI_1 and SI_2 in S. Let MN_1 and MN_2 be normal to Σ_1 and Σ_2. The optical paths leading from N_1 to S' and from N_2 to S' are equal to $(SI_1I_1'S')$ and $(SI_2I_2'S)$ respectively.

The path difference in S' between the two rays emitted by M is

$$\delta_M = (MN_2) + (SI_2I_2'S') - (MN_1) - (SI_1I_1'S'), \tag{3.22}$$

and, according to (3.21),

$$\delta_M = \delta + (MN_2) - (MN_1).$$

Now $l_1 = MN_1$ and $l_2 = MN_2$. Therefore,

$$\delta_M - \delta = l_2 - l_1; \tag{3.23}$$

$\delta_M - \delta$ represents the variation of the path difference passing from S to M.

We now calculate $\delta_M - \delta$ by taking point M in the plane SI_1I_2 (Fig. 3.12) and choosing a coordinate system Sxy so that Sx and Sy are the interior and the exterior bisectrices of the angle $I_1SI_2 = \theta$. The centers of the wavefronts Σ_1 and Σ_2 are located at C_1 and C_2. The coordinates of C_1 and C_2 are

$$C_1 \bigg| \quad R_1 \cos\frac{\theta}{2} \quad R_1 \sin\frac{\theta}{2},$$

$$C_2 \bigg| \quad R_2 \cos\frac{\theta}{2} \quad -R_2 \sin\frac{\theta}{2}.$$

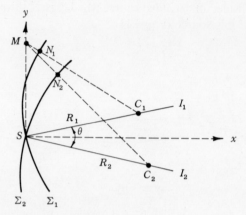

Fig. 3.12   Variation of path difference when passing from S to M.

If y is the ordinate of M, we have

$$C_1 M = R_1 + l_1 = \left[R_1{}^2 \cos^2 \frac{\theta}{2} + \left(y - R_1 \sin \frac{\theta}{2} \right)^2 \right]^{1/2}, \qquad (3.24)$$

$$C_2 M = R_2 + l_2 = \left[R_2{}^2 \cos^2 \frac{\theta}{2} + \left(y + R_2 \sin \frac{\theta}{2} \right)^2 \right]^{1/2}. \qquad (3.25)$$

Let us assume that the dimensions of the source are small compared with R_1. We can expand and neglect the powers of y/R_1 higher than the square. We now have

$$C_1 M = R_1 - y \sin \frac{\theta}{2} + \frac{y^2}{2R_1} \cos^2 \frac{\theta}{2},$$

from which

$$l_1 = -y \sin \frac{\theta}{2} + \frac{y^2}{2R_1} \cos^2 \frac{\theta}{2}. \qquad (3.26)$$

We also find that

$$l_2 = y \sin \frac{\theta}{2} + \frac{y^2}{2R_2} \cos^2 \frac{\theta}{2} \qquad (3.27)$$

and

$$\delta_M - \delta = 2y \sin \frac{\theta}{2} + \frac{y^2}{2} \left(\frac{1}{R_2} - \frac{1}{R_1} \right) \cos^2 \frac{\theta}{2}. \qquad (3.28)$$

If θ is small,

$$\delta_M - \delta = y\theta + \frac{1}{2}\left(\frac{1}{R_2} - \frac{1}{R_1}\right)y^2. \tag{3.29}$$

If M is no longer on Sy but occupies an arbitrary position (x, y, z) in the neighborhood of S, we have

$$\delta_M - \delta = y\theta + \frac{1}{2}\left(\frac{1}{R_2} - \frac{1}{R_1}\right)(y^2 + z^2). \tag{3.30}$$

This expression shows that $\delta_M - \delta$ does not depend on x. If the point M stays close to S, the source can have an arbitrary form.

Equation 3.30 expresses the variation of the path difference in S' (Fig. 3.11) when passing from point S to point M. If $y = z = 0$, that is, if the source is infinitely small, $\delta_M = \delta$. When M moves away from S', the difference is no longer δ; it becomes δ_M. In order for the state of interference in S' to be independent of the position of M in the neighborhood of S', meaning thereby that we may use an extended source, it is necessary that $\delta_M - \delta$ vary very little.

There are two terms in (3.30). We neglect to begin with the term of second order and have

$$\delta_M - \delta = y\theta. \tag{3.31}$$

We can use an extended source in S without causing a change in the state of interference in S' if $\theta = 0$. Hence $\theta = 0$ means that SI_1 and SI_2 (Fig. 3.12) coincide. In order to observe the interferences in S' with an extended source, it is necessary that the two rays $I_1'S'$ and $I_2'S'$, which end at S', originate in the same incident ray coming from S. We then have the arrangement in Fig. 3.13: the points C_1, C_2, and S' are aligned, and if M is displaced in the neighborhood of S the path difference varies only a little at S'. We indeed see that at S' and for the two compounded rays coming from S, the path difference is

$$\delta = C_1 C_2 = R_2 - R_1.$$

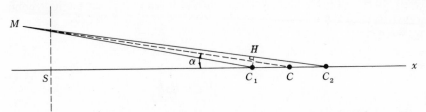

FIG. 3.13   Path differences do not depend on the abscissa of the point considered at the source.

For an arbitrary point M near S we have a path difference in S':

$$\delta_M = C_2 H = C_1 C_2 \cos \alpha,$$

where α is the angle under which we see SM from C.

$$\delta_M - \delta = C_1 C_2 (\cos \alpha - 1) \simeq (R_1 - R_2)\frac{\alpha^2}{2};$$

$\delta_M - \delta$ therefore varies very little if M stays close to S.

The preceding expression is nothing but the second-order term of (3.30) in which $R = \frac{1}{2}(R_1 + R_2)$ and $\alpha = [(y^2 + z^2)^{1/2}]/R$.

In Fig. 3.13 the path difference $\delta_M = C_2 H$ remains constant if α is constant. Hence the difference does not depend on x, as shown by (3.30).

If we change the position of the point S' (point S remains fixed), the coordinate axes and the orientations of SI_1 and SI_2 also change.

Let us assume that the condition $\theta = 0$ is satisfied for point S'; that is, the two rays ending at S' originate from the same incident ray $SI_1 I_2$. For S' we can use an extended source in the neighborhood of S almost without changing the state of interference in S'. We could find another point, S'' (i.e., another position of S'), in which the two rays arriving at S'' also originate from the same ray, which was emitted by S (different from $SI_1 I_2$). For S', as for S'', we can use an extended source in the neighborhood of S almost without changing the state of interference in S' and in S''.

For all points such as S', S'', ..., which have been found in this way, and only for them, we may use an extended source in the neighborhood of S' because they all satisfy the condition $\theta = 0$. For other points an extended source cannot be used; that is, the fringes are not visible with an extended source beyond the surface that is the locus of points such as S'. This surface is the surface of localization of the fringes.

If a source has a certain size, the phenomenon of interference is localized on a surface that is the locus of the points of intersection of the rays which originate from one incident ray coming from S.

It should be noted that the visibility of the phenomenon in S' varies with the size of the source. The influence of this size is given by the second-order term in y if $\theta = 0$.

We have

$$\delta_M - \delta = \frac{1}{2}\left(\frac{1}{R_2} - \frac{1}{R_1}\right) y^2. \tag{3.32}$$

In order that the state of interference in S' may remain constant in spite of the size of the source, it is necessary that $\delta_M - \delta$ be smaller than a certain fraction of the wavelength (e.g., $\lambda/4$). We then have (3.31)

$$\frac{1}{2}\left(\frac{1}{R_2} - \frac{1}{R_1}\right)y^2 \leqslant \frac{\lambda}{4},$$

from which

$$\alpha = \frac{y}{R} \leqslant \left(\frac{\lambda}{2|R_1 - R_2|}\right)^{1/2}. \tag{3.33}$$

The visibility of the fringes is still good if the angular radius of the source, seen from point C, does not exceed the value given by (3.33).

Consequently, (3.29) indicates (a) the region of localization if we use an extended source (first term), (b) the upper limit of the size of an extended source (second term).

The preceding results, which are general, permit us to localize the fringes. The search for the surface of localization must be made for each case. In the plane parallel plate (3.1) $\theta = 0$, when S' is in the focal plane of an objective. R_1 and R_2 are infinite whatever the position of S. Hence we can observe the fringes with a source of any size.

3.6   Special Case of Thin Film Fringes

Consider the interferences produced by a plate of index n contained between two surfaces of glass of index of refraction n' which make a small angle ε (Fig. 3.14).

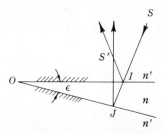

FIG. 3.14   Localization of fringes of an air wedge (S' real).

The incident ray SI (Fig. 3.14) is reflected along IS' on the first plate and along JS' on the second. The two rays JS' and IS' coincide in S' and originate from the same incident ray SI. If J and O are on the same side with respect to the normal in I, S' is real (Fig. 3.14). If O and J are on different sides of the normal in I, S' is virtual (Fig. 3.15). We take the case of Fig. 3.14 and follow the same reasoning: we imagine a point source in S' and search for the positions of the centers C_1 and C_2 (Fig. 3.16).

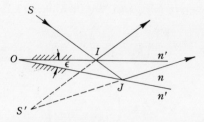

FIG. 3.15   Localization of fringes of an air wedge (S' virtual).

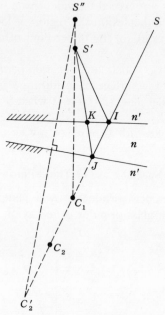

FIG. 3.16   Calculation of the distance C_1C_2 in an air wedge.

We assume that we have normal incidence. After refraction in K, the ray $S'K$ appears to come from the point S'' such that

$$\frac{KS''}{KS'} = \frac{n}{n'}.$$

After reflection in J, the ray JI appears to come from the point C_2', symmetrical to S'', with respect to the lower face of the wedge. After refraction in I, the ray IS appears to come from C_2 such that

$$\frac{IC_2'}{IC_2} = \frac{n}{n'}.$$

The ray $S'I$, which is reflected in I, appears to come from C_1, symmetrical to S', with respect to the upper face of the wedge. We have

$$IC_2' = IJ + JC_2' = IJ + JK + KS'',$$

$$IC_2 = IC_2'\frac{n'}{n} = \frac{n'}{n}(IJ + JK + KS''),$$

$$IC_2 = \frac{n'}{n}\left(2e + \frac{n}{n'}KS'\right) = 2e\frac{n'}{n} + KS';$$

hence

$$KS' \simeq IS' = IC_1,$$

from which

$$IC_2 - IC_1 = R_2 - R_1 = \frac{2ne'}{n}. \tag{3.34}$$

AIR WEDGE: SOURCE AT FINITE DISTANCE

We ignore the thickness of the glass plates forming the wedge which changes neither our reasoning nor the results. In Fig. 3.17 the centers C_1 and C_2 are symmetrical to S' with respect to the two surfaces of the air wedge. Points C_1 and C_2 are the centers of the wavefronts Σ_1 and Σ_2 considered earlier (Fig. 3.11). We now have

$$R_2 - R_1 = C_2S - C_1S.$$

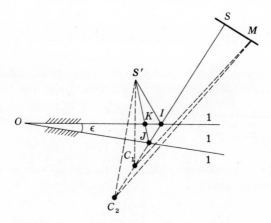

FIG. 3.17   Air wedge. Influence of the size of the source.

For a point M near S (Fig. 3.18) and located on the plane tangent to Σ_1 and Σ_2 the path difference in S', according to (3.23), is

$$\delta_M - \delta = l_2 - l_1.$$

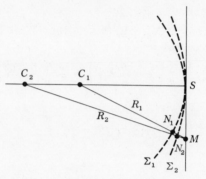

FIG. 3.18   Calculation of the path difference.

A simple calculation (Fig. 3.19) shows that

$$l_2 - l_1 = C_1 C_2 \frac{\alpha^2}{2} = (R_2 - R_1)\frac{\alpha^2}{2}.$$

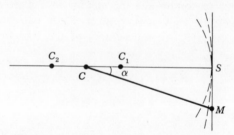

FIG. 3.19   Calculation of the angle 2α under which the source is seen.

The state of interference in S' does not change if we replace the point source S by a source subtending an angle α under the condition that $\delta_M - \delta = l_2 - l_1$ is smaller than $\lambda/4$. We therefore have

$$(R_2 - R_1)\frac{\alpha^2}{2} \leqslant \frac{\lambda}{4}, \qquad \alpha \leqslant \left(\frac{\lambda}{2|R_2 - R_1|}\right)^{1/2}.$$

We find again the relation (3.32). In the case of an air wedge (3.34) $R_2 - R_1 = 2e$ from which

$$\alpha \leqslant \left(\frac{\lambda}{4e}\right)^{1/2}. \tag{3.35}$$

Let us take an air wedge of a mean thickness of 0.1 mm and $\lambda = 0.55\,\mu$. We then have

$$\alpha \leqslant 2°.$$

AIR WEDGE: SOURCE AT INFINITY

Let us now consider a source at infinity (Fig. 3.20). The two rays IS' and JS', originating from the incident ray SI, intersect at S'. Points like S', which satisfy the same condition $\theta = 0$, are located on OS'. For all points of OS' we can see fringes with an extended source at infinity. The region of localization of the fringes is the plane OS', which passes through the edge of the wedge. Equation 3.34 shows that

$$C_1 C_2 = R_2 - R_1 = 2e = \delta.$$

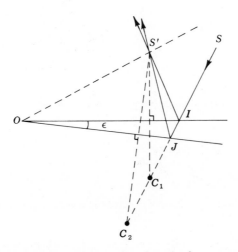

FIG. 3.20 Localization of fringes of an air wedge for a source at infinity.

Hence, for a ray that comes from S, the path difference at S' is

$$\delta_M = C_2 H = C_1 C_2 \cos \alpha,$$

$$\delta_M = \delta \cos \alpha = \delta \left(1 - \frac{\alpha^2}{2}\right),$$

$$\delta_M - \delta = \frac{\alpha^2}{2}\delta = (R_2 - R_1)\frac{\alpha^2}{2}.$$

Once again we find the relation (3.32).

If we neglect the second-order terms, the state of interference will remain unchanged in S' when we replace the point source S' with the extended source of radius SM (Fig. 3.21). This is true of the same source for all points of the plane OS'. In fact, the entire plane OS' is illuminated in the same fashion by the rays emitted by S. The entire plane OS' is likewise illuminated by the rays emitted by M. It is possible to see the fringes on OS' if we adjust the size of the source SM accordingly. If e is the mean thickness of the wedge in near normal incidence, then $\delta = 2e$, which is sufficient to satisfy condition (3.35); α is the angle under which the source is seen from point O.

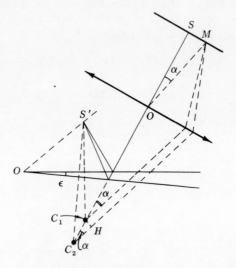

FIG. 3.21   Influence of the angular diameter 2α of the source on fringe visibility.

In a wedge of index of refraction n, placed in air, we have

$$R_2 - R_1 = \frac{2e}{n},$$

from which

$$\alpha \leqslant \left(\frac{n\lambda}{4e}\right)^{1/2}. \tag{3.36}$$

If the wedge is very thin, OS' coincides with the plate, and the fringes are localized on the film. If the angle of the wedge goes to zero, the two emerging rays become parallel, but because they are very close to each other point S' is no longer defined.

The localization disappears. The fringes are visible on the film and beyond it.

FRINGES OF THE AIR WEDGE

We consider a thin film, contained between two glass plates which form a small angle ε (Fig. 3.22). The fringes localized on the film outline the wedge's contours which are straight lines parallel to its apex. In near normal incidence in a region of thickness e the path difference by reflection is (3.3)

$$\delta = 2e + \frac{\lambda}{2}.$$

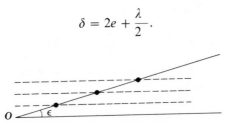

FIG. 3.22   Distance between successive fringes in an air wedge.

When we pass from one fringe to the next (two fringes of the same type) the path difference changes by λ. We then have

$$p_1 = \frac{\delta_1}{\lambda} = \frac{2e_1}{\lambda} + \frac{1}{2}, \qquad p_2 = \frac{\delta_2}{\lambda} = \frac{2e_2}{\lambda} + \frac{1}{2},$$

from which

$$e_2 - e_1 = \frac{\lambda}{2}.$$

In normal incidence the thickness varies by $\lambda/2$.

The fringes are the lines of intersection of one face of the plate with planes parallel to the other face. We see that the air wedge is crossed by equidistant fringes parallel to its apex. If one plate is shifted in a continuous movement with respect to the other one, the fringes keep their form, but they move into the field of observation. When the displacement becomes equal to half a wavelength, each fringe is replaced by its neighbor.

The fringes are shifted toward the locus of minimum thickness as the order of the fringes increases with the thickness. If we increase the distance of the surfaces, the first visible fringe will be of a higher and higher order.

If we move the surface A away from the surface B, as shown by (1) in Fig. 3.23, the fringes move in the direction of (2). In oblique incidence the path difference becomes (3.2)

$$\delta = 2e \cos i + \frac{\lambda}{2}.$$

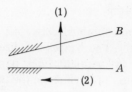

FIG. 3.23   Fringes displaced toward areas of lesser thicknesses when the distance between the air-wedge surfaces is changed.

If the angle of incidence increases, the path difference diminishes and the fringes separate.

The fringes of the air wedge can be observed in transmission but they have a low contrast (Section 3.4).

NEWTON'S RINGS

A spherical surface S (a plane convex lens of large radius) is placed on a plane surface of glass P (Fig. 3.24). We observe, in reflection, the interferences produced by the thin air film between the two surfaces. The fringes, indicating contours of equal thickness, are circular and are centered on A'. These are known as Newton's rings.

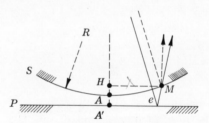

FIG. 3.24   Newton's rings.

The air film of thickness e_0 between the lens and the plane disappears only if there is optical contact between the two surfaces. At a certain point M the thickness of the air film is e. If $HM = x$ and AH is small,

$$x^2 = AH(2R - AH) \simeq 2R\,AH,$$

$$e = AH + e_0 = \frac{x^2}{2R} + e_0.$$

The path difference in M is

$$\delta = 2e + \frac{\lambda}{2} = \frac{x^2}{R} + 2e_0 + \frac{\lambda}{2}.$$

There will be a dark ring in M if

$$p = \frac{\delta}{\lambda} = \frac{x^2}{R\lambda} + \frac{2e_0}{\lambda} + \frac{1}{2} = K + \frac{1}{2};$$

that is, if

$$\frac{x^2}{R\lambda} + \frac{2e_0}{\lambda} = K,$$

the radius x of this dark ring is given by

$$x = \left[R\left(K - \frac{2e_0}{\lambda} \right)\lambda \right]^{1/2}. \tag{3.37}$$

By setting

$$K_0 = \frac{2e_0}{\lambda} \tag{3.38}$$

we have

$$x = [R(K - K_0)\lambda]^{1/2}. \tag{3.39}$$

If $K_0 = 0$ (optical contact), $x = (RK\lambda)^{1/2}$; the radii of the dark rings vary like the square roots of successive integers.

The difference $K - K_0$ is the difference in the orders of interference in M and A; it represents the number of fringes seen between the center A and M.

3.7 Influence of the Size of the Source on the Contrast of Fringes of Equal Thickness

We have studied in a general way the influence of the size of the source on the visibility of the fringes with respect to localization. We shall now investigate in more detail the fringes of equal thickness of a thin film.

If we consider a plate illuminated by a source at infinity, the fringes are almost entirely localized in the plate. We observe the image I' of the plate L as given by the objective O_2 (Fig. 3.25) and study the contrast of these fringes in near normal incidence. The source is circular and its axis SO_1 is normal to the plate L. Plate G inclined at 45° permits the observation of the phenomenon.

The path difference in K for point M is:

$$\delta_M = 2ne \cos i' + \frac{\lambda}{2}.$$

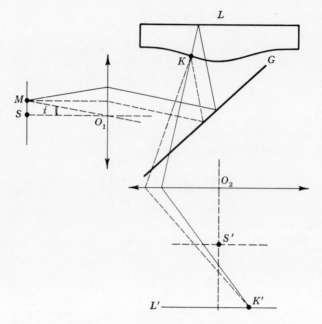

FIG. 3.25   Observation of fringes of equal thickness by reflection.

We can write

$$\delta_M = 2ne\left(1 - \frac{i'^2}{2}\right) + \frac{\lambda}{2};\tag{3.40}$$

$\delta = 2ne + \lambda/2$ is the path difference in K if we consider point S of the source. We will then have

$$\delta_M = \delta - nei'^2 = \delta - \frac{ei^2}{n}.\tag{3.41}$$

If point M illuminates only plate L, the intensity at a point K, where the thickness is e, will be proportional to $1 + \cos 2\pi\delta_M/\lambda$:

$$1 + \cos\frac{2\pi\delta_M}{\lambda} = 1 + \cos\frac{2\pi}{\lambda}\left(\delta - \frac{ei^2}{n}\right).$$

The intensity at K due to a small elementary ring seen from point O_1 under the angle di is

$$2\pi\left[1 + \cos\frac{2\pi}{\lambda}\left(\delta - \frac{ei^2}{n}\right)\right]i\,di$$

and the intensity at K due to the entire source, which is seen from O_1 under the angle α, is

$$I = 2\pi \int_0^\alpha \left[1 + \cos \frac{2\pi}{\lambda} \left(\delta - \frac{ei^2}{n} \right) \right] i \, di, \qquad (3.42)$$

from which

$$I = \pi\alpha^2 + \frac{n\lambda}{e} \cos \frac{2\pi\delta}{\lambda} \sin \frac{\pi e\alpha^2}{n\lambda}. \qquad (3.43)$$

In order to study the variations of I we must vary δ in (3.43) because the ratio e/n is based on (3.41) in which i alone varies and in which e is the mean thickness of the plate whose defects are always small.

The bright and the dark fringes are given by

$$\cos \frac{2\pi\delta}{\lambda} = \pm 1, \qquad (3.44)$$

$$\frac{\pi\alpha^2 e}{n\lambda} = m. \qquad (3.45)$$

The contrast (2.5) is given by

$$\gamma = \frac{2 \sin m}{m + \sin m}; \qquad (3.46)$$

$2m$ represents the phase difference in K due to the inclination of the rays if we pass from the center to the edge of the source. The variations of γ as a function of m are shown in Fig. 3.26. This calculation is in fact that of the

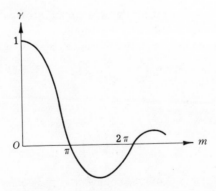

FIG. 3.26   Contrast of fringes of equal thickness as a function of angular diameter of the source.

degree of partial coherence. The contrast vanishes for $m = \pi$ which results in

$$\alpha = \left(\frac{n\lambda}{e}\right)^{1/2}. \tag{3.47}$$

The phenomenon can be explained as follows: instead of observing the image L' of the plate L, we focus on the focal plane S' of the objective O_2. Because the defects of the plate are small, we see at S' rings of average thickness at infinity of plate L. If we compare (3.8) and (3.47), we can see that the angle α, given by (3.47), corresponds to a variation of the path difference equal to λ if we set $K = 1$ ($\delta = \lambda$) in (3.8).

We observe the rings at infinity at S' by assuming a dark center at S'.

Equation 3.47 shows that the contrast will be zero if the diameter of the source is such that the edge of its image falls into the minimum of the first ring (Fig. 3.27).

FIG. 3.27   Relation between the rings at infinity and the visibility of fringes.

Hence, to show good contrast between fringes of equal thickness, it is necessary that the source diameter be smaller. We take a source with an angular diameter in which the path difference $e\alpha^2/n$ is equal to $\lambda/4$. We then have

$$\frac{e\alpha^2}{n} = \frac{\lambda}{4} \tag{3.48}$$

from which

$$\alpha = \frac{1}{2}\left(\frac{n\lambda}{e}\right)^{1/2}. \tag{3.49}$$

According to (3.45) and (3.48) the value $2m = \pi/2$ corresponds to the value of α, which produces $\gamma \simeq 0.95$, an excellent contrast.

The identity of the expressions (3.36) and (3.49) should be noted.

The preceding calculations are applied to a circular source with its axis normal to the plate. If this axis is not normal to the plate, we have oblique incidence. We know that the rings become smaller if we leave the center. If we use the source defined by (3.49) in oblique incidence, the variation of the path difference due to the inclination of the rays will be larger than $\pi/2$ and contrast between the fringes will diminish.

The more oblique the incidence, the more we must reduce the aperture of the source in order to conserve contrast between fringes. Therefore, our interest in the observation of fringes in normal incidence is continuous.

Let us return to the circular source in which the axis is normal to the plate. Equation 3.44 permits us to calculate the variation of the thickness of the plate when we pass from one fringe to the next. For the dark fringes we have (3.44)

$$\frac{\delta}{\lambda} - \frac{e\alpha^2}{2n\lambda} = K + \frac{1}{2}$$

$$\frac{2ne}{\lambda} + \frac{\lambda}{2} - \frac{e\alpha^2}{2n\lambda} = K + \frac{1}{2},$$

from which

$$e = \frac{K\lambda}{2n - \alpha^2/n} = \frac{K\lambda}{2n(1 - i'^2/2)}. \qquad (3.50)$$

In passing from one dark fringe to the next, the thickness of the plate varies by

$$\frac{\lambda}{2n(1 - i'^2/2)}. \qquad (3.51)$$

We can compare (3.50) and (3.51) with (3.16).

3.8   Thin Films in White Light

When we observe a thin film in white light, an order of interference $p = \delta/\lambda$ corresponds to each radiation. At any point in the film the order of interference varies with the wavelength. In the light reflected by the thin film in the region under observation the radiations for which $p = \delta/\lambda = K + \frac{1}{2}$ will be absent (3.13).

If only one to three radiations are extinguished, the thin film will appear to be colored, and if constant thickness is lacking the colors observed will not be the same at all points in the film. One value of δ and a determined color correspond to each thickness. Whether the film is an air film or made of a substance with refractive index n, the phenomena are almost the same.

In fact, as the wavelength varies from simple to double, from one extremity of the visible spectrum to the other, the index of refraction varies at most by 1 or 2 per cent. For example, in a thin air film observed in reflection the thickness is zero, and, according to (3.11), $I = 0$ for all radiations; therefore we have black. We increase the thickness e steadily, assuming always that it remains plane parallel; that is, the color is uniform over the entire film. If e is very small, the short waves are reflected best, and the first color is blue. For $e = \lambda/4$ with $\lambda = 0.56\,\mu$ (medium yellow) we obtain a maximum of reflection for this wavelength. Because it corresponds to the maximum sensitivity of the eye, the film takes on a yellowish, almost white cast. For $e = \lambda/2$ with $\lambda = 0.56\,\mu$ the reflected light is composed of the extremities of the spectrum. The result is purple, which is called a sensitive color. The same phenomenon holds for $e = \lambda$, $3\lambda/2$, etc., but as the phase difference increases the colors become less and less pure. Classification is by different order separated by sensitive colors (Newton's color scale).

Similar phenomena exist in transmission, but the contrast is poor and the colors are not pure. With Young's slits the phase shift is zero in the center for all radiations and we have white light. As we move away from the axis, the phase difference increases, and we see a whole sequence of colors different from those observed in reflection from a thin film.

The colors resulting from these phenomena, beginning with black or white, are catalogued in Newton's scale (Table 3.2). In this table the path differences between two interfering vibrations (due to the thickness of the thin film only) are shown.

Let us consider a simple radiation which carries a certain energy flux. Suppose that this flux is divided by the interference apparatus into two equal fluxes. If the path difference is δ, they interfere and the resulting flux is proportional to $1 - \cos 2\pi\delta/\lambda$ (scale 1).

In a phenomenon with a white center (Young's fringes) the resulting flux is proportional to $1 + \cos 2\pi\delta/\lambda$ (scale 2).

In a narrow spectral band $d\lambda$ corresponding to an elementary flux $d\Phi_0 = E(\lambda)\,d\lambda$, $E(\lambda)$ denotes the spectral distribution of the energy of the light source. After the interference, one will have

$$d\Phi_1 = \left(1 - \cos\frac{2\pi\delta}{\lambda}\right) d\Phi_0 \qquad \text{(scale 1)}$$

or

$$d\Phi_2 = \left(1 + \cos\frac{2\pi\delta}{\lambda}\right) d\Phi_0. \qquad \text{(scale 2)}$$

TABLE 3.2

Path difference (in microns)	Scale 1 Phenomena with center black	Scale 2 Phenomena with center white
0.040	Iron gray	White
0.097	Lavender-gray	Yellowish white
0.158	Blue-gray	Brownish white
0.218	Light gray	Yellow-brown
0.234	Greenish white	Brown
0.259	White	Clear red
0.267	Yellowish white	Carmine red
0.275	Pale straw yellow	Dark red-brown
First order		
0.281	Straw yellow	Dark violet
0.306	Light yellow	Indigo
0.332	Bright yellow	Blue
0.430	Yellow-brown	Blue-gray
0.505	Red-orange	Blue-green
0.536	Warm red	Pale green
0.551	Dark red	Yellow-green
0.565	Purple	Light green
0.575	Violet	Yellow-green
0.589	Indigo	Yellow-gold
0.664	Sky blue	Orange
0.728	Yellow-green	Orange-brown
0.747	Green	Light carmine red
0.826	Light green	Purple

If the incident light is white, the colors observed after the interference will be characterized by

$$\Phi_1 = \int E(\lambda) \left[1 - \cos \frac{2\pi\delta}{\lambda} \right] d\lambda \qquad \text{(scale 1)} \qquad (3.52)$$

or

$$d\Phi_2 = \int E(\lambda) \left[1 + \cos \frac{2\pi\delta}{\lambda} \right] d\lambda. \qquad \text{(scale 2)} \qquad (3.53)$$

The superposition of these two types of interference produces

$$\Phi_1 + \Phi_2 = \int E(\lambda)\, d\lambda, \qquad (3.54)$$

which represents the incident white light. The colors in the two scales which correspond to the same path differences are complementary. Their superposition restores the incident white light.

3.9   Channeled Spectra of Thin Films

The calculations in Section 2.6 can be applied here. However, the path difference δ is now produced by the film. For a film of index n and thickness e we have $\delta = 2ne + \lambda/2$ for an observation of reflection in air of near normal incidence.

As an example we use the setup shown in Fig. 3.28. The image of a small region I of the film L is projected on the slit of a spectroscope. The thin film L is illuminated by the source S (white light) after reflection by the semi-transparent plate G inclined at 45°. In this way we can study the spectral composition of the reflected light in the region I. If the thickness of the film amounts to several microns, the reflected light is no longer colored. It will have become white of a higher order. Examination by spectroscope shows the spectrum crossed by channels. The black channels correspond to the wavelengths for which $p = \delta/\lambda = K + \frac{1}{2}$, the bright channels to $p = \delta/\lambda = K$. If λ_1 and λ_2 are two wavelengths of the spectrum, there are as many bright channels between λ_1 and λ_2 as there are integers between $p_1 = \delta/\lambda_1$ and $p_2 = \delta/\lambda_2$. By determining the number of channels, we can measure the phase difference caused by the film. Let K be the number of bright channels between λ_1 and λ_2. Because p is not known, we have

$$p = \frac{\delta}{\lambda_1}, \qquad p + K = \frac{\delta}{\lambda_2}, \qquad \delta = \frac{K\lambda_1\lambda_2}{\lambda_1 - \lambda_2}.$$

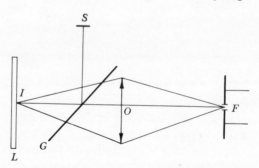

FIG. 3.28   Observation of a channeled spectrum.

3.10   Observation of the Phenomena

FRINGES OF EQUAL INCLINATION

The angular radius of the rings at infinity is given by (3.8). If the order of interference in the center is an integer, the angular radius of the first ring will be

$$i = \sqrt{\frac{n\lambda}{e}}.$$

Consider a glass plate of index 1.5. By taking $\lambda = 0.55\,\mu$ we can find the angular radius of the first ring for plates of different thicknesses. Some values are given in Table 3.3.

TABLE 3.3

e (mm): 0.1	1	10	20
i: 6°	2°	38′	22′

The angular radius of the first ring for a 20-mm plate is approximately equal to the apparent diameter of the sun, hence visible to the naked eye.

The fringes can be observed at infinity by placing the eye against a sheet of white paper in which a hole of 3 to 4 mm diameter has been cut and through which the plate in Fig. 3.29 can be seen. The sheet E is illuminated by a monochromatic source (e.g., a mercury vapor lamp). By reflection on the plate the image of the hole T shows up as a small black spot surrounded by rings.

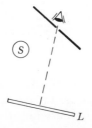

FIG. 3.29   Observation of rings at infinity by reflection.

To observe the fringes of equal inclination in transmission it is sufficient to place the plate before the eye and to gaze steadily at an extended surface uniformly lighted by a monochromatic source. The rings are found by disaccommodation and by orienting the plate.

Observation of rings at infinity has always required a plane parallel plate. Fabry's device (Fig. 3.30) permits this observation even with a plate that is only approximately plane parallel.

The image of a source S is formed on the plate L by means of a lens O_1, and after reflection on the semitransparent plate G, inclined at 45°. The rings are observed through a small telescope focused at infinity and consisting of an objective O_2 and an eyepiece O_3 with a magnification of approximately $\frac{1}{2}$. We place a diaphragm in which a pinhole has been made over the eyepiece, and an image of this minute opening is cast on the plate L. By this method we use a very small part of the plate. If the plate is not perfect in its entirety, the region used is small enough to be considered plane parallel.

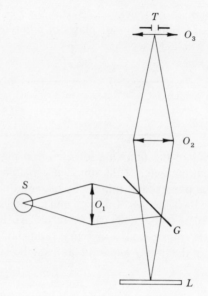

FIG. 3.30   Observation of rings at infinity in a small region of a plate.

FRINGES OF EQUAL THICKNESS

Equation 3.49 shows that the thinner the plate, the larger the source used. In fact, because the pupil of the eye has only a very small aperture, it also diaphragms the beams. An example is given in Fig. 3.31 in which the eye utilizes only a small part of the source. For a pupil equal to 4 mm and a distance from the eye to the plate equal to 25 cm we have $2\alpha = 0.016$.

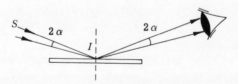

FIG. 3.31   Limitation of a light beam by the pupil of the eye.

Then, according to (4.45) $m \simeq 0.1\pi e/n$ (e in millimeters), and a contrast of $\gamma \simeq 0.7$ with a plate 2 mm thick, observed in monochromatic light, is produced.

For the observation of fringes in white light, Newton's scale shows that because the colors become rapidly weaker a thickness of the order of $1\,\mu$ must not be exceeded. With sufficiently thin plates a method of observation analogous to that in Fig. 3.29 can be used. A white light source S illuminates a white diffusing screen with an opening *T* through which the eye looks at the surface of the thin film *L*. By means of the screen *E* the film is fully illuminated, and the eye sees the fringes which trace the contours of equal thickness.

To observe narrow closely aligned fringes, in monochromatic light, we use a low power microscope focused on the thin film *L* (Fig. 3.32). A mirror *G*, inclined at 45°, reflects the light from the source *S* on the film *L*. For observation in normal incidence the focusing microscope *V* must have a convenient aperture so that the inclination of the rays it admits is within the desired tolerances.

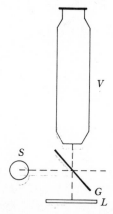

FIG. 3.32 Observation of fringes of equal thickness in a thin plate by reflection.

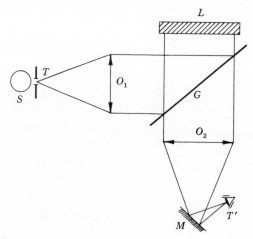

FIG. 3.33 Observation of fringes of equal thickness in a plate of any thickness.

For plates several centimeters thick it is necessary to operate in normal incidence with a beam that is sufficiently parallel. The device shown in Fig. 3.33 can be used. A hole T of variable diameter and illuminated by a monochromatic source is placed at the focus of a lens O_1. A beam of parallel light falls on a mirror, G, inclined at 45°, and then on the plate L to be studied. After reflection, the beam is made convergent by the lens O_2 and the eye is placed at T', the image of T on the other side of the system. The eye sees the well-lighted plate and the fringes clearly, without accommodation, if care has been taken to place L in the object focus of the lens O_2.

Chapter IV

Two-Beam Interferometers

In certain cases it is helpful to use an interference apparatus in which the two beams are completely separated before they are reunited, for each beam can be acted upon separately to make the task of adjusting and measuring easier.

4.1   Michelson's Interferometer

Michelson's interferometer (Fig. 4.1) consists of two mirrors M_1 and M_2 and a glass plate inclined at 45° with respect to their normals. G_1, called a beam splitter, is a semitransparent plate that reflects as much light as it transmits.

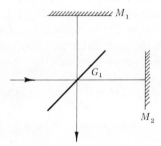

FIG. 4.1   Principle of Michelson interferometer.

We take a point source S at the focus of an objective, O_1 (Fig. 4.2). The interferometer is illuminated by a beam of parallel rays, and we follow the path of one of them through the apparatus. The ray SA is divided in two when it arrives at A on the semireflecting face of the beam splitter G_1. The ray AB is reflected in B_1 on the mirror M_1, retraces its path, crosses G_1, and falls into the objective O_2.

The other ray crosses G_1, is reflected in B_2 by the mirror M_2, returns and is reflected on the semireflecting face A of G_1, recrosses G_1, and is superposed on the first ray when it reaches the objective O_2. The eye of the observer is located below the objective O_1 and is not shown in Fig. 4.2.

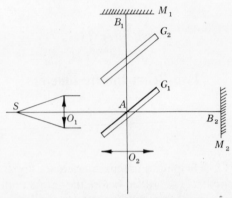

FIG. 4.2   Scheme of Michelson interferometer with separator G_1, and compensator G_2.

The first ray crosses the beam splitter G_1 only once, whereas the second crosses it three times. In order that the two trajectories along which the rays travel may be identical, we place a "compensator," G_2, in the first beam. This plate must have the same thickness and be made of the same glass as G_1. Because a strict equality of the thicknesses of G_1 and G_2 is difficult to achieve, it is possible to compensate the very small differences that may exist by slightly turning the compensator plate G_2. Let i be the angle of incidence of the rays on the plate G_2 (Fig. 4.3), i', the angle of refraction, e, the thickness of the compensator plate, and n, its index of refraction. We calculate the path difference between a ray that passes as if there were no plate and a ray that crosses the plate. We have

$$\delta = nIJ - IH = \frac{e}{\cos i'}[n - \cos(i - i')],$$

$$\delta = e(n \cos i' - \cos i).$$

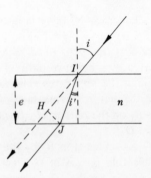

FIG. 4.3   Path difference between a ray that passes through a plate and a ray that passes in the absence of the plate.

If we incline the compensator plate by a small angle di from this position, the path difference is changed by $d\delta$ and we have

$$d\delta = e(-n \sin i' \, di' + \sin i \, di) = \frac{e \sin(i - i')}{\cos i'} \, di. \qquad (4.1)$$

Thus it is possible to compensate a small inequality in the thicknesses of G_1 and G_2 by a slight variation of the inclination of the compensator plate.

OBSERVATION OF FRINGES OF EQUAL THICKNESS

The mirror M_2 has, by reflection on the semireflecting side A of the beam splitter G_1, an image in M_2' (Fig. 4.4). Everything behaves as if the interferences were produced by an air plate contained between the mirror

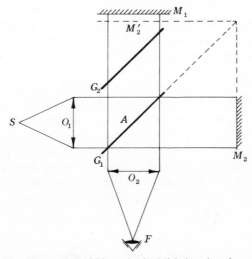

FIG. 4.4 Observation of fringes in the Michelson interferometer.

M_1 and the image M_2' of the mirror M_2. Thus, if the image M_2' is not parallel to M_1, we have an air wedge. If the different optical components which make up the instrument are perfect, the fringes are parallel and equidistant straight lines. The eye is placed at the focus F of the objective lens O_2 to observe them. The focal length of the objective lens must be chosen to permit the observation of the region of the localization of the fringes. If M_2' intersects M_1, we see the fringes in white light. However, the fringe that corresponds to the intersection of M_2' and M_1 is not completely white. As a matter of fact, after reflection at B_2 the ray AB_2 (Fig. 4.2) has undergone in A a reflection glass → semireflecting film. The path difference therefore is equal to the difference of the geometric paths (zero for the intersection of M_2' with M_1) plus a small path difference. If the source S is very small, the fringes are not localized and can be observed everywhere. If S has a certain size, the fringes become localized on the plate M_1M_2'. The diameter of the source S must be smaller as the plate M_1M_2' becomes thicker.

If the plate between M_1 and M_2' is very thin, it is possible to observe the fringes in white light if the optical paths followed by the two beams are identical. If the plates G_1 and G_2 have the same thickness but not the same index of refraction, the path difference can be zero for one radiation but not for the others. The path difference varies rapidly with the wavelength, and the fringes cannot be observed in white light.

OBSERVATION OF FRINGES OF EQUAL INCLINATION

If the image M_2' is exactly parallel to M_1, we can observe the rings of the air plate formed at infinity. They are localized at the focus of the objective lens O_2. Thus we can examine the focal plane F with a magnifying glass. The combination of the objective lens O_2 and the magnifying glass form a telescope adjusted to infinity, and the magnification chosen is a function of the angular diameter of the observed rings.

The source S must be replaced by a larger source. Furthermore, it is possible to replace the collimator by a large diffusing white surface illuminated by a monochromatic source. By moving one of the mirrors parallel to itself the diameter of the rings can be varied. If the two plates G_1 and G_2 are sufficiently parallel, the rings at infinity are perfectly circular. They are deformed if G_2 is inclined to G_1. At first the rings at infinity become elliptical; if the inclination is increased they become hyperbolic.

Note   Consider a point source S at a finite distance (Fig. 4.5). Everything behaves as if the light originated from two sources S_1 and S_2, which are the images of S after reflection on G_1 and on M_1 and M_2. If S_1S_2 is perpendicular to Ax (Fig. 4.6), the experiment can be compared with Fresnel's

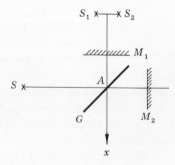

FIG. 4.5   Observation of fringes with a point source.

mirror experiment and straight fringes are observed. If S_1S_2 is parallel to Ax, we observe rings whose radii can be changed by moving one of the mirrors parallel to itself.

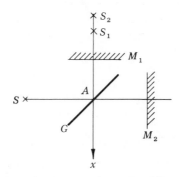

FIG. 4.6   Production of rings with a point source.

4.2   Study of the Monochromaticity of the Source and of the Visibility of Fringes by Michelson's Interferometer

We shall now discuss Michelson's interferometer because it is simpler to describe the phenomena with a given instrument. In addition, these phenomena can be most easily observed with Michelson's interferometer. However, it should be well understood that the following results are of general validity. The study of the phenomena based on the notion of partial coherence will be undertaken in Chapter 8.

We consider Michelson's interferometer adjusted for the observation of fringes of equal thickness at the air wedge located between M_1 and M_2' (Fig. 4.4). The source S is a nonmonochromatic point source. The phenomenon we observe on the wedge M_1M_2' is the combination of the phenomena that correspond to different monochromatic radiations of the source. Because the interspace of the fringes is not the same for all radiations, the superposition of these fringe systems diminishes the contrast of the phenomenon. We can ask what requirements are to be fulfilled by the source in respect of monochromaticity so that the fringes have good contrast.

We have seen that it is necessary for good fringe visibility that the value given by (3.39) remain unsurpassed by the angular radius α of the source. This limits the variation of the order of interference to less than $\frac{1}{4}$ ($d\delta = \lambda/4$) for passing from the center to the edge of the source. If we consider a nonmonochromatic point source, we can say that the variation of the order of interference at a point at which the phenomenon is observed is no longer due to a variation of the inclination of the incident rays but to a variation of the wavelength. In applying the preceding rule, we state that the variation of the order of interference caused by a variation of the wavelength of the incident light is not larger than $\frac{1}{4}$. We assume that the variation is small enough to allow the spectral sensitivity of the eye to remain constant. We now have

$$p = \frac{\delta}{\lambda},$$

from which

$$dp = -\frac{\delta \, d\lambda}{\lambda^2} = -p \frac{d\lambda}{\lambda}. \tag{4.2}$$

It is necessary therefore that

$$p \frac{d\lambda}{\lambda} \leqslant \frac{1}{4}. \tag{4.3}$$

It is sufficient to replace $2m = 2\pi p(d\lambda/\lambda) = \pi/2$ in (3.46) to achieve fringe contrast. We now have, as before, $\gamma \simeq 0.95$. The ratio $\lambda/d\lambda$ is called the coefficient of finesse of the radiation utilized. We shall assume that the source emits the radiation with the coefficient of finesse $\lambda/d\lambda$ and study the phenomena in a more precise manner.

For example, we adjust the mirror M_1 so that the mean thickness of the air wedge $M_1 M_2'$ becomes very small. The visibility of the fringes of equal thickness is perfect. We now move the mirror M_1 parallel to itself to increase e and, in consequence, the path difference δ. We then trace the curve that shows the contrast of the fringes as a function of the path difference δ.

At any point of the wedge $M_1 M_2'$ the intensity is proportional to $1 + \cos 2\pi\delta/\lambda = 1 + \cos 2\pi\sigma\delta$. The path difference δ corresponds to a certain region of the wedge, but we take it also as the mean value of the path difference that characterizes the mean distance between M_1 and M_2'. For a small spectral interval characterized by $d\sigma$ the intensity at the point under consideration is

$$dI = (1 + \cos 2\pi\delta\sigma) \, d\sigma \; ; \tag{4.4}$$

the intensity I, if the source emits the radiations contained between σ_1 and σ_2 symmetrical with respect to a central value σ_0, is

$$I = \int_{\sigma_1}^{\sigma_2} f(\sigma - \sigma_0)(1 + \cos 2\pi\sigma\delta) \, d\sigma. \tag{4.5}$$

The function $f(\sigma - \sigma_0)$ (Fig. 4.7) characterizes the energy emitted by the source as a function of the wavelength.

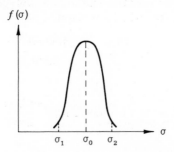

FIG. 4.7   A curve that characterizes the spectral distribution of energy emitted by the source.

By setting $\sigma' = \sigma - \sigma_0$ (Fig. 4.8) we can write

$$I = \int_{-\sigma'}^{+\sigma'} f(\sigma') \left[1 + \frac{e^{j2\pi(\sigma_0+\sigma')\delta} + e^{-j2\pi(\sigma_0+\sigma')\delta}}{2} \right] d\sigma'. \qquad (4.6)$$

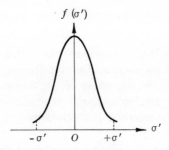

FIG. 4.8   The curve of Fig. 4.7 with a change of origin.

We put

$$A = \int_{-\sigma'}^{+\sigma'} f(\sigma') e^{j2\pi\sigma'\delta} \, d\sigma' \qquad (4.7)$$

and

$$B = \int_{-\sigma'}^{+\sigma'} f(\sigma') e^{-j2\pi\sigma'\delta} \, d\sigma'. \qquad (4.8)$$

We find

$$I = \int_{-\sigma'}^{+\sigma'} f(\sigma') \, d\sigma' + \tfrac{1}{2} [e^{j2\pi\sigma_0\delta} A + e^{-j2\pi\sigma_0\delta} B]. \qquad (4.9)$$

The integrals A and B are the Fourier transforms of the function $f(\sigma')$. They are equal if $f(\sigma - \sigma_0)$ is symmetrical with respect to σ_0. To begin with we consider the case of a source with a constant spectral distribution (Fig. 4.9); that is, a source for which $f(\sigma')$ equals constant. We have

$$A = B = 2\sigma' \frac{\sin 2\pi\sigma'\delta}{2\pi\sigma'\delta}, \tag{4.10}$$

from which

$$I = 2\sigma' \left[1 + \cos 2\pi\sigma_0\delta \frac{\sin 2\pi\sigma'\delta}{2\pi\sigma'\delta} \right]. \tag{4.11}$$

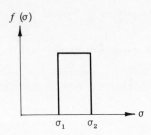

FIG. 4.9   A source that emits constant energy in the interval $\sigma_1\sigma_2$.

The term $(\sin 2\pi\sigma'\delta)/2\pi\sigma'\delta$ represents the influence of the spectrum of width $2\sigma'$ emitted by the source. For the study of the variations of I as a function of δ, that is, for the study of the fringes, we must not vary the factor δ in the term $(\sin 2\pi\sigma'\delta)/2\pi\sigma'\delta$. This factor corresponds to a mean value of the path difference and it changes only if we move M_1 away from M_2'.

The bright and the dark fringes are still given by

$$\cos 2\pi\sigma_0\delta = \pm 1.$$

The contrast of the fringes then is (Fig. 4.10)

$$\gamma = \frac{2 \sin 2\pi\sigma'\delta}{2\pi\sigma'\delta + \sin 2\pi\sigma'\delta}. \tag{4.12}$$

Let us consider the factor $2\sigma'\delta$. Because $\sigma' = \sigma - \sigma_0$, we have

$$2\sigma'\delta = 2\delta\left(\frac{1}{\lambda} - \frac{1}{\lambda_0}\right) \simeq 2\delta\frac{\lambda_0 - \lambda}{\lambda_0{}^2}.$$

If the spectral width of the line is equal to $d\lambda$, we obtain $d\lambda = 2(\lambda_0 - \lambda)$, because $\sigma' = 1/\lambda - 1/\lambda_0$ corresponds to one half the spectral interval.

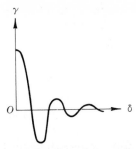

FIG. 4.10 Contrast of fringes as a function of the path difference when the source is characterized by the curve in Fig. 4.9.

Thus we have

$$2\sigma'\delta = \delta\frac{d\lambda}{\lambda_0^2} = p\frac{d\lambda}{\lambda_0}. \qquad (4.13)$$

The term $2\sigma'\delta$ represents the variation of the order of interference at the point at which the phenomenon is observed. This variation is caused by a variation $d\lambda$ of the wavelength. By valuing p so that the variation of the path difference does not exceed $\lambda/4$, we have

$$2\sigma'\delta = \tfrac{1}{4}.$$

The expression (4.12) results in $\gamma = 0.95$, a value that has already been found.

The path difference ne for a given spectral bandwidth 2σ must not exceed the value

$$\delta = \frac{1}{2\sigma'}. \qquad (4.14)$$

The contrast of the fringes will be good under these conditions, and we increase the path difference δ progressively without changing $2\sigma'$, that is, by always using the same line. It is sufficient to move the mirror M_1 to increase its distance from the image M_2'; (4.12) shows that the fringe contrast diminishes and vanishes for

$$2\sigma'\delta_e = 1. \qquad (4.15)$$

In fact, the eye will perceive no fringes at all much before the path difference has reached the value δ_e, but because physical detectors detect weaker contrasts than the eye we can choose δ_e as a limiting value.

Equation 4.15 shows that we can see the fringes up to a path difference corresponding to

$$p < \frac{\lambda_0}{d\lambda}. \qquad (4.16)$$

With a line of the wavelength $\lambda_0 = 0.6\,\mu$ and a coefficient of finesse $\lambda_0/d\lambda = 10^6$, the maximum value of δ_e is

$$p = \frac{\delta_e}{\lambda_0} = 10^6\,;$$

that is, $\delta_e = 60\,\text{cm}$.

Note   In (4.6) $f(\sigma') = $ constant between σ_1 and σ_2, that is, a spectral line with the energy profile given by Fig. 4.9.

This explains that γ assumes values different from zero for $\delta > \delta_e$. The curve $\gamma = f(\delta)$ (Fig. 4.10), representing the variations of γ, in effect oscillates about the x-axis beginning with $\delta > \delta_e$.

In general the spectral line has a profile of the type shown in Fig. 4.8 and the contrast decreases smoothly if δ increases. The oscillations of γ are indeed due to the integrals A and B which cause the appearance of the Fourier transform of a rectangular function (Fig. 4.9). Suppose that $f(\sigma')$ is a Gaussian function of the form (Fig. 4.11)

$$e^{-\sigma'^2/a^2}.$$

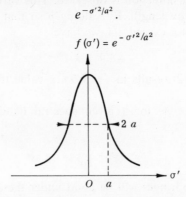

FIG. 4.11   Spectral distribution of a source characterized by a Gaussian function.

The line width can be characterized by the interval $2\sigma' = 2a$, corresponding to $1/e = 0.37$. The Fourier transform of a Gaussian function is a Gaussian function.

The oscillating term $(\sin 2\pi\sigma'\delta)/2\pi\sigma'\delta$ disappears and is replaced by a continuously decreasing term.

The integrals A and B become

$$A = \int_{-\infty}^{+\infty} e^{-\sigma'^2/a^2}\, e^{j2\pi\sigma'\delta}\, d\sigma' = a\sqrt{\pi}\, e^{-\pi^2 a^2 \delta^2}, \tag{4.17}$$

$$B = \int_{-\infty}^{+\infty} e^{-\sigma'^2/a^2}\, e^{-j2\pi\sigma'\delta}\, d\sigma' = a\sqrt{\pi}\, e^{-\pi^2 a^2 \delta^2}. \tag{4.18}$$

The integrals A and B are equal; according to (3.63) we find

$$I = a\sqrt{\pi}[1 + \cos 2\pi\sigma_0\delta \cdot e^{-(\pi a\delta)^2}] \qquad (4.19)$$

and (Fig. 4.12)

$$\gamma = \frac{2e^{-(\pi a\delta)^2}}{1 + e^{-(\pi a\delta)^2}}. \qquad (4.20)$$

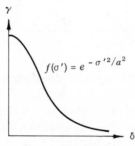

FIG. 4.12 Contrast of fringes as a function of the path difference δ when the source is characterized by the curve of Fig. 4.11.

We take as the limiting contrast $\gamma = 0.02$, the minimum perceptible by the eye. We have

$$\pi a\delta_e = 1.48.$$

According to (4.13), $2\sigma'\delta$ represents the variation of the order of interference due to a wavelength variation $d\lambda$. Because $2a = 2\sigma'$ is the line width, we obtain

$$2\sigma'\delta_e = 2a\delta_e = \frac{2.96}{\pi} = p\frac{d\lambda}{\lambda_0}.$$

The fringes will be visible up to an order of interference

$$p = \frac{\delta_e}{\lambda_0} = \frac{2.96}{\pi}\frac{\lambda_0}{d\lambda}.$$

With a line of the wavelength $\lambda_0 = 0.6\,\mu$ and a coefficient of finesse $\lambda_0/d\lambda = 10^6$ ($d\lambda$ corresponds to $2a$), we can achieve a maximum path difference $\delta_e = 60$ cm.

4.3 Mach–Zehnder Interferometer

The Mach–Zehnder interferometer contains two beam splitters, L_1L_2, and two mirrors, M_1M_2, as shown in Fig. 4.13. An incident ray SI falls on a semireflecting plate L_1 and is divided in two parts. The ray IJ is reflected by the mirror M_1 and at K passes through a second semireflecting plate, L_2.

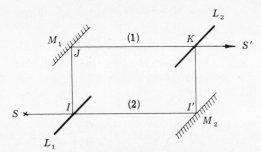

FIG. 4.13   A Mach–Zehnder interferometer.

The ray transmitted at I is reflected at I' on the mirror M_2 and again at K on the semireflecting plate L_2 to combine with the first ray. The semireflecting faces in Fig. 4.14 are marked by heavy lines.

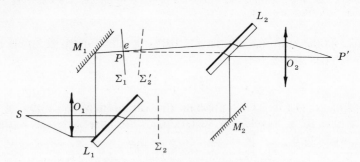

FIG. 4.14   Localization of fringes in a Mach–Zehnder interferometer.

We place the source S at the focal point of an objective O_1 to illuminate the interferometer in parallel light and assume that the mirror M_1 is slightly inclined with respect to the other three elements. Let Σ_1 be a plane wave corresponding to beam (1) and Σ_2 corresponding to beam (2). The wave Σ_2' is the image of Σ_2 after reflection on the semireflecting face of L_2. We observe the fringes of the wedge formed by the two waves Σ_1 and Σ_2'. Let P be a region in which the distance from P to the wave Σ_2' is e. The path difference is

$$\delta = ne, \tag{4.21}$$

where n is the index of refraction of the medium between Σ_1 and Σ_2'.

The bright fringes correspond to $ne = K\lambda$, the dark fringes, to $ne = (K + \frac{1}{2})\lambda$. If P and P' are conjugated by an objective lens O_2, we find the fringes again in P'.

If the source is extended, the fringes are localized in the region in which the two emerging rays originating from the same incident ray meet. This region can be moved about by modifying the orientations of the elements which act on the relative inclination of Σ_1 and Σ_2.

If we turn M_1 around an axis perpendicular to the plane of Fig. 4.15, the region P of localization is near M_1. By turning M_1 and L_2, P becomes located between M_1 and L_2. Thus it is possible to control the location of the region of localization.

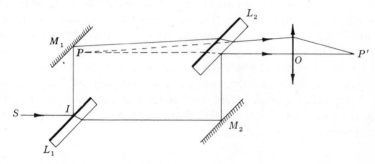

FIG. 4.15   Localization of fringes in a Mach–Zehnder interferometer.

4.4   Jamin's Interferometer

Jamin's interferometer (Fig. 4.16) consists of two thick plane-parallel glass plates L_1 and L_2. The back faces A_1B_1 and A_2B_2 are reflecting (opaque aluminum or silver coated). We adjust the two plates parallel to each other and consider the incident ray SI on the first plate, which is divided in two parts, one reflected at I and the other at J after refraction in the plate. The ray II', which has undergone the reflection on glass in I, has a weaker intensity than the ray IJK.

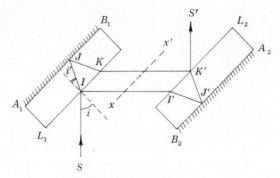

FIG. 4.16   A Jamin interferometer.

The two rays II' and KK' are parallel and have a great path difference between them because of the thickness of the plates. Arriving at plate L_2, they give rise to several reflected and refracted rays. We consider only the reflected ray $K'S'$ caused by the ray KK', and the ray $I'J'K'S'$, caused by II'. The two rays $SII'J'K'S'$ and $SIJKK'S'$, which are superposed, have traveled along symmetrical paths, have undergone the same reflections and refractions, and have had the same amplitude. If the two plates are strictly parallel, the path difference is zero, whatever the inclination of the rays may be. We let the fringes at infinity appear by slightly inclining one of the plates with respect to the other. The path difference depends only on the direction of the rays that interfere, and we obtain good fringes of equal inclination. The extended source can have any position, and the fringes are observed by means of a telescope adjusted to infinity. We assume that the angles of incidence of the rays are approximately 45° and that the edge of the wedge formed by the two plates is projected along xx'. The fringes at infinity are fringes parallel to xx', with angular spacing between two consecutive fringes given by

$$\alpha = \frac{\lambda}{4e\theta} (2n^2 - 1)^{1/2}, \qquad (4.22)$$

where e and n are the thickness and the index of refraction of the plates, respectively, and 2θ is the angle between their normals.

Chapter V

Standing Waves

In the interference instruments discussed in Chapter 4 the two waves which arrive and interfere at the point of observation have almost the same direction. We can also observe the interferences of two waves propagated in opposite directions. This phenomenon occurs when an incident wave interferes with a wave reflected by a plane mirror.

5.1 Normal Incidence

A beam of parallel light is directed at normal incidence toward a plane mirror M (Fig. 5.1). The reflected rays interfere with the incident rays and we have standing waves. We can assume that the vibrations which interfere at some point A originate at the source and its image with respect to the mirror M. If $OA = x$, the path difference of these two vibrations is $\delta = 2x$. If φ is the phase change due to the reflection in O on the mirror, the phase difference of the two vibrations is

$$\frac{4\pi x}{\lambda} + \varphi. \tag{5.1}$$

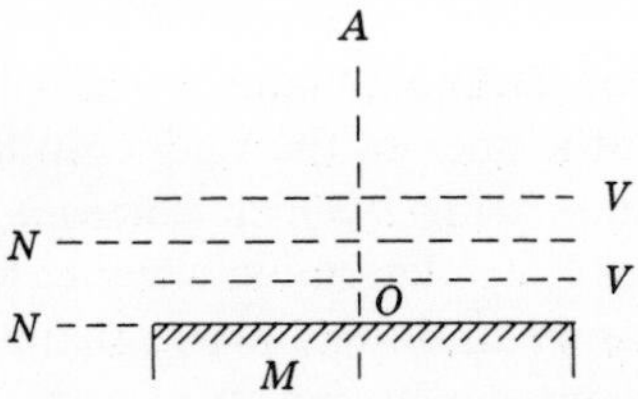

FIG. 5.1 Stationary waves in normal incidence.

If $\sqrt{I_1}$ and $\sqrt{I_2}$ are the amplitudes of the vibrations transported by the two rays, the intensity is

$$I = I_1 + I_2 + 2\sqrt{I_1}\sqrt{I_2} \cos\left(\frac{4\pi x}{\lambda} + \varphi\right). \tag{5.2}$$

101

There will be a maximum for

$$\frac{4\pi x}{\lambda} + \varphi = 2K\pi, \qquad x = \left(K - \frac{\varphi}{2\pi}\right)\frac{\lambda}{2}. \tag{5.3}$$

The planes located at a distance x from the mirror, and which satisfy (5.3), are antinodal planes. Their separation is $\lambda/2$.

The intensity I is minimum for

$$\frac{4\pi x}{\lambda} = \varphi = (2K + 1)\pi, \qquad x = \left(K + \frac{1}{2} - \frac{\varphi}{2\pi}\right)\frac{\lambda}{2}. \tag{5.4}$$

The planes defined by (5.4) are nodal, and their separation is also $\lambda/2$. All of these planes are equidistant; the distance from a nodal to an antinodal plane is $\lambda/4$. There is a maximum of light on the antinodal planes, a minimum on the nodal. In spite of the very small separation (of the order of $0.1\,\mu$) between an antinodal and a nodal plane, Wiener succeeded in demonstrating them by photographing the phenomenon on a collodion emulsion with silver bromide of a thickness of $\lambda/30$. The emulsion is deposited at a very small angle to the mirror M on the plane surface (AB) of a glass plate (Fig. 5.2). The mirror is metalized so that the amplitudes $\sqrt{I_1}$ and $\sqrt{I_2}$ are nearly equal and the contrast of the phenomenon is adequate.

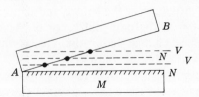

FIG. 5.2   Wiener's experiment.

The emulsion cuts the antinodal and nodal planes into a system of straight lines parallel to the apex of the wedge. In fact, we observe a series of parallel and equidistant fringes which correspond to the intersections with the antinodal planes V. To determine whether the surface of the mirror corresponds to a nodal or an antinodal plane, that is, whether the reflection occurs with or without a change in sign, the sensitive emulsion is deposited not on a plane but on a spherical surface to obtain optical contact. AB is deposited on a glass lens L (Fig. 5.3). The lower surface of L is blackened to

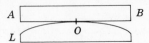

FIG. 5.3   Phase change of π brought about by air-glass reflection.

avoid all parasitic reflections. The photograph shows a system of rings analogous to Newton's rings and the central part O corresponds to a light minima. Hence there is a node for the luminous vibration at the contact of L in O and $\varphi = \pi$. The same is true of the mirror M whose surface corresponds to a nodal plane. It is the electric field vector that has a node on the mirror, and it is the electric field vector that corresponds to the photochemical action of the luminous vibration recorded in Wiener's experiments. On a metalized surface and, for example, on a silvered surface the reflecting surface is not exactly a node. The system of standing waves would be the same if the first node were contained within the metal at a distance from the surface of $\lambda/20$. Because the thickness of the collodion film in Wiener's experiment is of the same order of magnitude, this difference cannot be demonstrated.

Wiener's experiment was repeated by Drude and Nernst who replaced the photographic film with a thin fluorescent emulsion. The fluorescent film is deposited on the surface of a half-metalized glass plate and the device is illuminated by ultraviolet light. It is found that the nonmetalized region shows a stronger fluorescence than the metalized region, in which the stationary waves are weak because of the large difference in amplitudes. Because the fluorescence is less visible on the metalized part, the waves annihilate one another. To the accuracy of the experiment the reflection introduces a phase change of π.

5.2 Color Photography

We consider a mirror M (Fig. 5.4) covered with a sensitive, rather thick film of silver chloride of extremely fine grain. We illuminate it normally with a beam of monochromatic light λ_0. On all the antinodal planes the

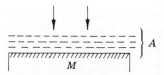

FIG. 5.4 Color photography with the help of stationary waves (Lippmann).

silver is reduced, and we obtain a series of reflecting layers of reduced silver separated by $\lambda_0/2$. We illuminate them with white light: for the radiation λ_0 the reflected light for all these planes is in phase, for, because of the reflection, the path difference between two planes is twice $\lambda_0/2$. For another radiation, even for one near λ_0, this is no longer so if there is a large number of layers. We calculate the spectral bandwidth of the reflected light in the neighborhood of the wavelength λ_0, which has served to expose the sensitive film. We assume that the system is illuminated by white light, but we study the behavior near λ_0. As phase origin we take the phase of the first reflected ray. If φ is the phase difference between one ray and the next, the vibrations reflected by the surfaces 2, 3, 4, ..., etc. (Fig. 5.5), are written

$$e^{-j\varphi}, e^{-j2\varphi}, e^{-j3\varphi}, \ldots .$$

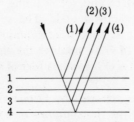

FIG. 5.5   Rays reflected by the layers of reduced silver.

If we assume (in order to simplify) that all the amplitudes are equal, the total amplitude is

$$U = 1 + e^{-j\varphi} + e^{-j2\varphi} + \cdots + e^{-j(n-1)\varphi},$$

where n is the number of reflecting planes. We then have

$$U = \frac{1 - e^{-jn\varphi}}{1 - e^{-j\varphi}}. \tag{5.5}$$

We get the intensity by multiplying this quantity by its conjugate (Fig. 5.6).

$$I = \frac{\sin^2(n\varphi/2)}{\sin^2(\varphi/2)}. \tag{5.6}$$

The path difference from one plane to the next is λ_0. Thus $\varphi = (2\pi/\lambda)\lambda_0$ and we can write I in the form

$$I = \frac{\sin^2(n\pi\lambda_0/\lambda)}{\sin^2(\pi\lambda_0/\lambda)}.$$

The first minimum occurs for the wavelength λ given by

$$\frac{n\pi\lambda_0}{\lambda} = n\pi \pm \pi.$$

We have therefore

$$\lambda - \lambda_0 = \frac{\lambda_0}{n}.$$

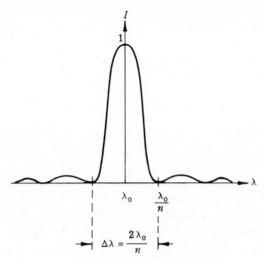

FIG. 5.6   Spectral width of the reflected light.

If we take $d\lambda$, the width corresponding to the first two null minima of the curve, as the width of the spectral band we have

$$d\lambda = \frac{2\lambda_0}{n},$$

taking $n = 500$ and $\lambda_0 = 0.5\,\mu$; we get $d\lambda = 20$ Å. The reflection can be very selective. The plate, illuminated by white light reflects almost entirely monochromatic light of wavelength λ_0 to which it was originally exposed. If we illuminate an extremely fine-grained film, backed by a reflecting mirror, with white light, we obtain in each point of the plate a whole system of reflecting films, characteristic of the radiations received at this point. By observing the plate in reflection at normal incidence in white light, we see that the light reflected by each point of the plate reproduces the color to which it was exposed. This is the principle of interferential color photography invented by Lippmann in 1891.

5.3   Oblique Incidence

We direct a beam of parallel rays to a mirror M (Fig. 5.7) at almost grazing incidence ($i \simeq \pi/2$). A ray such as SI produces a reflected ray IR which can interfere with an incident ray ST. In this way we obtain plane parallel standing waves on the mirror M. For an angle of incidence i the separation of the planes is $\lambda/2 \cos i$. Because the incidence is almost grazing,

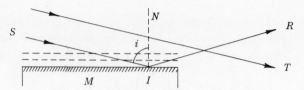

FIG. 5.7   Stationary waves in grazing incidence.

we can see dark fringes in a plane N normal to M, which are the inter-sections of the nodal planes with the plane of observation N. We find that there is a dark fringe in the plane of the mirror which once again shows the phase change equal to π, introduced by the air–glass reflection.

We assume that the mirror M (Fig. 5.8) is illuminated by a beam of parallel rays under an oblique nongrazing incidence; for example, under the angle of incidence 45°. It is necessary that the mirror M has a high

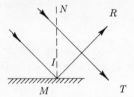

FIG. 5.8   Stationary waves for an incidence near 45°.

reflectance so that the amplitudes of the interfering amplitudes may be approximately equal. We polarize the light in such a way that the incident vibrations are in the plane of incidence. The fringes are not visible. In fact at A, in the reflected beam (Fig. 5.9) the vibration is directed along Ax, whereas in the transmitted ray IT the vibration Ay is unchanged. The two rectangular vibrations Ax and Ay produce an elliptical vibration whose intensity is always equal to the sum of the intensities of the component vibrations, whatever their phase difference may be. If the light is polarized so that the incident vibrations are perpendicular to the plane of incidence

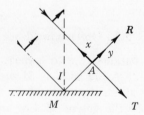

FIG. 5.9   Vibrations in the plane of incidence cannot interfere at A.

(Fig. 5.10) in A, the vibrations are parallel and there are interferences. In fact, we find that the fringes have their maximum visibility.

The phenomenon is the same at the luminous source: if the vibrations originating from the source are orthogonal, there is no interference.

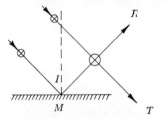

FIG. 5.10   Vibrations perpendicular to the plane of incidence interfere at A.

Chapter VI

Multiple Beam Interferences

6.1 Introduction

In the phenomena already studied we have considered interferences produced by only two waves, originating from the same point of the source and having a certain path difference. We have not taken into account the waves produced by reflection because, in general, the plate has a small reflectance and these waves have negligible amplitudes. However, if we make the plate highly reflective, we can no longer neglect them. We shall now study the phenomena they produce. To begin with, we define the reflectance of a surface as the ratio

$$R = \frac{\text{reflected energy}}{\text{incident energy}}. \tag{6.1}$$

The reflectance R is always smaller than 1. If we consider the reflection, no longer in intensity but in amplitude, we can define a complex coefficient of reflection r. If ρ is the reflected fraction of the amplitude and φ' the phase delay at reflection, we have

$$r = \rho e^{-j\varphi'} \tag{6.2}$$

with

$$R = rr^* = \rho^2. \tag{6.3}$$

In the reflection from glass r is real ($\varphi' = 0$ or $\varphi' = \pi$) and easily calculated with Fresnel's equations. In metallic reflection r is complex. We define transmittance as the ratio

$$T = \frac{\text{transmitted energy}}{\text{incident energy}}. \tag{6.4}$$

If τ is the transmitted fraction of the amplitude and φ', the phase delay introduced in crossing the surface or the semireflecting film, we define a complex transmission coefficient as

$$t = \tau e^{-j\varphi'} \tag{6.5}$$

108

with

$$T = tt^* = \tau^2.\tag{6.6}$$

In the case of transparent media t is real and we have $t = \tau$. In metallic films t is complex. If the media are transparent, all the incident energy reappears in the reflected and transmitted energy. The conservation of the energy permits us to write

$$R + T = 1.\tag{6.7}$$

In metallic reflection a fraction A of the energy is lost by absorption. We have

$$R + T + A = 1.\tag{6.8}$$

6.2   Fringes Produced by a Plane Parallel Plate at Infinity by Transmission

We consider two parallel semireflecting surfaces AB and $A'B'$ (Fig. 6.1). An incident ray SI_1 produces a whole series of reflected rays, J_1I_2, I_2J_2, J_2I_3, etc., and from the system formed by AB and $A'B'$ a beam of parallel rays (1) (2) (3) emerges. We calculate the complex amplitudes of these rays.

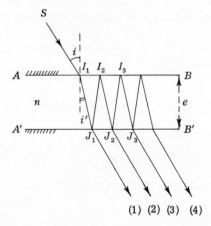

FIG. 6.1   Multiple-beam interference by transmission.

The amplitude and the intensity of the incident ray SI_1 are assumed to be unity. We also assume that the media located above AB and below $A'B'$ are identical. This means that the reflections on AB and $A'B'$ (between AB and $A'B'$) are identical. The separating surfaces AB and $A'B'$ can be characterized by the same coefficient t (transmission) and the same coefficient r (reflection).

Rays	Amplitude
I_1J_1	t
J_1I_2	tr
I_2J_2	tr^2
J_2I_3	tr^3
$\vdots$	$\vdots$

These amplitudes take into account the phase shifts at reflection and transmission by the surfaces AB and $A'B'$.

The transmitted vibrations corresponding to the rays (1), (2), (3), are

$$t^2, t^2r^2e^{-j\varphi}, t^2r^4e^{-j2\varphi}, \ldots,$$

with

$$\varphi = \frac{4\pi ne \cos i'}{\lambda}, \tag{6.9}$$

where e is the thickness of the plate between AB and $A'B'$ and n is its index of refraction.

All rays are parallel and can interfere at infinity. We observe therefore the phenomena in the focal plane F of lens O (Fig. 6.2), as in the case of

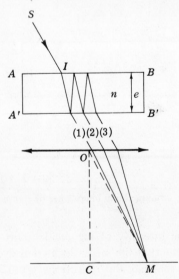

FIG. 6.2 Observation of multiple-beam fringes at infinity by transmission.

fringes of two waves at infinity. At a point M on the focal plane the amplitude of the vibration is given by the sum

$$U_M = t^2 + t^2 r^2 e^{-j\varphi} + t^2 r^4 e^{-j2\varphi} + \cdots. \tag{6.10}$$

Hence for an infinite number of beams we have

$$U = \frac{t^2}{1 - r^2 e^{-j\varphi}}. \tag{6.11}$$

If φ' is the phase shift at reflection given by (6.2), the intensity in M is given by

$$I_M = \frac{t^2}{1 - r^2 e^{-j\varphi}} \cdot \frac{(t^*)^2}{1 - (r^*)^2 e^{j\varphi}} = \frac{T^2}{1 - 2R\cos(\varphi + 2\varphi') + R^2}. \tag{6.12}$$

We set

$$\Phi = \varphi + 2\varphi' \tag{6.13}$$

to obtain

$$1 + R^2 - 2R\cos\Phi = (1 - R)^2 + 4R\sin^2\frac{\Phi}{2}, \tag{6.14}$$

from which

$$I_M = \frac{T^2}{(1-R)^2}\left[1 + \frac{4R}{(1-R)^2}\sin^2\frac{\Phi}{2}\right]^{-1}. \tag{6.15}$$

The maximum intensity is given by

$$I_0 = \frac{T^2}{(1-R)^2}. \tag{6.16}$$

By choosing

$$F = \frac{4R}{(1-R)^2} \tag{6.17}$$

we obtain

$$I_M = \frac{I_0}{1 + F\sin^2(\Phi/2)} \tag{6.18}$$

Equations 6.12, 6.15 or 6.18 are called Airy's formulas.
There is a bright ring in M if $\sin^2(\Phi/2) = 0$.

$$\frac{\Phi}{2} = \frac{\pi 2ne\cos i'}{\lambda} + \varphi' = K\pi \tag{6.19}$$

Equation 6.18 shows that the minima corresponding to $\sin^2(\Phi/2) = 1$ are no longer equal to zero. Their intensity is $I_0/(1 + F)$ and the contrast is

$$\gamma = \frac{I_{\max} - I_{\min}}{I_{\max}} = \frac{F}{1 + F} = \frac{4R}{(1 + R)^2}. \tag{6.20}$$

Being weak when R is small, the contrast improves when R approaches 1.

Figure 6.3 shows the variations of $I = f(\Phi)$ according to (6.18).

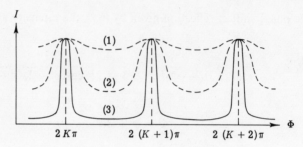

FIG. 6.3   Distribution of intensity in multiple-beam fringes.

The curves (1), (2), (3) represent the structure of the fringes for increasing values of R.

If R is high, the fringes appear in the form of fine, bright fringes against an almost black background. If p is the order of interference in some point M of the focal plane of the lens, we have

$$p = \frac{\Phi}{2\pi} = \frac{2ne \cos i'}{\lambda} + \frac{\varphi'}{2\pi}. \tag{6.21}$$

At the center c:

$$p_0 = \frac{2ne}{\lambda} + \frac{\varphi'}{2\pi}. \tag{6.22}$$

If K represents the number (integers or fractions) of the fringes visible between c and M, we have

$$p = p_0 - K$$

and

$$i = \sqrt{\frac{n\lambda}{e}} \sqrt{K}. \tag{6.23}$$

If we have a bright center in c, (6.23) gives the radius of the Kth bright fringe. The same results obtain for the rings at infinity, taking into account only two waves.

6.3 Fringes Produced by a Parallel Plate: Fringes at Infinity by Reflection

We can also observe the fringes due to multiple waves by reflection (Fig. 6.4), but the calculations are more complicated because the first ray (1), which has not passed through the metallic film AB, does not belong to the same series as (2), (3), (4), etc., which have all penetrated it twice.

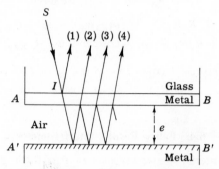

FIG. 6.4   Multiple-beam interference by reflection.

Let ρ_1 be the factor of reflection in amplitude of the metal $A'B'$. The factor of reflection in amplitude air–metal of AB is ρ_2. It is different from ρ_3, which corresponds to the glass–metal reflection. The phase changes at the air–metal $A'B'$, air–metal AB, and glass–metal $A'B'$ reflections are equal to φ_1', φ_2' and φ_3', respectively. The phase change due to the transmission of the metal film AB is β. The factor of transmission in amplitude of AB is τ. The amplitudes of the reflected rays are

(1) $\rho_3 e^{j\varphi_3'}$,
(2) $\tau^2 \rho_1 e^{j(2\varphi + \varphi_1' + 2\beta)}$,
(3) $\tau^2 \rho_1 \rho_2 \rho_1 e^{j(2\varphi + \varphi_1' + \varphi_2' + 2\varphi + \varphi_1' + 2\beta)}$,

$$\vdots$$

with

$$\varphi = \frac{2\pi e \cos i}{\lambda}. \tag{6.24}$$

The resulting amplitude U in the direction of the reflected rays is

$$U = \rho_3 e^{j\varphi_3'} + \tau^2 \rho_1 e^{j(2\varphi + \varphi_1' + 2\beta)}[1 + \rho_2 \rho_1 e^{j(\varphi_2' + 2\varphi + \varphi_1')} + \cdots],$$

from which

$$U = \rho_3 e^{j\varphi_3'} + \frac{\tau^2 \rho_1 e^{j(2\varphi + \varphi_1' + 2\beta)}}{1 - \rho_2 \rho_1 e^{j(\varphi_2' + 2\varphi + \varphi_1')}}. \tag{6.25}$$

We multiply the second term of the second member of (6.25) by the conjugate of the denominator. We have

$$U = \rho_3 e^{j\varphi_3'} + \frac{\tau^2 \rho_1 e^{j(2\varphi + \varphi_1' + 2\beta)} - \tau^2 \rho_2 \rho_1{}^2 e^{j(2\beta - \varphi_2')}}{1 + \rho_2{}^2 \rho_1{}^2 - 2\rho_2 \rho_1 \cos(\varphi_2' + 2\varphi + \varphi_1')}. \tag{6.26}$$

By taking the product UU^* we obtain the intensity I, and by setting $\rho_1{}^2 = R_1$, $\rho_2{}^2 = R_2$, $\rho_3{}^2 = R_3$, and $\tau^2 = T$, we have

$$I = R_3 + \frac{T^2 R_1 + T^2 R_2 R_1{}^2 - 2T^2 \rho_1 \rho_2 R_1 \cos(2\varphi + \varphi_1' + \varphi_2')}{[1 + R_1 R_2 - 2\rho_1 \rho_2 \cos(2\varphi + \varphi_1' + \varphi_2')]^2}$$

$$+ \frac{2\rho_1 \rho_3 T \cos(2\varphi + \varphi_1' + 2\beta - \varphi_3') - 2\rho_2 \rho_3 R_1 T \cos(2\beta - \varphi_2' - \varphi_3')}{1 + R_1 R_2 - 2\rho_1 \rho_2 \cos(2\varphi + \varphi_1' + \varphi_2')}.$$

$$\tag{6.27}$$

6.4   Fabry–Perot's Interferometer

Fabry–Perot's interferometer consists of two thick glass plates whose separation can be adjusted. The opposite faces AB and $A'B'$ (Fig. 6.5) have a high reflectance. We have given these plates a slightly prismatic form so that the rings produced by the two other faces are rejected outside the field.

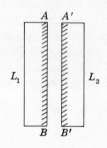

FIG. 6.5   A Fabry–Perot interferometer.

We then observe the rings at infinity produced by the air plate contained between AB and $A'B'$. The observation is made with a telescope focused at infinity (Fig. 6.6).

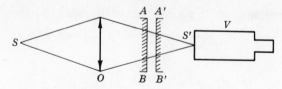

FIG. 6.6   Observation of fringes in a Fabry–Perot interferometer.

If a source S of small dimensions is available, it is convenient to project its image S' near the entrance pupil of the telescope by means of a lens O. The interferometer is placed in front of the objective lens of the telescope.

A mechanical device permits us to fix the distance between the two faces AB and $A'B'$ by using three spacers of the same thickness. In this way we obtain an interferometric standard.

6.5   Study of the Phenomena Inside the Fabry–Perot Interferometer

By considering the applications of the Fabry–Perot interferometer as a resonant cavity for lasers we can study the phenomena inside the inter-ferometer. We take a point M located between the two surfaces AB and $A'B'$, which constitute the interferometer (Fig. 6.7). We assume that the thin films that produce the semireflection at the faces AB and $A'B'$ are dielectric and that there are no losses by absorption. Hence the relation $R + T = 1$ is satisfied. The coefficients r and t are real. The interferometer is illuminated by a beam of parallel rays with an angle of incidence i and we assume that the two surfaces AB and $A'B'$ are identical. To simplify the calculations we also assume that the index of refraction n is the same inside and outside the interferometer. Two distinct series of rays arrive in M:

(a)   Rays $a_1, a_2, a_3, \ldots$,

(b)   Rays $b_1, b_2, b_3, \ldots$,

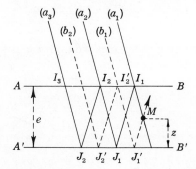

FIG. 6.7   Phenomena in the interior of a Fabry–Perot interferometer.

The amplitudes of the rays a are

rays: $IM, \qquad I_2 J_1 I_1 M, \qquad I_3 J_2 I_2 J_1 I_1 M, \ldots,$

amplitudes: $t, \qquad tr^2, \qquad tr^4, \ldots.$

These rays in M according to (6.10), (6.11) and (6.15) have an amplitude of

$$U_a = \frac{t}{1 - r^2} \left(1 + F \sin^2 \frac{\varphi}{2} \right)^{-1/2}. \tag{6.28}$$

The amplitudes of the rays of the series b are given by

rays: $I_2'J_1'M, \qquad I_3J_2'I_2'J_1'M, \dots,$

amplitudes: $tr, \qquad tr^3, \dots.$

In M these rays have an amplitude of

$$U_b = \frac{tr}{1 - r^2} \left(1 + F \sin^2 \frac{\varphi}{2} \right)^{-1/2}. \tag{6.29}$$

The phase difference between these two systems is

$$\psi = \frac{4\pi nz \cos i}{\lambda}, \tag{6.30}$$

where z is the distance between M and the plane $A'B'$. We assume that the inclination i of the rays remains small, and under these conditions the vibrations in M are parallel. The intensity in M is

$$I = U_a^2 + U_b^2 + 2U_aU_b \cos \psi \cdot$$

where

$$I = (U_a - U_b)^2 + 4U_aU_b \cos^2 \frac{\psi}{2}. \tag{6.31}$$

If the factor of reflection of the planes AB and $A'B'$ is large enough, we can neglect $(U_a - U_b)^2$ and write

$$I = 4U_aU_b \cos^2 \frac{\psi}{2}. \tag{6.32}$$

Then

$$4U_aU_b = \frac{4T\sqrt{R}}{(1 - R)^2} \left(1 + F \sin^2 \frac{\varphi}{2} \right)^{-1} = \frac{4\sqrt{R}}{1 - R} \left(1 + F \sin^2 \frac{\varphi}{2} \right)^{-1}.$$

We set

$$\frac{4\sqrt{R}}{1 - R} \left(1 + F \sin^2 \frac{\varphi}{2} \right)^{-1} = I_1, \tag{6.33}$$

and have, for a given inclination,

$$I = I_1 \cos^2\left(\frac{2\pi n z \cos i}{\lambda}\right).$$
(6.34)

A whole series of fringes appears between AB and $A'B'$ (Fig. 6.8). The intensity is constant in all points of a plane corresponding to a particular value of z. A plane corresponds to a maximum of intensity if

$$z = \frac{K\lambda}{2n \cos i},$$
(6.35)

and the interval Δz which separates two planes of maximum intensity is

$$\Delta z = \frac{\lambda}{2n \cos i}.$$
(6.36)

FIG. 6.8   Calculation of the distance ΔZ separating two planes of maximum intensity.

The variation of the intensity along a direction perpendicular to AB and $A'B'$ is sinusoidal.

According to (6.33), (6.34), and (6.35), the intensity of the bright fringes (antinodal planes) is

$$I_1 = \frac{4\sqrt{R}}{1 - R}\left(1 + F \sin^2 \frac{\varphi}{2}\right)^{-1}.$$

The maximum value of I_1 corresponds to

$$I_1 = \frac{4\sqrt{R}}{1 - R},$$

and with $R = 0.94$ we have $I_1 = 64$. Hence there are plane zones inside the interferometer in which the luminous intensity is much larger than in the incident wave. The number of plane fringes is given by

$$\frac{e}{\Delta z} = \frac{2ne \cos i}{\lambda} = K.$$
(6.37)

If K is even, the median plane is nodal. It is antinodal for odd K. We take a coordinate system $Oxyz$ (Fig. 6.9) in which Oz is normal to the planes AB and $A'B'$, Ox is parallel to AB and $A'B'$ and in the plane of incidence, and Oy is normal to the plane of incidence. The vibration in M due to series a has an amplitude U_a and its phase at the point M is $[n(x \sin i - z \cos i)]/c$.

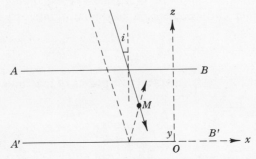

FIG. 6.9   Choice of a system of axes for the calculation of the phenomena in Fabry–Perot interferometer.

The vibration in M can be written

$$U_a \cos \omega \left(t - \frac{x \sin i - z \cos i}{c/n} \right).$$

Similarly, the vibration in M due to series b is written

$$U_b \cos \omega \left(t - \frac{x \sin i + z \cos i}{c/n} \right),$$

from which the resulting vibration in M is

$$V^{(r)}(t) = 2U_a U_b \cos \frac{2\pi nz \cos i}{\lambda} \cos \omega \left(t - \frac{x \sin i}{c/n} \right).$$

The phase of this vibration is

$$\Phi = \frac{\omega x \sin i}{c/n} = \frac{2\pi}{\lambda}(nx \sin i). \tag{6.38}$$

The phase is constant along Oz and Oy because Φ depends only on x. In normal incidence the phase is also constant along Ox. When we pass from one fringe to another (from one antinodal plane to another) $\cos 2\pi nz/\lambda$ changes its sign and consequently the phase changes abruptly by a factor π. Hence the phase is constant at the center of the volume of one fringe, but two consecutive fringes oscillate in phase opposition. The wave inside the Fabry–Perot is a standing wave.

6.6 Fabry–Perot Interferometer with Confocal Spherical Surfaces
(P. Connes)

In the multiple reflection interferometer due to P. Connes the two semi-reflecting surfaces are spherical and their focal planes are coincident. The center of curvature of each mirror is located on the opposite mirror. Figure 6.10 is a diagram of the instrument. The lower half of each mirror is totally reflecting, the upper half (above M_1 and M_2) semitransparent. SI is an incident ray that reaches the mirror M_2 at a point J located in the semi-reflecting region. One part travels along JT, but others are reflected at J, I', J', and I, and beginning at this point the reflected ray is combined with the initial ray IJ. In the paraxial region the path difference between the

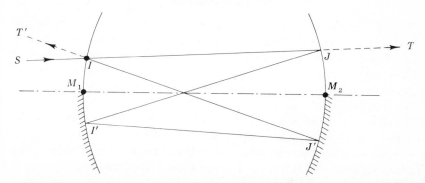

FIG. 6.10 A Fabry–Perot interferometer with confocal spherical surfaces (P. Connes).

initial ray IJ which travels along JT and the ray $IJI'J'IT$ which also travels along JT is equal to $4e$ if $e = M_1M_2$. One part of the ray $IJI'J'IT$ is reflected in J and the phenomenon repeats itself. A third ray travels along JT which has followed the same path as before and which has a path difference of $4e$ with the preceding ray or $8e$ with the initial ray. Hence we have a whole series of rays which originate from the incident ray SI and travel along JT. Instead of obtaining a series of *parallel* emerging rays originating from one incident ray, as in the Fabry–Perot interferometer, we have a series of overlapping rays traveling along JT. The phase difference φ between two consecutive emerging rays is given by

$$\varphi = \frac{2\pi}{\lambda}(4e), \tag{6.39}$$

which is independent of the inclination of the rays and their azimuth within the limits of the Gaussian approximation. The luminous intensity is given by (6.18) in which the phase difference Φ (by neglecting φ') has the value given by (6.39). Hence we observe a flat tint all over the field. If the rays are inclined on the axis, the third-order aberrations produce variations of the path difference. In fact, we find that the original flat tint is surrounded by circular fringes. It is possible to reduce the aberrations by placing two identical circular diaphragms centered on M_1 and M_2. This interferometer is particularly suited to the large path differences corresponding to a high spectral resolution. Connes' interferometer is readily adaptable to a resonant cavity for lasers. The adjustment consists only in selecting the distance M_1M_2 and there is no need to worry about the orientation of the mirrors.

6.7   Phenomena Produced if the Incident Light is Composed of Two Simple Radiations

If several simple radiations simultaneously illuminate an interferometric instrument for multiple reflections, each radiation transmits a system of bright fringes, and because of the fineness of the fringes they can be placed side by side without overlapping. We shall study the case in which the incident beam contains two monochromatic radiations and use the Fabry–Perot interferometer.

We take a radiation of wavelength λ; at a point on the observation plane at which the phase difference Φ equals $2\pi\delta/\lambda$ the order of interference is $p = \delta/\lambda$. If we have a second radiation λ', the order of interference $p' = \delta/\lambda'$ at the same point differs from p. The radiation λ' also produces a system of bright fringes, but the fringes corresponding to λ' will be more widely spaced than those corresponding to λ if $\lambda < \lambda'$.

To simplify these calculations we arrange the two systems of bright fringes, one above the other (Fig. 6.11). By varying the spacing e of the

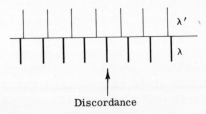

Discordance

FIG. 6.11 Disposition of fringes when the light is composed of two simple radiations (discordance).

interferometer, we observe the following phenomenon: for a certain value of e one fringe of the system of wavelength λ appears approximately at the center of the interval separating two fringes of the wavelength λ'; there is discordance.

For another spacing of the interferometer we observe two fringes of wavelength λ between two fringes of wavelength λ'. We define this as coincidence (Fig. 6.12). This separation, followed by discordance and a new coincidence, is repeated again and again. Let us calculate the period of the coincidences.

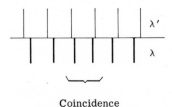

Coincidence

FIG. 6.12 Disposition of fringes when the light is composed of two simple radiations (coincidence).

If δ_1 is the path difference in the region of observation for a coincidence, we have

$$\frac{\delta_1}{\lambda} = \frac{\delta_1}{\lambda'} + K,$$ (6.40)

where K is the difference between the orders of interference corresponding to λ and λ'. It represents the number of coincidences counted from the path difference zero ($\delta = 0$). By varying e we observe in the same region the following coincidence when the path difference is equal to δ_2. Between these two coincidences one of the systems has one fringe more than the other. Therefore we can write

$$\frac{\delta_2}{\lambda} = \frac{\delta_2}{\lambda'} + K + 1.$$ (6.41)

If we observe n coincidences, we will have for the nth

$$\frac{\delta}{\lambda} = \frac{\delta}{\lambda'} + K + n.$$ (6.42)

$N = K + n$ is the true number of these coincidences from the path difference zero ($\delta = 0$). Equation 6.42 can be written

$$\delta = N \frac{\lambda\lambda'}{\lambda' - \lambda}.$$ (6.43)

The quantity $\lambda\lambda'/(\lambda' - \lambda)$ is called the period of the coincidences of the two radiations. These coincidences repeat themselves for all values of δ

that are multiples of length $\lambda\lambda'/(\lambda' - \lambda)$. According to (6.21), we have

$$\delta = 2e \cos i' + \frac{\varphi'}{2\pi},$$

from which the path difference at the center is

$$\delta = 2e + \frac{\varphi'}{2\pi}.$$

Between two successive coincidences corresponding to δ_1 and δ_2 (6.43) gives

$$\delta_2 - \delta_1 = 2(e_2 - e_1) = \frac{\lambda\lambda'}{\lambda' - \lambda}. \tag{6.44}$$

The period of the coincidences corresponds to a variation in the spacing $e_2 - e_1$ of the interferometer which is obviously always the same (φ' does not enter into the calculation).

Equations 6.43 and 6.44 are also applied to the discordances that are very easily observed.

We assume that the spacing e at the center is such that there is discordance. It is sufficient to modify the spacing of the interferometer slightly so that the rings λ are no longer exactly in the center of the rings λ' and lack of symmetry can be easily observed.

For the thickness e_2 the next discordance occurs according to relation (6.44). Let m be the number of rings, corresponding to wavelength λ, which pass through a given point of the field when the thickness varies by $e_2 - e_1$. We have

$$2(e_2 - e_1) = m\lambda = \frac{\lambda\lambda'}{\lambda' - \lambda}. \tag{6.45}$$

The phenomena of coincidence and discordance can also be observed in the fringes of two beams. The formulas are the same, but the fringes are much broader and disappear completely at the moment of discordance.

6.8   Limit of Resolution of the Fabry–Perot Interferometer

Figure 6.13 shows that it is possible to separate two radiations with wavelengths close to each other if the fringes are correspondingly fine.

Let us define the width of a fringe by the interval between two points at which the intensity is equal to one half its maximum value (Fig. 6.13). According to (6.18) we have

$$\frac{I_0}{1 + F \sin^2 \Phi/2} = \frac{I_0}{2},$$

from which

$$\sin\frac{\Phi}{2} = \frac{1}{\sqrt{F}}. \tag{6.46}$$

Because the fringes are fine, this value is reached for a value of Φ close to $2K\pi$:

$$\Phi = 2K\pi + d\Phi. \tag{6.47}$$

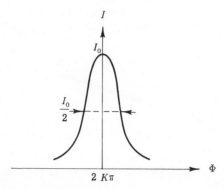

FIG. 6.13   The width of a fringe can be characterized by the interval in whose interior the intensity is equal to half the maximum intensity.

By carrying over into (6.46) we have

$$d\Phi = \frac{2}{\sqrt{F}} = \frac{1 - R}{\sqrt{R}}. \tag{6.48}$$

This expression gives the half-width of the fringe as a function of R. If we have two neighboring radiations, λ and $\lambda + d\lambda$, a variation $d\lambda$ of the wavelength corresponds to a variation $d\Phi'$ of the phase difference Φ' given by

$$\Phi' = \frac{2\pi\Delta'}{\lambda} \qquad \frac{d\Phi'}{\Phi'} = -\frac{d\lambda}{\lambda}. \tag{6.49}$$

To separate these two wavelengths, it is necessary that the distance separating the center of a bright fringe of wavelength λ from the center of a bright fringe of wavelength $\lambda + d\lambda$ be equal to double the value $d\Phi$ given by (6.48). We have

$$d\Phi' = \Phi'\frac{d\lambda}{\lambda} \geqslant \frac{2(1 - R)}{\sqrt{R}}.$$

In this expression we have $\Phi' = 2K\pi$. Hence

$$d\lambda \geqslant \lambda\frac{1 - R}{K\pi\sqrt{R}}. \tag{6.50}$$

We define the resolving power $\mathscr{R}$ as the ratio

$$\mathscr{R} = \frac{\lambda}{d\lambda} = \frac{K\pi\sqrt{R}}{1-R}. \tag{6.51}$$

The distance separating two bright fringes is equal to 2π in phase difference. The width $[2(1-R)]/\sqrt{R}$ of a fringe can be expressed as a fraction of the interval of two bright fringes. If the width of a fringe is N times smaller than the distance separating two fringes, we obtain

$$\frac{2\pi}{N} = \frac{2(1-R)}{\sqrt{R}}, \qquad N = \frac{\pi\sqrt{R}}{1-R}$$

from which

$$\mathscr{R} = KN; \tag{6.52}$$

but according to (6.47) K is just the order of interference $p = \Phi/2\pi$ corresponding to the phase difference $\Phi = 2K\pi$. Consequently the expression (6.52) can be written

$$\mathscr{R} = pN. \tag{6.53}$$

For a given value of N, depending on the reflectance R, it is, therefore advantageous to make p as large as possible. According to (6.22), and by neglecting φ', we have $p = 2ne/\lambda$.

Hence we obtain high resolving powers by choosing large thicknesses. As a result, we can, theoretically, separate the components of a double line, close as they may be, by giving sufficient spacing to the interferometer. Obviously, each component must produce clear fringes and, therefore, its width should not be too great. The resolving power of the Fabry–Perot interferometer is limited only by the widths of the spectral lines to be separated.

6.9   Interference Filters

We illuminate an interferential Fabry–Perot standard in parallel light. Let us use a white-light source and analyze the transmitted light with a spectroscope. According to (6.18), the wavelengths corresponding to $\sin^2(\Phi/2) = 0$ produce maxima of light. Beyond the values of λ, defined by this equation, light is not transmitted. We observe therefore a channeled spectrum formed of fine bright bands against an almost black background. If the surfaces of the interferential Fabry–Perot standard have a high reflective power, the bands are narrow. By giving the standard suitable spacing we can achieve the transmission of one bright band only in the visible spectrum. This is the principle of the transmission interference filters. In reality interference filters are true Fabry–Perot standards of narrow width in which the air plate has been replaced by a solid transparent plate (thin film). We assume that the two semireflecting surfaces of the filter are identical so that we may apply the formulas in Section 6.1. If the filter is illuminated in normal incidence, according to (6.18) the wavelengths of the bright bands are given by

$$\frac{\Phi}{2\pi} = K.$$

According to (6.19),

$$\frac{\Phi}{2\pi} = \frac{2ne}{\lambda} + \frac{\varphi'}{\pi},$$

from which, if $\varphi' = 2\pi\delta'/\lambda$,

$$\frac{\Phi}{2\pi} = \frac{2ne}{\lambda} + \frac{2\delta'}{\lambda} = \frac{\Delta}{\lambda} = K \tag{6.54}$$

The wavelengths of the bright bands are given by the values $\lambda_1 = \Delta$, $\lambda_2 = \Delta/2, \ldots$. Let us assume that $\Delta = 1.09 \,\mu$. The bands occupy these positions:

$$\lambda_1 = 1.09 \,\mu, \qquad \lambda_2 = 0.54 \,\mu, \qquad \lambda_3 = 0.36 \,\mu, \ldots.$$

In this way we obtain a filter that passes the green at $0.54 \,\mu$. The width $d\lambda$ of the transmitted band around the wavelength λ is given by (6.50):

$$d\lambda = \lambda \frac{1 - R}{K\pi\sqrt{R}}. \tag{6.55}$$

Take $R = 0.9$ and $\lambda = 0.546 \,\mu$. For the filter ($\Delta = 1.09 \,\mu$) we have approximately $\lambda = 0.546 \,\mu$, a bandwidth of the order of 80 Å ($K = 2$). Equation 6.54 shows that the bandwidth $d\lambda$ diminishes as p increases, but at the same time the distance between the bands decreases. In place of $\Delta = 1.09 \,\mu$, we take $\Delta = 2.18 \,\mu$. There are now three bright bands in the visible spectrum with wavelengths $\lambda_1 = 0.76 \,\mu$, $\lambda_2 = 0.55 \,\mu$, and $\lambda_3 = 0.44 \,\mu$. For $R = 0.9$ the band $\lambda_2 = 0.55$, has a width of $d\lambda = 45$ Å ($K = 4$). Hence we have a finer band. The other bands, $\lambda_1 = 0.76 \,\mu$ and $\lambda_3 = 0.44 \,\mu$, are separated and can be eliminated with an ordinary absorbing filter or with a larger interference filter. The fabrication of reflective interference filters is based on an analogous principle.

Remark When a Fabry–Perot interferometer with dielectric multilayers is used, the phase change with wavelength is important. This phenomenon enlarges the pass-band of an interference filter and also intervenes in the measurements of wavelength. The dispersion of phase change can be determined both theoretically and experimentally.

6.10 Fringes of Multiple Reflections of Thin Films with Variable Thickness

When the reflectance of the surfaces of a thin film is increased, the fineness of the fringes of equal thickness increases. In this way we can more easily determine very small variations of thickness or the index of refraction.

We take a wedge of an index of refraction n and an angle ε illuminated in parallel light at normal incidence (Fig. 6.14). After reflection in the plate, the emerging rays form the angles $i_1, i_2, i_3, \ldots$, with the normal at the lower surface. We then have

$$\sin i_1 = n \sin \varepsilon, \tag{6.56}$$

and for the pth ray

$$\sin i_p = n \sin(2p - 1)\varepsilon. \tag{6.57}$$

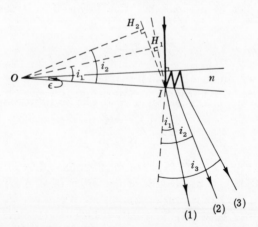

FIG. 6.14 Multiple-beam fringes due to a thin plate of variable thickness.

The path difference between ray (2) and ray (1) is

$$\delta = IH_2 - IH_1,$$

$$\delta = OI(\sin i_2 - \sin i_1) = \frac{e}{\varepsilon}(\sin i_2 - \sin i_1),$$

where e is the thickness of the wedge in the region I. The path difference between ray (p) and ray (1) is

$$\delta_p = \frac{e}{\varepsilon}(\sin i_p - \sin i_1),$$ (6.58)

or, according to (6.56), (6.57) and (6.58),

$$\delta_p = \frac{e}{\varepsilon}[n \sin(2p - 1)\varepsilon - n \sin \varepsilon],$$ (6.59)

$$\delta_p = 2n\frac{e}{\varepsilon}\cos p\varepsilon \sin(p - 1)\varepsilon.$$ (6.60)

If we take the phase shift at reflection into account, we add $(2p - 1)\delta'$ to the second member of (6.60).

If the number (p) of the rays is limited, we can expand (6.60). We assume that ε is small enough that we may neglect the terms in ε of higher order than the second.

$$\delta_p = 2ne(p - 1) - ne(p - 1)\varepsilon^2\left(\frac{4p^2 - 2p + 1}{3}\right).$$ (6.61)

The amplitudes of the transmitted waves are

$$Te^{-j\varphi_1}, TRe^{-j\varphi_2}, \ldots, TR^{p-1}e^{-j\varphi_p},$$

with

$$\varphi_p = \frac{2\pi\delta_p}{\lambda} \qquad (\varphi_1 = 0).$$ (6.62)

The amplitude in I, which results from the superposition of all these waves, is

$$U = T \sum_{p=1}^{\infty} R^{p-1}e^{-j\varphi_p}$$

and the intensity is

$$I = T^2 \left|\sum_{p=1}^{\infty} R^{p-1}e^{-j\varphi_p}\right|^2.$$ (6.63)

It is not necessary to use an infinite number of terms to have a good representation of the phenomena. For example, with 120 terms ($p = 120$), if $R = 0.93$, our error is not larger than 0.01 for the intensity. The expansion (6.61) is therefore justified.

If ε^2 can be neglected, (6.61) reduces to

$$\delta_p = 2ne(p - 1).$$ (6.64)

The phase difference between two consecutive rays $\varphi = 4\pi ne/\lambda$ is constant and the amplitude becomes

$$U = T(1 + Re^{-j\varphi} + R^2 e^{-j2\varphi} + \cdots).$$ (6.65)

This is equivalent to (6.11). The observed fringes have the same intensity distribution as the fringes at infinity given by a plane parallel plate. The bright fringes correspond to

$$2ne = K\lambda,$$ (6.66)

or, if we take phase shift at reflection into account,

$$2ne + 2\delta' = K\lambda.$$

The fringes are parallel to the apex of the wedge and their mutual separation is $\lambda/2n\varepsilon$.

To represent the phenomena by (6.64), (6.65), and (6.66) it is necessary that the term containing ε^2 in (6.61) be negligible. This term must therefore be much smaller than $\lambda/2$

$$ne(p-1)\varepsilon^2 \frac{4p^2 - 2p + 1}{3} \ll \frac{\lambda}{2}.$$ (6.67)

If p is large enough, we can write

$$ne\varepsilon^2 \frac{4p^3}{3} \ll \frac{\lambda}{2},$$

in which where

$$ne \ll \frac{3\lambda}{8p^3\varepsilon^2}.$$ (6.68)

We take a wedge with an angle ε so that the separation between the fringes is approximately 1 mm. If $n = 1$ and $\lambda = 0.55\,\mu$, we have $\varepsilon \simeq 2.5 \times 10^{-4}$. If $p = 50$, we obtain

$$ne \ll 50\lambda.$$

It is therefore necessary to observe the wedge in the very thin regions, that is, near its apex. If we cannot neglect ε^2, the phenomena are modified. In particular, the fringes are displaced and are no longer symmetrical. In a thin film of variable thickness the fringes no longer indicate lines of equal thickness. In conclusion we can say that multiple beam fringes must be used with caution. These fringes indicate the lines of equal thickness if the film is sufficiently thin.

6.11   Fringes of Superposition

We know that it is not possible to observe fringes in white light if the path difference is larger than a few wavelengths. We can observe these fringes by using two thick plates in which the path difference caused by the first is compensated in the second. We consider two plane parallel plates of approximately equal thickness, e_1 and e_2, which together form a small angle, ω (Fig. 6.15). We begin by illuminating the plates with monochromatic light. The two plane parallel plates are semireflecting, and we

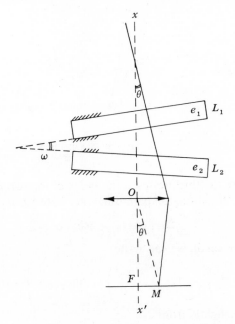

FIG. 6.15   Fringes of superposition at infinity.

choose plates whose rings at infinity, too close to one another, are almost invisible. The plane of the figure is normal to the apex of the dihedron formed by the two plates. We calculate the path difference in the direction θ with respect to the axis xx', equally inclined to the two plates. This axis coincides with the optical axis of an objective lens O, and we observe the phenomena in the focal plane F. An arbitrary incident ray produces pairs of rays which undergo internal reflections in the two plates. We consider two rays R_1 and R_2 which originate at the incident ray SI (Fig. 6.16): R_1 is reflected on the two surfaces of the plate L_1 and crosses L_2; R_2 passes through L_1 and is reflected by the two faces of L_2 before it emerges. Naturally, these rays can undergo additional reflections in the plates. It is necessary to take these reflections into account in a complete study of the phenomenon. We consider only those rays that have followed paths similar to R_1 and R_2.

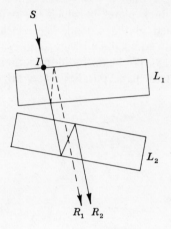

FIG. 6.16   The path of rays that interfere.

If e_1 and e_2 are the thicknesses, n the index of the two plates and r_1 and r_2, the angles of refraction, the path difference between R_1 and R_2 is

$$\delta = 2ne_1 \cos r_1 - 2ne_2 \cos r_2. \qquad (6.69)$$

If r_1 and r_2 are small, we can write

$$\delta = 2ne_1\left(1 - \frac{r_1^2}{2}\right) - 2ne_2\left(1 - \frac{r_2^2}{2}\right) = 2n(e_1 - e_2) + (r_2^2 e_2 - r_1^2 e_1)n.$$

If e_1 differs only slightly from e_2,

$$\delta = 2n(e_1 - e_2) + ne_1(r_2^2 - r_1^2).$$

According to Fig. 6.17, it can be seen that

$$i_1 = \theta + \frac{\omega}{2}, \qquad i_2 = \theta - \frac{\omega}{2},$$

and, because

$$i_1 = nr_1, \qquad i_2 = nr_2,$$

we have

$$r_2^2 - r_1^2 = \frac{2\theta\omega}{n^2},$$

from which

$$\delta = 2n(e_1 - e_2) + 2\theta\omega\frac{e_1}{n}. \tag{6.70}$$

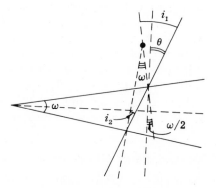

FIG. 6.17   Calculation of path difference.

As the thickness e_1 and e_2 are constant, δ varies proportionally to θ, and the fringes at infinity are straight lines parallel to the apex of the dihedron formed by the plates. We will have a bright fringe in the direction θ if

$$p = \frac{\delta}{\lambda} = \frac{2n(e_1 - e_2)}{\lambda} + 2\theta\omega\frac{e_1}{n\lambda} = K.$$

The next bright fringe is found in the direction θ' given by

$$\frac{2n(e_1 - e_2)}{\lambda} + 2\theta'\omega\frac{e_1}{n\lambda} = K + 1,$$

in which the distance that separates the two fringes is

$$\theta' - \theta = \frac{n\lambda}{2\omega e_1}. \tag{6.71}$$

The fringes are separated and the central fringe corresponds to $\delta = 0$ (6.70):

$$2n(e_1 - e_2) + 2\theta\omega\frac{e_1}{n} = 0,$$

$$\theta = \frac{n^2(e_2 - e_1)}{e_1\omega}. \tag{6.72}$$

When we vary one thickness, the fringes move parallel to themselves. For a decrease in ω they become wider and we obtain uniform illumination for $\omega = 0$. The fringes form rings at infinity in a plate of thickness $e_2 - e_1$. In fact, we have

$$\delta = 2n(e_1 - e_2). \tag{6.73}$$

We now turn to white light and again take up plates that form a small angle ω. If the path difference δ given by (6.70) is sufficiently small, the fringes are visible in white light. The central fringe, corresponding to $\delta = 0$, is a white fringe and its position is given by (6.73). It is surrounded by colored fringes called fringes of superposition which increase their width when ω diminishes. For $\omega = 0$ we have a flat tint; the path difference is given by (6.73), and for $e_1 = e_2$ the tint is white. A more complete exposition of the calculation of the intensity of these fringes follows.

6.12   Fringes of Superposition of Two Plates of Variable Thicknesses

We now observe the fringes of superposition of two plates, L_1 and L_2, of variable thickness (Fig. 6.18). We assume that they are air plates and that the semireflecting films deposited on their faces are identical.

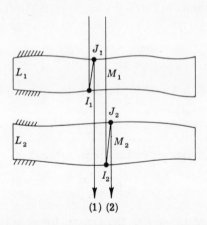

Fig. 6.18   Fringes of superposition with two plates of variable thicknesses.

We consider ray (1) reflected in I_1 and J_1 on the semireflecting faces of plate L_1 and passing through L_2. We also consider ray (2), which passes through L_1 and is reflected in I_2 and J_2 on the faces of L_2. If the thickness of L_1 in M_1 is e_1 and that of L_2 in M_2 is e_2, the path difference between (1) and (2) is

$$\delta = 2(e_1 - e_2); \tag{6.74}$$

$\delta = 0$ for $e_1 = e_2$, and if we illuminate the plates with white light we see a white fringe in the corresponding region (it is shown later how this phenomenon is observed). This fringe traces the locus of the points for which $e_1 = e_2$. It is bordered by other fringes of symmetrical colorations, and the lines of equal coloration trace the lines of equal difference of thickness of the two plates.

It must be pointed out that white-light fringes appear not only when the two thicknesses are equal but also whenever the two thicknesses are in simple ratio. In fact, when (1) undergoes $2m_1$ reflections in L_1 and $2m_2$ reflections in L_2 and (2) undergoes $2p_1$ reflections in L_1 and $2p_2$ reflections in L_2, the path difference between (1) and (2) is

$$\delta = (p_1 - m_1)\Delta_1 + (p_2 - m_2)\Delta_2, \tag{6.75}$$

where Δ_1 and Δ_2 are the path differences corresponding to each plate. The path difference δ is zero for any wavelength if

$$\frac{\Delta_2}{\Delta_1} = \frac{p_1 - m_1}{m_2 - p_2}. \tag{6.76}$$

If the ratio Δ_2/Δ_1 is commensurable, integers p_1, m_1, p_2, m_2 will always satisfy (6.76). The rays under consideration give then a fringe system in white light in which the central fringe traces the locus of points for which the ratio Δ_2/Δ_1 has a simple constant value. As Δ_2/Δ_1 gradually becomes less simple, a greater part of the white light can no longer interfere and the fringes become increasingly pale.

We calculate the intensity distribution in these fringes by assuming that the thickness of each plate is large enough so that, taken alone, it produces no white-light fringes.

We resume the calculations done in Section 6.2 in a slightly different form. Let R_1 and R_2 be the reflectance on the plates L_1 and L_2 and T_1 and T_2, their transmittance. The ray that has undergone $2p$ reflections has an amplitude of TR^p if the amplitude of the incident ray is taken as unity. We have, therefore, an infinity of rays coming out of L_1 with amplitudes

$$T_1, T_1R_1, T_1R_1^2, \ldots, T_1R_1^p,$$

and having with respect to the first directly transmitted ray, path differences

$$0, \Delta_1, 2\Delta_1, \ldots, p\Delta_1.$$

If we take L_1 alone, we have, after passing through M_1, an intensity I_1 corresponding to a path difference Δ_1. This intensity is obtained by Fresnel's rule for all vibratory motions. We then find that

$$I_1 = T_1^2 \sum R_1^{2p} + 2T_1^2 \sum R_1^{p+q} \cos(p - q)\frac{2\pi\Delta_1}{\lambda}. \tag{6.77}$$

This expression contains a constant term

$$T_1^2 \sum R_1^{2p} = \frac{T_1^2}{1 - R_1^2} \tag{6.78}$$

and a series of terms which has as a factor the cosine of a multiple of $2\pi\Delta_1/\lambda$. If we set $p - q = m$, the factor $\cos[m(2\pi\Delta_1)/\lambda]$ is found in all these terms, and the coefficient of the cosine is

$$2T_1^2 R_1^m (1 + R_1^2 + R_1^4 + \cdots) = \frac{2T_1^2 R_1^m}{1 + R_1^2}. \tag{6.79}$$

The intensity I_1 is written

$$I_1 = \frac{2T_1^2}{1 - R_1^2}\left(\frac{1}{2} + R_1 \cos\frac{2\pi\Delta_1}{\lambda} + R_1^2 \cos\frac{4\pi\Delta_1}{\lambda} + \cdots\right). \tag{6.80}$$

Similarly, if we observe the plate L_2 alone through the region M_2 corresponding to a path difference Δ_2, we would have

$$I_2 = \frac{2T_2^2}{1 - R_2^2}\left(\frac{1}{2} + R_2 \cos\frac{2\pi\Delta_2}{\lambda} + R_2^2 \cos\frac{4\pi\Delta_2}{\lambda} + \cdots\right). \tag{6.81}$$

If the light penetrates the two plates successively and the eye is directed normally toward them so that M_1 is projected on M_2, we obtain in M_1M_2 an intensity

$$I = I_1 \times I_2 = \frac{4T_1^2 T_2^2}{(1 - R_1^2)(1 - R_2^2)}\left[\frac{1}{2} + R_1 \cos\frac{2\pi\Delta_1}{\lambda} + \cdots\right]$$
$$\times \left[\frac{1}{2} + R_2 \cos\frac{2\pi\Delta_2}{\lambda} + \cdots\right]. \tag{6.82}$$

By taking the product of these two series we have

$$I = \frac{4T_1^2 T_2^2}{(1 - R_1^2)(1 - R_2^2)}\left[\frac{1}{4} + \sum \frac{1}{2}R_1^p \cos\left(\frac{2p\pi\Delta_1}{\lambda}\right) + \sum\frac{1}{2}R_2^p\cos\left(\frac{2p\pi\Delta_2}{\lambda}\right)\right.$$
$$\left. + \sum R_1^p R_2^q \cos\left(\frac{2p_1\pi\Delta_1}{\lambda}\right)\cos\left(\frac{2p_2\pi\Delta_2}{\lambda}\right)\right]$$

or

$$I = \frac{4T_1^2 T_2^2}{(1 - R_1^2)(1 - R_2^2)}\left\{\frac{1}{4} + \sum\frac{1}{2}R_1^p\cos\left(\frac{2p\pi\Delta_1}{\lambda}\right) + \sum\frac{1}{2}R_2^p\cos\left(\frac{2p\pi\Delta_2}{\lambda}\right)\right.$$
$$+ \sum\left[\frac{1}{2}R_1^p R_2^q \cos 2\pi\left(\frac{p_1\Delta_1 + p_2\Delta_2}{\lambda}\right)\right.$$
$$\left.\left. + \frac{1}{2}R_1^p R_2^q \cos 2\pi\left(\frac{p_1\Delta_1 - p_2\Delta_2}{\lambda}\right)\right]\right\}. \tag{6.83}$$

The expression (6.83) gives the intensity for one wavelength, and we superpose the intensities for all. We have assumed that each plate taken alone
would have no fringes. Therefore in the sum of the expressions analogous to
(6.83) for all wavelengths the terms containing $\cos(2p\pi\Delta_1/\lambda)$, $\cos(2p\pi\Delta_2/\lambda)$
and $\cos 2\pi[(p_1\Delta_1 + p_2\Delta_2)/\lambda]$ disappear. In fact, these terms take into
account only the fringes of each plate or of a plate of even greater thickness.
The intensity I_B for white light for a source of a spectrum of equal energy
becomes

$$I_B = \frac{2T_1{}^2T_2{}^2}{(1 - R_1{}^2)(1 - R_2{}^2)} \left[\frac{1}{2} + \sum \left(R_1{}^p R_2{}^q \sum_{\lambda_1}^{\lambda_2} \cos 2\pi \frac{p_1\Delta_1 - p_2\Delta_2}{\lambda} \right) \right]. \quad (6.84)$$

If the ratio Δ_1/Δ_2 is commensurable, the expressions $p_1\Delta_1 - p_2\Delta_2$ are zero.
The term in parenthesis in (6.84) is zero and the intensity I_B is uniform.
If, on the contrary, Δ_1/Δ_2 approaches a commensurable ratio m/n, in which
m and n are two prime numbers, we have a series of nonvanishing terms.
The intensity becomes equal to

$$I_B = \frac{2T_1{}^2T_2{}^2}{(1 - R_1{}^2)(1 - R_2{}^2)} \left[\frac{1}{2} + R_1{}^n R_2{}^m \sum_{\lambda_1}^{\lambda_2} \cos 2\pi \frac{n\Delta_1 - m\Delta_2}{\lambda} \right.$$
$$\left. + (R_1{}^n R_2{}^m)^2 \sum_{\lambda_1}^{\lambda_2} \cos 4\pi \frac{n\Delta_1 - m\Delta_2}{\lambda} + \cdots \right]. \quad (6.85)$$

By comparing (6.84) and (6.79) we see that this intensity, obtained with a
single plate, produces up to a constant factor a path difference $n\Delta_1 - m\Delta_2$
in which the reflectance of each face would be $R_1{}^n R_2{}^m$. Therefore we have a
system of fringes visible in white light whenever Δ_1/Δ_2 approaches a commensurable ratio m/n. The central fringe traces the locus of the points in
which $\Delta_1/\Delta_2 = m/n$.

We assume that R_1 and R_2 are equal and that the plate has a reflectance
equal to R^{m+n} for each of its faces. If $m + n$ increases, R^{m+n} diminishes, for
R is always smaller than unity. The colorations are therefore less vivid,
the larger the $m + n$. If the reflectance is not very high, the contrast between
the fringes of a system diminishes rapidly beyond the first system.

Table 6.1 shows the contrast γ in the central fringe of the first systems in
white light for two reflectances.

TABLE 6.1

Δ_1/Δ_2	$m + n$	R^{m+n} (R = 0·75)	γ	R^{m+n} (R = 0·65)	γ
1	2	0.56	0.52	0.42	0.35
2 or $\frac{1}{2}$	3	0.42	0.35	0.27	0.15
3 or $\frac{1}{3}$	4	0.32	0.24	0.18	0.09

We then have

$$\gamma = \left(\frac{2R^{m+n}}{1 + R^{m+n}} \right)^2 .$$

To observe the fringes of superposition we can use the scheme shown in Fig. 6.19. We project an image of the plate L_1 on the plate L_2 with an afocal system consisting of two lenses O_2 and O_3. L_1 and L_2 are illuminated in parallel light by the collimator SO_1, and O_4 permits to focus L_2. We find

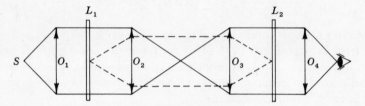

FIG. 6.19   Observation of fringes of superposition.

fringes in the areas in which the thicknesses of L_1 and L_2 are equal or in a simple ratio. In this way we can measure the thickness of L_1 if that of L_2 is known. Let us assume that L_1 is an air-plate and replace L_2 by a calibrated airwedge, that is, one whose thickness is known at each point. The white fringe corresponding to $e_1 = e_2$ is easily recognized. We locate the area of L_2 in which it is projected to obtain the desired thickness e_1. For the

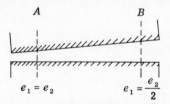

FIG. 6.20.   Calibration of a wedge with the help of fringes of superposition.

calibration of the wedge it is sufficient to locate A and B, in which the white fringes corresponding to $e_1 = e_2$ and $e_1 = e_2/2$ are found, on the wedge-shaped plate L_2 (Fig. 6.20). L_2 is removed from the instrument and its fringes of equal thickness are observed in white light. It serves to count the fringes visible between A and B to find the difference between these thicknesses. This difference is equal to e_1, which permits the calibration of the wedge.

Chapter VII

Polarization Interferometers

7.1 Introduction

In all interferometric instruments based on the interference of two waves the incident wave emanating from the source is divided into two waves which follow different optical paths. These two waves, which are then superposed, generate interference phenomena in the region of superposition. The interferometers differ from one another in their methods of doubling. For example, in the interferometers with amplitude division similar to that of the Michelson and Mach–Zehnder instruments, doubling is produced by a semireflecting plate inclined at 45° to the incident beam. It is possible to produce an amplitude division by means of a double-refracting plate and consequently to observe the variations of the optical path of an isotropic object by using the phenomena of polarization.

The fundamental element of the polarization interferometer is the double-refracting system that produces shearing of the incident wave. First we shall describe the instruments in order to promote a better understanding of the principles involved.

The double-refracting devices are based on two types: systems that produce linear shear and systems that produce angular shear.

7.2 Double-refracting Systems with Linear Shearing: Savart's Polariscope

Savart's polariscope (Fig. 7.1) consists of two identical uniaxial plates, cut at 45° and crossed. We show the projection of the axis of the second plate on the plane of the figure. In reality, the axis forms an angle of 45° with the plane.

In the first plate the incident ray is sheared in two: the ordinary ray O and the extraordinary ray E. Because the second plate is oriented at 90° with respect to the first, the ordinary ray O in the first plate becomes the extraordinary E in the second and vice versa. The path indicated by the dotted line shows that OE, is not in the plane of the figure, but this ray is parallel to the ray *EO* which is in the plane of the figure. The paths of these rays may be more easily understood by studying Fig. 7.2 and 7.3.

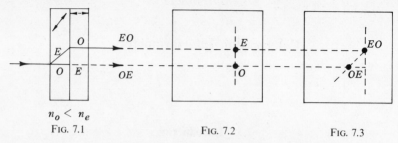

$$n_o < n_e$$

FIG. 7.1   FIG. 7.2   FIG. 7.3

FIG. 7.1   A Savart polariscope.

FIG. 7.2   Mechanism of the passage of rays in a Savart polariscope (first plate).

FIG. 7.3   Mechanism of the passage of rays in a Savart polariscope (second plate).

Figure 7.2 shows the passage of the rays in the plane normal to direction of incidence after passing through the first plate. The ordinary ray is at *O*, the extraordinary at *E*; Fig. 7.3 shows the passage of the rays in the normal plane after passing through the second plate. *EO* is an extension of *E*, but *OE* is displaced horizontally (the plane of the figure is considered to be vertical). The displacement of *OE* with respect to *O* is the same in the horizontal plane as the displacement of *E* with respect to *O* in the vertical plane. To study the structure of fringes given by a Savart polariscope an extended and uniform source *S* which emits monochromatic light is placed at the focus of an objective lens O_1 (Fig. 7.4). The polariscope is at *Q*, and we observe the phenomenon in the focal plane of a second objective lens O_2. The double-refracting elements, regardless of their number, always appear between crossed polarizers.

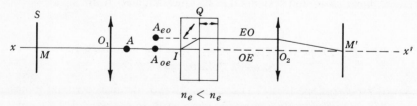

$$n_e < n_e$$

FIG. 7.4   Fringes at infinity in a Savart polariscope.

The incident ray, which we assume is emitted by a point source *A*, is split in two at *I* (*EO* and *OE*). The emerging ray *OE* is parallel to *EO* but is not in the plane of the figure. *EO* and *OE* appear to originate from the two images A_{oe} (corresponding to *OE*) and A_{eo} (corresponding to *EO*). A_{eo}, in the plane of the figure, and A_{oe}, outside the plane, are projected on *AI*. These images are located in the same vertical plane parallel to the face of the polariscope. In fact, the two paths *EO* and *OE* in the two plates of the polariscope are identical. This is true for any other ray emitted by *M* (Fig. 7.5). *EO* and *OE* are in phase and the shear remains the same. The state of interference in *M'* (Fig. 7.4) is the same regardless of the path from *M'*. Therefore we can study the interferences in *M'* by considering only two rays (*OE* and *EO*) which originate from the two sources A_{oe} and A_{eo} of Fig. 7.4. The state of interference in *M'* is the same as if the rays came from A_{eo} and A_{oe} with the polariscope removed.

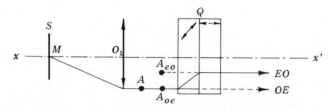

FIG. 7.5   Fringes at infinity of a Savart polariscope.

What happens now to a ray that is not normally incident on the polariscope (Fig. 7.6)? Let us take point *A* at the same distance from the polariscope as in Fig. 7.4. We can show that if the angle of incidence *i* remains small the emerging rays *EO* and *OE* will still appear to come from the same two points A_{eo} and A_{oe}. We can follow the same reasoning and say that the phenomenon of interference at infinity, in the direction *i*, is the same for all rays coming from *M'*. It can therefore be studied by considering the two sources A_{eo} and A_{oe} in Fig. 7.6, which are the same as in Fig. 7.4. The state of interference at infinity in the direction *i* is the same as if the rays came from two sources in phase A_{eo} and A_{oe}.

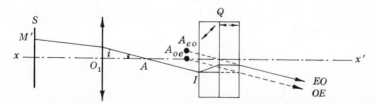

FIG. 7.6   Rays coming from two sources A_{oe} and A_{eo}.

Finally, we can describe the phenomenon by assuming that the rays come from the two sources A_{eo} and A_{oe} in Fig. 7.4 with the polariscope removed.

Figure 7.7 shows the analogy of the phenomenon with Young's experiment. The polariscope is omitted, and only the two sources A_{eo} and A_{oe} of Fig. 7.4 and an arbitrary direction *i* of the two rays *EO* and *OE* appear.

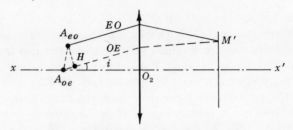

FIG. 7.7 Calculation of path difference at M.

As in Young's experiment, these two sources produce at infinity straight, parallel, and equidistant fringes which are in the focal plane of O_2 and are directed perpendicularly to the line $A_{oe}A_{eo}$ (OE, EO in Fig. 7.3). The fringes are therefore at an angle of 45° to the principal sections of the two plates in the polariscope. The analogy with Young's experiment permits us to find immediately the orientation of the fringes with respect to the polariscope. Following is the calculation of the angular distance of the fringes. In the direction i the path difference is

$$\Delta = \overline{A_{oe}H}.$$

Then, if $d = \overline{A_{oe}A_{eo}}$ is the shear produced by the polariscope, we have

$$\Delta = id. \tag{7.1}$$

If the thickness of the polariscope is equal to $2e$, the doubling d is given by

$$d = e\sqrt{2}\,\frac{n_e{}^2 - n_o{}^2}{n_e{}^2 + n_o{}^2}, \tag{7.2}$$

where n_0 and n_e are the ordinary and extraordinary indices of the crystal.

For quartz $d = 7 \times 10^{-3}e$ and for calcite $d = 0.15e$. According to (7.1) and (7.2) we have

$$\Delta = e\sqrt{2}\,\frac{n_e{}^2 - n_o{}^2}{n_e{}^2 + n_o{}^2}\,i. \tag{7.3}$$

If the polariscope is placed between crossed polarizers, the transmitted intensity is given by $I = \sin^2 \pi\Delta/\lambda$, and we have a bright fringe if

$$\Delta = (2K + 1)\frac{\lambda}{2};$$

that is, if the angle of incidence i has the values given by

$$i = \left(K + \frac{1}{2}\right)\frac{n_e{}^2 + n_o{}^2}{n_e{}^2 - n_o{}^2}\,\frac{\lambda}{e\sqrt{2}} \tag{7.4}$$

from which the angular spacing between two consecutive bright (or dark) fringes

$$i_f = \frac{n_e^2 + n_o^2}{n_e^2 - n_o^2} \frac{\lambda}{e\sqrt{2}}. \tag{7.5}$$

For quartz

$$i_f = \frac{0.068}{e_{mm}};$$

for calate

$$i_f = \frac{0.37 \times 10^{-2}}{e_{mm}}; \qquad (\lambda = 0^\mu.56).$$

7.3 Double-refracting Systems with Linear Shearing: Modified Savart's Polariscope (Françon)

Equation 7.3 is in fact an approximation. A more precise calculation shows that the second member of (7.3) is the first term of a series expansion which contains second, third, and higher orders. These terms are small and can be neglected in a first approximation. The fringes in Savart's polariscope are therefore not exactly straight lines. For certain applications—their usefulness is made clear later—it may be advantageous to have even straighter fringes. Figure 7.8 is a diagram of a polariscope for which the fringes are straight lines to the third order. This polariscope consists of two identical plates cut at 45° to the axis with their principal sections parallel.

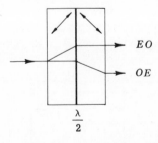

FIG. 7.8   Modified Savart polariscope (Françon).

The optical axes are perpendicular, and a half-wave plate with the preferred directions at 45° to the principal sections of the plate is inserted between the two plates. It is seen immediately that the rays stay in the plane and that the shearing equal to

$$d = 2e \frac{n_e^2 - n_o^2}{n_e^2 + n_o^2} \tag{7.6}$$

is twice that of a simple plate and $\sqrt{2}$ times that of Savart's polariscope. The path difference according to (7.1) is

$$\Delta = 2e \frac{n_e^2 - n_o^2}{n_e^2 + n_o^2} i. \tag{7.7}$$

Equation 7.7 is accurate to the third order. The angular spacing between two consecutive bright (or dark) fringes is

$$i_f = \frac{n_o^2 + n_e^2}{n_o^2 - n_e^2} \frac{\lambda}{2e}. \tag{7.8}$$

We refer again to the reasoning of Section 7.2: because the two rays are in the plane of the figure, so are the two points A_{eo} and A_{oe}. The fringes are oriented perpendicularly to the principal sections of the plates of the polariscope.

7.4   Double-refracting Systems with Linear Shearing: Polariscope with Fringes of Variable Spacing (Steel)

Let us separate the elements of the polariscope in Fig. 7.8. A polarizer $\mathscr{P}_1$ is fixed to a plate L_1 and a polarizer $\mathscr{P}_2$, to a plate L_2 with the usual correct orientations. We turn L_1 and L_2 around the axis xx' normal to the plates (Fig. 7.9). We turn them in opposite directions at the same speed with the polarizers fixed to the plates. The position of the plates is shown in Fig. 7.10 after a rotation of 90° for each. The path of the rays indicated in the upper part of the diagram shows that there is no shearing, and theoretically the fringes at infinity are infinitely spaced (analogous to Young's experiment). If we bring the sources A_{eo}, A_{oe} closer, the spaces between fringes become wider.

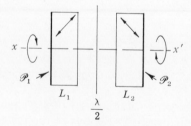

FIG. 7.9   A polariscope giving variable fringes (Steel).

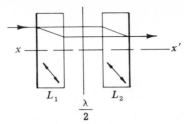

FIG. 7.10 A polariscope giving variable fringes (Steel).

As an initial orientation we take the position of Fig. 7.10, in which the principal sections and the axes are parallel. If we turn each plate by an angle α (in opposite directions), the angular distance between two consecutive bright (or dark) fringes is

$$i_f = \frac{n_o^2 + n_e^2}{n_o^2 - n_e^2} \frac{\lambda}{2e \sin \alpha}. \tag{7.9}$$

For $\alpha = 0$ the fringes are infinitely spaced, and for $\alpha = \pi/2$ we have the spacing (7.8) of the fringes in Fig. 7.8.

7.5 Double-refracting Systems with Linear Shearing: Polariscope with Fringes of Variable Spacing (Tsuruta)

This is a Savart polariscope divided into four identical prisms and oriented as shown in Fig. 4.11. The elements A and B, as well as C and D, are fixed to one another in a way such that the combination forms a plane parallel plate. By arranging the plates in the order $DABC$ we have a real Savart polariscope. The axis xx' passes through the four plates in a region in which all thicknesses are equal. Let us move AB and CD the same distance but in opposite directions. The axis xx' still intersects the plates in a region in which all thicknesses are equal, but in which the thickness of the combination (the thickness of the equivalent Savart polariscope) diminishes or increases. It increases in Fig. 7.11. Thus we have a Savart polariscope of a variable thickness $2e$ and with variable spacing of the fringes (7.5).

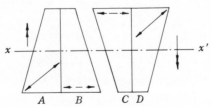

FIG. 7.11 Polariscope with variable fringes (Tsuruta).

7.6   Double-refracting Systems with Angular Shearing:
Wollaston Prism

A Wollaston prism consists of two prisms cut parallel to the optical axis and with the axes crossed. Both have the same angle θ, and their combination forms a plane parallel plate (Fig. 7.12). Let xx' be the axis that intersects the Wollaston prism in a region C in which the thicknesses of the two prisms are equal. We consider an incident ray normal to the Wollaston and located at a distance y from the axis xx'.

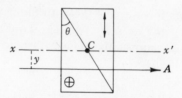

FIG. 7.12   A Wollaston prism.

There is no shearing of the incident ray in the first prism. The shearing occurs when the ray passes into the second. To simplify we assume weak shearing. Although it is not shown in Fig. 7.12, we know that it exists. The path difference between these two rays is given by:

$$\Delta = 2(n_o - n_e)y \tan \theta. \tag{7.10}$$

Because the prisms are crossed, the ordinary ray in the first prism becomes extraordinary in the second and vice versa. The path difference in the region $C(y = 0)$, in which the thicknesses are equal, is therefore zero. If we move parallel to the apex of the prisms ($y = $ constant), the path difference does not vary. In a direction perpendicular to the apex of the prisms (7.10) shows that Δ is a linear function of y. The fringes are equidistant straight lines parallel to the apex of the prisms and are localized in the Wollaston. The surface of localization is inclined by an angle of nearly $2\theta/3$ to the outer faces.

The distance y_f between two consecutive bright (or dark) fringes is given by

$$y_f = \frac{\lambda}{2(n_o - n_e) \tan \theta}. \tag{7.11}$$

If the Wollaston is placed between crossed polarizers, we have a dark central fringe at C. The colored fringes observed on both sides of C have colors in accordance with Newton's scale of colors with black center.

Figure 7.13 shows the angular shearing α produced by a Wollaston prism.

$$\alpha = 2(n_o - n_e) \tan \theta. \qquad (7.12)$$

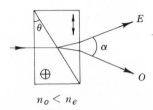

$$n_o < n_e$$

FIG. 7.13 Angular doubling produced by a Wollaston prism.

Equation 7.10 can be applied if the incident ray is normal to the Wollaston or very nearly so.

We now consider an incident ray, $M_1 I$, normal to W (Fig. 7.14) and another, $M_2 I$, which passes through the same point I at an angle i. In the study of path differences as a function of the inclination of these rays we can reason as follows: let us assume that the angle θ of the Wollaston is small. The region I, where the two incident rays meet, is small, and we can also assume that we are dealing with plane parallel plates cut parallel to the axis and crossed. Because θ is small, we neglect the shearing and assume that the two rays O and E, which originate in the same incident ray,

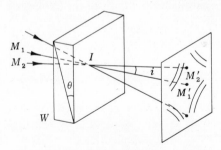

FIG. 7.14 The field of a Wollaston prism.

are almost parallel. If, under these conditions, we place a screen E sufficiently far away from the prism (for angles θ of the order of 5 to 6°, for example, and for quartz a distance of 15 to 20 cm between E and W is adequate to observe the phenomenon), we can make an observation similar to that obtained in convergent light with the two plates parallel to the axis and crossed: hyperbolas appear on the screen E. For the ray $M_1 I M'_1$, relation (7.10) can be used. For an angle of incidence i in a plane of incidence at 45°

from the asymptotes of the hyperbolas, the path difference becomes Δ', and we have

$$\Delta' = \Delta \left(1 - \frac{i^2}{2n_o{}^2}\right). \tag{7.13}$$

For example, for a 20-mm Wollaston prism (we assume that θ is small and that each plate is 10 mm thick in the region I) and for quartz we have

$$\Delta' = \Delta \left(1 - \frac{i^2}{4.74}\right).$$

For $i = 10°$ the variation $\Delta' - \Delta$ of the path difference is approximately one wavelength and therefore not tolerable. Consequently, the Wollaston must be used with beams of small aperture.

7.7 Double-refracting Systems with Angular Shear: Modified Wollaston (Nomarski)

The inclination of the surface of localization of the fringes in a Wollaston prism can be troublesome in certain instruments.

Nomarski proposed the use of two Wollastons separated by a half-wave plate and located as shown in Fig. 7.15. In this device the plane of localization of the fringes is parallel to the faces of the Wollaston.

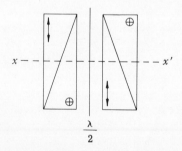

FIG. 7.15 A modified Wollaston prism (Nomarski).

A second device permits the moving of the plane of localization outside the Wollaston. This is a Wollaston in which one of the axes is inclined to the outer faces (Fig. 7.16) and is especially intended for the interferometers used in microscopy.

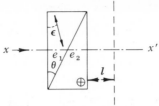

FIG. 7.16 Localization of the fringes in a modified Wollaston prism (Nomarski).

7.8 Double-refracting Systems with Angular Shear and a Wide Field

It is sometimes useful in certain instruments to pass a beam with a wide aperture through a Wollaston prism. Here, however, the path difference varies with the inclination of the rays and the Wollaston in its original form is unsuitable, as explained in Section 7.6. By referring once again to the diagram in Fig. 7.14 we can replace the Wollaston W with a system in which the screen is uniformly illuminated even for rather large angles i. This can be achieved by using the system shown in Fig. 7.17 (Nomarski).

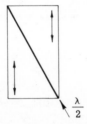

FIG. 7.17 A Wollaston prism with a large field (Nomarski).

The axes of the two elements are parallel and a half-wave plate is mounted between them. An instrument without the half-wave plate is shown on Fig. 7.18 (Françon). Its elements A and D are identical plane parallel quartz plates, and B and C make up an ordinary calcite Wollaston. Note the position of its axes. The quartz plates are 17,331 times thicker than the calcite prisms in the region in which the two prisms are equal.

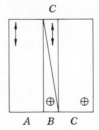

FIG. 7.18 A Wollaston prism with a large field (Françon).

7.9   Principle of the Polarization Interferometers

The principle involved in these instruments is the following: the wave deformed by the phase variations of the transparent object traverses a double-refracting system and is sheared. By means of a polarizer and an analyzer, we can make the two waves interfere and in this way recognize the details of a transparent isotropic phase-shifting object.

INTERFEROMETER WITH COMPLETE SHEAR

Let us consider a transparent object AC; for example, a glass plate which has in M a small region of a thickness different from the remainder of the plate (Fig. 7.19). The object AC is illuminated by a beam of parallel light

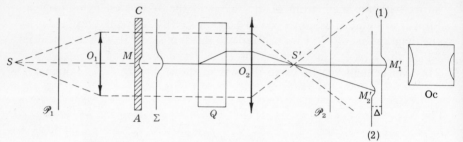

FIG. 7.19   A polarization interferometer with complete shear.

(the source S is very small), and the image $A'C'$ given by an optical system O_2 is observed with the eyepiece Oc. We place a plane-parallel, double-refracting system Q between the object AC and the objective lens O_2 (e.g., the polariscope of Fig. 7.1 or 7.8). The incident light is linearly polarized by a polarizer $\mathscr{P}_1$ which can be placed anywhere in front of the double-refracting system Q. The analyzer $\mathscr{P}_2$ can be set anywhere after it. Before passing through Q the incident wave Σ is a plane wave, except in its central part, in which it is slightly deformed because of the corresponding variation of the optical thickness of the object in this region. After traversing Q the wave Σ is sheared into two waves polarized at right angles (1) and (2) shown in Fig. 7.20. The shifting of these two waves in a direction perpendicular to the axis of the system is due to the double refraction of Q, and the shift in the direction of the axis is due to the path difference produced by Q.

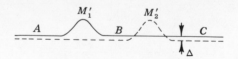

FIG. 7.20   Disposition of the two wavefronts in the total-shear method.

If we use a Savart polariscope, the path difference between the two waves (1) and (2) is just the path difference Δ between OE and EO in Fig. 7.1, given by (7.3). In fact, in accordance with Fig. 7.19, Fig. 7.21 shows that OE passing through P interferes with EO passing through M.

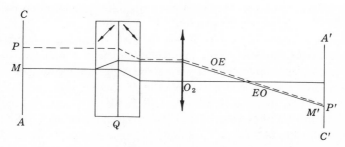

FIG. 7.21   Disposition of rays that interfere.

The two images of P and M which correspond to these two rays are combined in P' (or in M') in the image $A'C'$.

The difference, equal to Δ, between the optical paths $(POEP')$ and $(MEOM')$ occurs only in passing through the polariscope. This is obviously the path difference in the image $A'C'$ between the two waves corresponding to these two rays. It is sufficient to incline the polariscope with respect to the incident parallel beam to vary the path difference. We incline the interferometer slightly so that the path difference Δ between the two waves (1) and (2) in the nondeformed regions (Fig. 7.20) A, B, and C is equal to 0.565μ when working between crossed polarizers. We know that it is sufficient to vary the angle of incidence to change the path difference Δ. In the regions A, B, and C color, called purple of the first order, can be observed. In the regions M_1' and M_2', in which the two images of M are located, this is no longer so. The path difference becomes 0.565μ, plus or minus the path difference introduced by the object: the sensitive color changes at once, and thus the structure of the object is made visible. The color of the ordinary image is different from that of the extraordinary image because the path difference is $0.565 \mu + \delta$ (δ is the path difference introduced by the object itself) at M_1' and $0.565 \mu - \delta$ at M_2'. These colors are symmetrical to the sensitive colors on Newton's scale. Measurements, such as those we have just described, are performed by the method of flat tints, and by using Newton's scale, a comparison of the uniform color in the image of the object with the uniform color of the surrounding field will give us the optical thickness of the object.

It is generally more convenient, when measuring, to use straight fringes as in ordinary interferometers. We can use the following method: we place a second polariscope analogous to Q (not shown) between the eyepiece Oc and the eye (Fig. 7.19).

Because the second polariscope is not illuminated in parallel light, it projects its fringes, which are parallel and equidistant straight lines at infinity, onto the plane of observation.

These fringes trace the lines of equal path difference between the waves (1) and (2). The deformations produced by the object cause a displacement of the fringes, which, measured in terms of fringe spacing, gives the path differences in M_1' and M_2' in a manner completely identical to ordinary interferometric measurements. It should be noted in the utilization of a second polariscope inserted between Oc and the eye that the analyzer is displaced and that the polariscope also falls between $\mathscr{P}_1$ and $\mathscr{P}_2$. Figure 7.22 is a view of the field observation and the two sheared images, OE and EO. This method is useful for small isolated objects in which the images do not overlap one another.

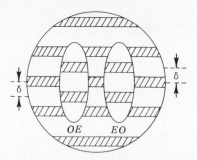

FIG. 7.22   Use of fringes in a polarization interferometer.

DIFFERENTIAL INTERFEROMETERS

We refer again to Fig. 7.19 to consider a polariscope Q in which the lateral displacement is small compared with the size of the object. To obtain this result the polariscope may be thinner than that required in the preceding method. Figure 7.23 shows the position of the waves (1) and (2).

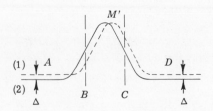

FIG. 7.23   Disposition of the two wavefronts in the differential method.

We adjust Q so that the path difference Δ between (1) and (2) in the plane parts such as A and D is equal to 0.565. As before, the areas A and D surrounding the image M' of the object show the sensitive purple of the first order.

On the other hand, in the area of the image M' itself the color is different. For example, because of the lateral shift, the path difference in B and C between (1) and (2) is modified, and the sensitive color changes immediately, thus making the slopes of the phase object visible.

Because this method does not reveal the optical path itself, but only its variations, it is a differential method. Here also by means of an additional polariscope we can produce fringes to facilitate the measurements.

USE OF A DOUBLE-REFRACTING SYSTEM OF ANGULAR SHEAR

We have discussed the principles of two methods of linear shearing in which the double-refracting system consists of plane parallel plates. The same rules apply if we use a system of angular shear (Fig. 7.24). In this case the Wollaston W or an analogous system is in focus under the objective lens O_2.

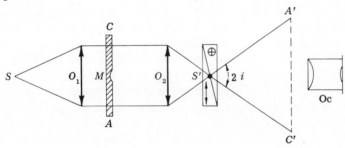

FIG. 7.24   Use of a Wollaston prism in a polarization interferometer.

The image S' of S is produced by the Wollaston prism. The rest of the instrument is described by Fig. 7.19, and the shearing of waves (1) and (2) follows the method given.

It should be noted that in Fig. 7.24 the light beam has been shown without any indication of the shearing of rays. The angle $2i$ is the aperture of the beam. However, Fig. 7.25 does show the shearing of an incident ray. The angle α is the same as that in Fig. 7.13. The difference Δ, representing the path difference between waves (1) and (2), is obviously rather exaggerated compared with Fig. 7.24.

As we have seen, the aperture $2i$ of the beam that passes through the Wollaston prism (Fig. 7.24) must be small. Otherwise, even with no phase-shifting object, the field will not be uniform.

This system is applicable to microscopy but cannot be used in macroscopic instruments. It is necessary, therefore, to use one of the devices described in Section 7.8.

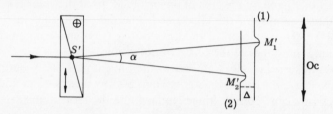

FIG. 7.25 Doubling of the wavefronts produced by a Wollaston prism.

7.10   Contrast of the Images or Fringes of Polarization Interferometers

In Section 7.9 we did not specify the form of the source to be used. We refer again to Fig. 7.19.

If S is an extended source, it is necessary, to have a well-contrasted image, that the path difference Δ be uniform at one point in the field, no matter what source point is considered. In fact, a given angle of incidence corresponds in the polariscope to a certain point in the source S, hence to a specified path difference Δ between waves (1) and (2) in the plane regions. For a given wavelength we have an intensity $I = \sin^2(\pi\Delta/\lambda)$ between crossed polarizers and $I = \cos^2(\pi\Delta/\lambda)$ between parallel polarizers. If Δ varies with the point of the source under consideration, the same is true of the intensity. Because the different points of the source are incoherent, the intensities must be added, and the contrast of the phenomenon diminishes. To avoid a decrease in contrast with an extended source, it is necessary that the path difference Δ be the same between waves (1) and (2) (plane regions).

It is now easy to determine the form that the source must be given in a Savart polariscope. We know that the fringes of the Savart at infinity are equidistant parallel straight lines, oriented at 45° to the principal sections of the plates. These fringes at infinity are projected into the focal plane passing through S'.

Let us consider source S as a slit parallel to the fringes at infinity and whose width is small with respect to the fringe intervals. Source S is a fine slit; all its points will give the same path difference Δ between waves (1) and (2). We know, in fact, that in all interference phenomena at infinity the path difference produced by a plane parallel plate does not vary if the source point is moved along a fringe at infinity. In the arrangement shown in Fig. 7.19 it is easy to see the fringes at infinity by observing the focal plane S' of the objective lens O_2. At the same time we note the image S' of the slit placed in S. This image must be oriented suitably (See Fig. 7.26).

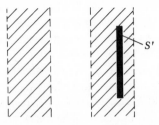

FIG. 7.26   Use of a slit source in a polarization interferometer.   .

Under these conditions all incoherent points of the slit S produce the same phenomenon in the image plane observed by means of the eyepiece Oc. With respect to the point source, the contrast of the image is the same, but the phenomenon is much brighter.

7.11   Compensation in Polarization Interferometers

The use of slits as light sources would severely limit the brightness of polarization interferometers. However, we shall see that double-refracting systems possess particular properties that permit the use of large sources.

Let us consider two identical, parallel polariscopes, Q_1 and Q_2 (e.g., of the type shown in Fig. 7.8). Q_2 is turned 180° with respect to Q_1 (Fig. 7.27). The two polarizers are not shown in Fig. 7.27 (as they are in subsequent figures), but we assume that all double-refracting elements fall between them. The first polarizer here would appear to the left of Q_1, the second, to the right of Q_2.

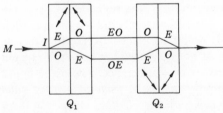

FIG. 7.27   Use of a broad source in a polarization interferometer (compensation).

We study the fringes of this system at infinity and note immediately that for an incident ray MI normal to the polariscopes the shearing produced by Q_1 is canceled by Q_2. What happens if we incline the ray MI?

The path difference between the two rays EO and OE as they pass through Q_1 is compensated by an equal path difference of opposite sign as they pass through Q_2. The recombination of these rays by the polariscope Q_2 occurs in oblique incidence. We can explain the phenomenon in the following way: we replace the polariscope Q of Fig. 7.19 with the two polariscopes Q_1 and Q_2 of Fig. 7.27. We now have Fig. 7.28. If the polariscope Q_1 were alone, it would produce parallel, equidistant, and straight fringes at infinity at E in the focal plane of the objective lens O_2. The same is true of Q_2, which, if it were alone, would give exactly the same fringes in the same position at E. For MI (we have not shown the shearing, assumed to be very small, in Fig. 7.28) EO is delayed with respect to OE, whereas at Q_2, turned by 180°, it is the opposite. The birefringences cancel each other, and because the fringes at infinity of each polariscope are identical and occupy exactly the same position, the phenomenon will occur in the same way at all the points of the field in the focal plane E. The path difference is zero at M_0' at the center of the field: it will also be zero at all the other points in the field.

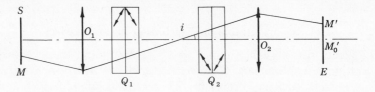

FIG. 7.28   Compensation obtained with birefringent elements with parallel faces.

The system of the two polariscopes produces infinitely spaced fringes at infinity, and we have a flat tint at E (this is true to approximately the third order for the inclination i). The path difference Δ between EO and OE varies very little with the inclination of the rays i, and we can use a large source S. This is termed compensation: the polariscope Q_1 compensates the polariscope Q_2. Figure 7.27 is therefore valid for oblique incidence.

Where must the object be placed? According to Fig. 7.27, it is obvious that the object must not be placed to the left of Q_1, for there would be no shearing and therefore no interference. The object must be placed between the two polariscopes. *This is a result of general validity: if two double-refracting systems compensate each other and permit the use of a large source, the object to be observed must be placed between the two double-refracting elements.*

More details on the complete set-up are given in the section following the description of the instruments.

In Figs. 7.27 and 7.28 the path difference is zero, and the field of observation is dark as in the case of the fine slit discussed in Section 7.10. We have seen that to vary contrast it is sufficient to modify the inclination of the polariscope. We must now change the inclination of Q_2 with respect to Q_1. The principle of the compensation can be applied to all the double-refracting systems described.

Two conditions must be fulfilled:

1. *It must be possible to superpose exactly the two fringe systems of the two double-refracting systems (fringes at infinity or localized in the double-refracting system).*

2. *The orientation of the two double-refracting systems must be such that the shear produced by the first is canceled by the second.*

A simplified diagram using Wollaston prism is shown in Fig. 7.29. Everything that has been said can be applied without change. The fringes of W_1 must be projected on the fringes of W_2: W_1 and W_2 must therefore be conjugate through O. The two polariscopes in Fig. 7.28 have no lenses between Q_1 and Q_2; hence the two fringe systems are identical if the polariscopes themselves are identical. However, in Fig. 7.29 the superposition of the planes of localization of the fringes is accomplished by the objective lens O. Because the spacing of the fringes of the Wollastons W_1 and W_2 is inversely proportional to the angles θ_1 and θ_2 if p_1 and p_2 are the distances from W_1 and W_2 to O, the condition that the fringes can be superposed evidently is

$$\frac{\theta_1}{\theta_2} = \frac{p_2}{p_1}. \tag{7.14}$$

If the Wollastons are at the principal points, W_1 and W_2 are identical.

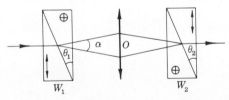

FIG. 7.29   Compensation obtained with two Wollaston prisms.

As in the case of the polariscope, the object must be placed between W_1 and W_2 to effect shearing and therefore interference. These results show that with two appropriate double-refracting systems an incident ray originating from the source is sheared by the first system into two rays EO and OE. The second system recombines these rays, and only one single ray corresponding to the incident ray emerges from the two systems. This phenomenon is not changed if we change the inclination of the incident ray.

Moreover, the path difference between *EO* and *OE* remains the same, regardless of the inclination. We can therefore illuminate the combination of the two double-refracting systems with a large source.

The object must be placed between the two systems. Under these conditions the shearing in the waves (1) and (2) in the image of the object is produced by the double-refracting system placed after the object. The path difference at an arbitrary point in the image of the object does not vary with the inclination of the rays. As a consequence, the contrast of the image is not modified by the use of a large source, and the device becomes very bright.

7.12   Description of the Principal Polarization Interferometers

INTERFEROMETERS USING DOUBLE-REFRACTING SYSTEMS WITH LINEAR SHEAR

The first polarization interferometer, constructed by Jamin (Fig. 7.30) consists of two identical plates cut at 45° with a half-wave plate between them. Because of the half-wave plate, vibrations are interchanged and the recombination of the rays occurs after passing through L_2. The object must be placed between L_1 and L_2, and the shear in the image of the object is produced by L_2. This arrangement is illustrated by Fig. 7.28. We replace Q_1 by L_1 and the half-wave plate and Q_2 by L_2. The two conditions given previously for compensation are fulfilled. Jamin's interferometer has been applied to microscopy by Lebedeff.

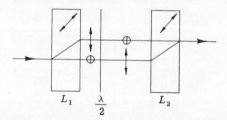

FIG. 7.30   Jamin polarization interferometer.

Figure 7.31 shows an interferometer (Françon–Yamamoto) in which the compensation is produced by an optical system. We let the image focal plane of the objective lens O_1 coincide with the object focal plane of the objective lens O_2. These two planes coincide at F. It does not matter where in front of O_1 we place a Savart polariscope Q_1 (or a polariscope of the type in Fig. 7.8) or where after O_2 we place another polariscope of the same type. Obviously the system is completed by two polarizers not shown. The device is illuminated by a large source so that the incident rays have all possible inclinations to give in F the fringes at infinity of the polariscope Q_1.

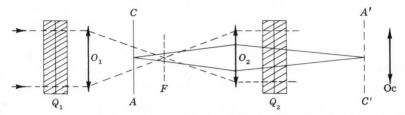

FIG. 7.31   Françon–Yamamoto polarization interferometer.

These fringes are parallel, equidistant straight lines. The same is true of the polariscope Q_2, which produces fringes at F which are, however, virtual. To obtain compensation the first condition is that the two fringe systems be identical. Now, according to (7.5) and (7.8), the angular spacing of the fringes is inversely proportional to e. If f_1 and f_2 are the focal lengths of the objective lenses O_1 and O_2, the condition for compensation is

$$\frac{e_1}{e_2} = \frac{f_1}{f_2}. \tag{7.15}$$

In addition, Q_1 and Q_2 must be oriented so that the birefringences subtract from one another. The plane F is thus uniformly illuminated. The object AC must be placed between O_1 and O_2, but not at F because the image of F will be moved out to infinity and, therefore, the polariscope Q_2 will not produce shearing. The object AC, for example, is slightly in front of F and its image $A'C'$ is observed by means of the eyepiece Oc.

INTERFEROMETERS USING DOUBLE-REFRACTING SYSTEMS WITH ANGULAR SHEAR

Smith's interferometer is described in Fig. 7.32. It consists of two Wollastons W_1 and W_2, placed at the focuses of the objectives O_1 and O_2. The object is at AC and its image $A'C'$, formed by the objective O_2, is observed

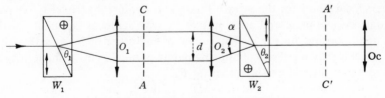

FIG. 7.32   Smith polarization interferometer.

with the eyepiece Oc. The first condition for compensation is that the two fringe systems can be superposed in W_2. If f_1 and f_2 are the focal lengths of O_1 and O_2, (7.14) becomes

$$\frac{\theta_1}{\theta_2} = \frac{f_2}{f_1}. \tag{7.16}$$

The angular shearing is given by (7.12) from which the linear shearing in the object plane AC is

$$d = 2f_2(n_o - n_e) \tan \theta_2. \tag{7.17}$$

The second condition for compensation is a suitable orientation of the Wollastons such that the birefringence is canceled out. The system is illuminated by covering W_1 with the image of a large source. The path difference, that is, the contrast of the images, is changed, for example, by displacing W_2 parallel to a front plane and perpendicular to its fringes.

For practical reasons it is sometimes difficult to reach the focal plane of the objective lenses O_1 and O_2. In this case the modified Wollaston by Nomarski (Fig. 7.16) is useful. In Fig. 7.33 the prism of the type shown in Fig. 7.16 is used under the assumption that the focal plane S' of the objective lens O_2 is not accessible. The plane of localization of the fringes of W_2 is at S', which is conjugate to W_1 through O_1 and O_2.

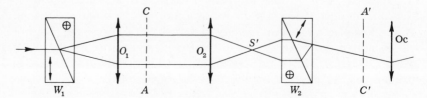

FIG. 7.33   Nomarski polarization interferometer.

In Dyson's interferometer the shear is produced by a calcite lens (Fig. 7.34). The triplet L_1 consists of a biconcave calcite lens cut parallel to the axis and cemented to two biconvex glass lenses. It has zero refracting power for the ordinary ray but behaves like a converging system of a few centimeters focal length for the extraordinary ray. Against the triplet L_1 we place a quarter-wave plate and an objective L_2 with its focus coinciding with a spherical concave mirror A. The center of curvature of A is on the triplet L_1, which receives a beam of approximately parallel light. A small image of the source is formed on the mirror at F_1.

Let us follow an incident ray MI parallel to the axis. After it passes through the triplet, it separates into two rays, O and E; O is not deviated, and after crossing the quarter-wave plate and the lens L_2 it converges into F_1 and is symmetrically reflected. It emerges from L_2 parallel to the axis and again passes through the quarter-wave plate. The quarter-wave plate, having been crossed twice, behaves like a half-wave plate, and the ray O becomes the ray E on the calcite element. It then converges at $F_1{}'$, where we find an image of the point source.

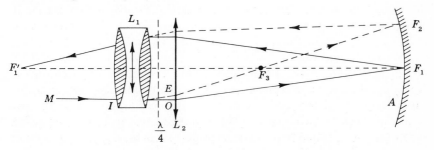

FIG. 7.34   Dyson polarization interferometer.

Now we follow the ray E as it emerges from L_1 and the quarter-wave plate. After traversing L_2, E arrives in F_3, is symmetrically reflected, passes through L_2 and the quarter-wave plate, and becomes ordinary in the calcite element. It converges on the same spot $F_1{}'$. We have shown the paths traveled by only one incident ray MI; a system of beams is represented in Fig. 7.35.

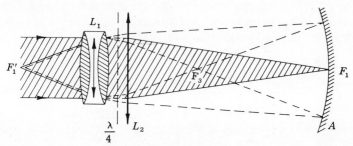

FIG. 7.35   Dyson polarization interferometer.

The incident beam is parallel to the axis; the ordinary beam, emerging at L_1, converges at F_1, and on return, at $F_1{}'$. The extraordinary beam, emerging at L_1, converges at F_3, the focus of the $L_1 + L_2$ combination for extraordinary rays. This beam covers the surface of the mirror A and, on return, converges at $F_1{}'$. Obviously, a semireflecting plate, not shown, on the left side of the diagram, shifts the direction of the returning rays to the side so that the eye may conveniently observe the phenomenon. Thus we see two images of the source in F_1' which originate from two beams: one covers the entire surface of A and the other only a small region in F_1. The object to be studied is placed against the mirror A and must cover, if not the entire surface at least a large part of it. The beam arriving at F_1 is the reference wave, and because it crosses only a very small part of the object we can say that it is not affected by it. The eye placed near F_1' observes the entire illuminated surface at A (lighted by the beam that leaves L_1 as the extraordinary beam and covers the surface at A). It also receives the reference wave originating at F_1 and converging at F_1'. In Fig. 7.35 these two waves are seen from F_1' under the same angle. We assume that there is no object in front of A and that this mirror is perfect. The eye, adjusted to A through L_1 and L_2, sees the mirror uniformly illuminated. Let us modify the orientation slightly at A: the two images corresponding to the two beams no longer coincide at F_1'. We have two small images of the source separated in a direction perpendicular to the axis of the device. We therefore see, parallel, straight fringes on the surface at A. If an object is placed in front of A or if the mirror is not perfect, the deformation of the fringes permits the measurement of the defects, as in a classical interferometer. If we combine the two images corresponding to the two beams at F_1' we observe the object by the flat-tint method.

Figure 7.36 describes an interferometer, designed by Lenouvel. In this instrument the double-refracting system is a Wollaston W, but to achieve a field that is large enough, it is preferable to use the prisms shown in Fig. 7.17 or 7.18. With the objective lens O_1 and after reflection on a mirror m, we form an image of the source S at the center of curvature of the spherical mirror A. We obtain by reflection an image, S_2', which we shift very slightly

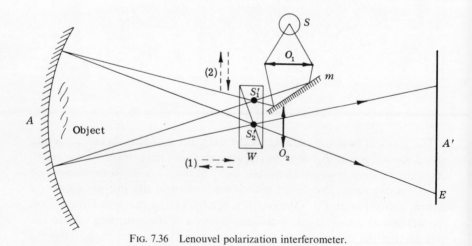

FIG. 7.36   Lenouvel polarization interferometer.

with respect to S_1'. We place a Wollaston W of the large field type on S_1' and S_2'. The light beam passes through the objective O_2 to form an image A' of the mirror A on the observation screen E. As usual, the instrument must be completed by two polarizers, one between O_1 and m, the other between W and O_2. It is also possible to use only one polarizer between W and m, which covers the entire surface of W and through which incident and reflected beams pass. This is equivalent to placing W between two parallel polarizers in perfect adjustment. To obtain the flat color we move W in the direction of the axis of the instrument (1). For a variation of the contrast we displace W in the direction perpendicular to (2).

The object is placed against the mirror A, and W produces the shear in image A' when it acts on the returning beam. By acting on the incident beam it is self-compensating.

Chapter VIII

Interference and Partial Coherence

8.1 Interferences in Quasi-monochromatic Light*

Let us consider Young's experiment (Fig. 8.1): an extended nonmonochromatic source S illuminates an opaque screen pierced by two pinholes T_1 and T_2, and we investigate the phenomenon of interference on the screen π. In this chapter we assume that a large number of wavetrains arrive on the detector during the time necessary to make one observation.

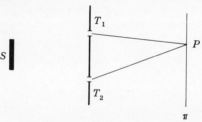

FIG. 8.1   Coherence of two holes T_1 and T_2 illuminated by a source S in Young's experiment.

According to the results of Chapter 1, which we utilize here, the vibrations at T_1 and T_2 produced by the source S can be represented by the functions $V_1^{(r)}(t)$ and $V_2^{(r)}(t)$, which are given by (1.15). For the calculation of these phenomena we associate two analytic signals $V_1(t)$ and $V_2(t)$ with these two real vibrations.

According to the notation of Section 1.8, we have

$$V_1(t) = 2\int_0^\infty v(T_1, v)e^{j2\pi vt}\, dv,$$

$$V_2(t) = 2\int_0^\infty v(T_2, v)e^{j2\pi vt}\, dv. \tag{8.1}$$

The vibration $V_1(t)$ emitted by T_1 follows the path T_1P, and can be characterized for each frequency by a complex number,

$$g(v)e^{-j2\pi v\theta_1},$$

* We follow the treatment given by E. Wolf.

162

where θ_1 is the time taken by light to travel from T_1 to P. The function $g(v)$ determines the ratio of the amplitudes at T_1 and P for the frequency v. The Fourier transformation of the vibration at P is given by

$$v(T_1, v)\, g(v) e^{-j2\pi v \theta_1}, \tag{8.2}$$

from which the vibration at P at time t, due to the pinhole T_1, is

$$V_P(T_1, t) = 2K_1 \int_0^\infty v(T_1, v)\, g(v) e^{j2\pi v(t-\theta_1)}\, dv\,; \tag{8.3}$$

K_1 depends on the dimension of the pinhole T_1, the angle of incidence of the ray at T_1, and the inclination of the diffraction ray $T_1 P$ with respect to the geometrical ray. To simplify we assume that the medium is homogeneous and transparent, with an index of refraction equal to 1.

The function $g(v)$ is now equal to $1/T_1 P$, and the decrease in the amplitude can be taken into account in the factor K_1. We write the vibration at P due to T_1 in this form:

$$V_P(T_1, t) = 2K_1 \int_0^\infty v(T_1, v) e^{j2\pi v(t-\theta_1)}\, dv = K_1 V_1(t - \theta_1), \tag{8.4}$$

where K_1 has been defined before. Now, however, K_1 is also inversely proportional to $T_1 P$. Finally, we write the vibration in P due to T_1 and T_2 as

$$V(t) = K_1 V_1(t - \theta_1) + K_2 V_2(t - \theta_2). \tag{8.5}$$

According to the Huygens–Fresnel principle, the vibrations diffracted by T_1 and T_2 have undergone a phase shift of $\pi/2$ with respect to the incident vibrations arriving at T_1 and T_2. The factors K_1 and K_2 are therefore pure imaginary numbers.

According to (1.79) the intensity in P up to a constant factor is given by the expression

$$I = \overline{V(t)\, V^*(t)} = 2\overline{V^{(r)2}(t)}.$$

The calculations in Section 1.8 can be applied; it is sufficient to introduce the factors K_1 and K_2. We have

$$I = K_1 K_1^* \,\overline{V_1 V_1^*} + K_2 K_2^* \,\overline{V_2 V_2^*}$$

$$+ K_1 K_2^* \,\overline{V_1(t + \theta) V_2^*(t)} + K_2 K_2^* \,\overline{V_1^*(t + \theta) V_2(t)}, \tag{8.6}$$

where, according to (1.84), $\theta = \theta_2 - \theta_1$. Because K_1 and K_2 are purely imaginary, (8.6) can be written

$$I = |K_1|^2 \,\overline{V_1 V_1^*} + |K_2|^2 \,\overline{V_2 V_2^*}$$

$$+ 2|K_1 K_2| \mathscr{R}[\overline{V_1(t + \theta) V_2^*(t)}]. \tag{8.7}$$

We set

$$I_1 = |K_1|^2 \overline{V_1 V_1^*}, \qquad I_2 = |K_2|^2 \overline{V_2 V_2^*}. \tag{8.8}$$

The intensities I_1 and I_2 are the intensities at P if T_1 and T_2 act separately. Let us introduce the complex degree of coherence (1.89) of the vibrations

$$\gamma_{12}(\theta) = \frac{\overline{V_1(t+\theta) V_2^*(t)}}{\sqrt{I_1}\sqrt{I_2}}, \tag{8.9}$$

where I_1 and I_2 are given by (8.8). We have

$$I = I_1 + I_2 + 2\sqrt{I_1}\sqrt{I_2}\mathscr{R}[\gamma_{12}(\theta)]. \tag{8.10}$$

As we have already seen in Section 1.8, this expression shows that to determine the light intensity at P we must know the intensity due to each source, acting separately, and the real part of the complex degree of coherence.

According to (1.92) and (1.93), we can write

$$I = I_1 + I_2 + 2\sqrt{I_1}\sqrt{I_2}|\gamma_{12}(\theta)|\cos[\alpha(\theta) + 2\pi\nu_0\theta], \tag{8.11}$$

where ν_0 is a mean frequency and $\alpha(\theta)$ is given by

$$\alpha(\theta) = \text{argument of} \quad \gamma_{12}(\theta) - 2\pi\nu_0\theta. \tag{8.12}$$

If the openings T_1 and T_2 are very small, we can say that at π, a region of generally small extension in which the phenomenon is observed, the intensity due to each aperture acting separately is constant. In (8.11) I_1 and I_2 are constants. We assume that this is true.

In addition, we consider the case in which the light emitted by S is quasi-monochromatic. Under these conditions, discussed in Section 1.14, $|\gamma_{12}(\theta)|$ varies very slowly in comparison to $\cos 2\pi\nu_0\theta$. We can assume that $|\gamma_{12}(\theta)|$ is constant for all points on the plane π, where the phenomenon is observed. With these hypotheses, the variations of the intensity I given by (8.11) depend only on the variations of $\cos[\alpha(\theta) + 2\pi\nu_0\theta]$, and we have a sinusoidal variation of the intensity on which a uniform background of intensity $I_1 + I_2$ is superposed. The results of Section 1.14 can be applied. The contrast of the fringes is given by (1.124)

$$\gamma = \frac{4\sqrt{I_1}\sqrt{I_2}|\gamma_{12}(\theta)|}{I_1 + I_2 + 2\sqrt{I_1}\sqrt{I_2}|\gamma_{12}(\theta)|}. \tag{8.13}$$

If the path difference $T_1 P - T_2 P$ remains small compared with the coherence length (length of the wavetrains), we can write (Section 1.15)

$$|\gamma_{12}(\theta)| \simeq |\gamma_{12}(0)|,$$

and finally the contrast is written as (1.130)

$$\gamma = \frac{4\sqrt{I_1}\sqrt{I_2}|\gamma_{12}(0)|}{I_1 + I_2 + 2\sqrt{I_1}\sqrt{I_2}|\gamma_{12}(0)|}. \tag{8.14}$$

If $I_1 = I_2$,

$$\gamma = \frac{2|\gamma_{12}(0)|}{1 + |\gamma_{12}(0)|}, \tag{8.15}$$

and the distribution of the intensities in the plane π is given by (1.129)

$$I = I_1 + I_2 + 2\sqrt{I_1}\sqrt{I_2}|\gamma_{12}(0)|\cos[\alpha(0) + 2\pi\nu_0\theta]. \tag{8.16}$$

In summing up, (8.14) and (8.15) can be applied if the following conditions are fulfilled:

1. The openings T_1 and T_2 are small enough so that in the region of the plane π, in which the phenomenon is observed, the intensities I_1 and I_2 produced separately by each opening are constant.

2. The light is quasi-monochromatic.

3. The path difference $T_1P - T_2P$ remains small compared with the length of the wavetrains.

Equations 8.14 and 8.15 show that for the calculation of fringe contrast we must know the degree of coherence $|\gamma_{12}(0)|$ of the vibrations emitted by T_1 and T_2. This is the degree of coherence of the two openings T_1 and T_2 illuminated by the source S. We perform this calculation in the next section.

8.2   Degree of Coherence of Two Points Illuminated by an Extended Source of Quasi-monochromatic Light

Two points T_1 and T_2 (Fig. 8.2) located in a plane yOz are illuminated by a source S. We want to calculate the degree of coherence of the vibrations at T_1 and T_2. We assume that the source S is an element of a plane parallel to the plane yOz and that its dimensions are small compared with the distance CO. If M is an arbitrary point of S, we assume that the angles between CO and MT_2 and MT_1 are small.

To simplify, T_2 is coincident with O and T_1's position is variable. According to (1.45), a vibration emitted by an atom M, as it leaves M, can be written by marking the atom with the index i:

$$a_i(t)e^{j2\pi\nu_0 t},$$

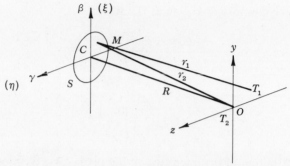

FIG. 8.2   Calculation of the degree of coherence of T_1 and T_2 illuminated by S.

and the two vibrations at T_1 and in T_2, evaluated at the instant at which they reach these two points, are written

$$a_{i1}(t) = a_i\left(t - \frac{r_1}{c}\right)\frac{\exp[j2\pi v_0(t - r_1/c)]}{r_1},$$

$$a_{i2}(t) = a_i\left(t - \frac{r_2}{c}\right)\frac{\exp[j2\pi v_0(t - r_2/c)]}{r_2}, \tag{8.17}$$

assuming that the medium has an index equal to 1 (c = speed of light).

The vibrations at T_1 and T_2, due to all the atoms at the source, are given by the expressions

$$a_1(t) = \sum a_i\left(t - \frac{r_1}{c}\right)\frac{\exp[j2\pi v_0(t - r_1/c)]}{r_1} = \sum a_{i1}(t),$$

$$a_2(t) = \sum a_i\left(t - \frac{r_2}{c}\right)\frac{\exp[j2\pi v_0(t - r_2/c)]}{r_2} = \sum a_{i2}(t), \tag{8.18}$$

so the mutual coherence function at T_1 and T_2 is given by

$$\Gamma_{12}(0) = \overline{a_1(t)\,a_2{}^*(t)} = \overline{\sum a_{i1}(t)\sum a_{i2}(t)}. \tag{8.19}$$

Now, the products for which $i \neq j$ correspond to different atoms which are incoherent, and it follows that

$$\Gamma_{12}(0) = \overline{\sum a_{i1}(t)\,a_{i2}{}^*(t)}. \tag{8.20}$$

We then have

$$\Gamma_{12}(0) = \overline{\sum a_i\left(t - \frac{r_1}{c}\right) a_i{}^*\left(t - \frac{r_2}{c}\right)\frac{\exp\left[j2\pi v_0\left(\dfrac{r_2 - r_1}{c}\right)\right]}{r_1 r_2}}. \tag{8.21}$$

and we may write

$$\overline{\sum a_i\left(t - \frac{r_1}{c}\right) a_i^*\left(t - \frac{r_2}{c}\right) \frac{\exp\left[j2\pi v_0\left(\frac{r_2 - r_1}{c}\right)\right]}{r_1 r_2}}$$

$$= \overline{\sum a_i(t) a_i^*\left(t - \frac{r_2 - r_1}{c}\right) \frac{\exp\left[j2\pi v_0\left(\frac{r_2 - r_1}{c}\right)\right]}{r_1 r_2}}.$$

The retardation $(r_2 - r_1)/c$ in a_i^* may be neglected if $r_2 - r_1$ is small compared with the coherence lengths of the light.

$$\Gamma_{12}(0) = \overline{\sum a_i(t) a_i^*(t)} \frac{\exp\left[j2\pi v_0\left(\frac{r_2 - r_1}{c}\right)\right]}{r_1 r_2}. \tag{8.22}$$

According to (8.16), we see that $\overline{a_i(t) a_i^*(t)}$ represents the energy emitted by the atom M. Because the atoms are numerous at the source, the sum can be replaced by an integral. if $J(S) dS$ is the energy emitted by an element dS at the source, we have

$$J(S) dS = \overline{a_i(t) a_i^*(t)} \tag{8.23}$$

and

$$\Gamma_{12}(0) = \int_S J(S) \frac{\exp[jK_0(r_2 - r_1)]}{r_1 r_2} dS, \tag{8.24}$$

with

$$K_0 = \frac{2\pi v_0}{c} = \frac{2\pi}{\lambda_0},$$

in which the complex degree of coherence is

$$\gamma_{12}(0) = (J_1 J_2)^{-1/2} \int_S J(S) \frac{\exp[jK_0(r_2 - r_1)]}{r_1 r_2} dS, \tag{8.25}$$

with

$$J_1 = \int_S \frac{J(S)}{r_1^2} dS \qquad J_2 = \int_S \frac{J(S)}{r_2^2} dS ; \tag{8.26}$$

J_1 and J_2 are the intensities at T_1 and T_2. Let us assume that the source is replaced by a screen pierced by an opening of the same form and dimensions as the source. If this opening limits a spherical wave front with the center T_2, we have on the plane yOz a certain amplitude distribution that is just the phenomenon of diffraction at T_2, if T_2 were the image of a fictitious point source. Equation 8.25 shows that the complex degree of coherence of T_1 and T_2 is represented by the amplitude at T_1. This is the van Cittert–Zernike theorem.

We calculate $r_2 - r_1 = MT_2 - MT_1$. The coordinates of M are ξ and η and those of T_1 are y and z. By setting $CO = R$ we have

$$r_1{}^2 = (y - \xi)^2 + (z - \eta)^2 + R^2 , \tag{8.27}$$

$$r_1 \simeq R + \frac{(y - \xi)^2 + (z - \eta)^2}{2R}, \tag{8.28}$$

and

$$r_2 \simeq R + \frac{\xi^2 + \eta^2}{2R}, \tag{8.29}$$

from which

$$r_2 - r_1 \simeq - \frac{y^2 + z^2}{2R} + \frac{y\xi + z\eta}{R}. \tag{8.30}$$

Then

$$\frac{\xi}{R} = \beta, \qquad \frac{\eta}{R} = \gamma , \tag{8.31}$$

and we have

$$r_2 - r_1 = - \frac{y^2 + z^2}{2R} + \beta y + \gamma z . \tag{8.32}$$

By setting

$$\psi_{12} = - K_0 \left(\frac{y^2 + z^2}{2R} \right) \tag{8.33}$$

the complex degree of coherence (8.25) can be written

$$\gamma_{12}(0) = \frac{e^{j\psi_{12}}}{(J_1 J_2)^{1/2}} \iint_S \frac{J(\beta, \gamma)}{R^2} e^{jK_0(\beta y + \gamma z)} \, d\beta \, d\gamma . \tag{8.34}$$

Now

$$J_1 \simeq J_2 = \iint \frac{J(\beta, \gamma)}{R^2} \, d\beta \, d\gamma , \tag{8.35}$$

from which finally

$$\gamma_{12}(0) = \frac{e^{j\psi_{12}} \iint_S J(\beta, \gamma) e^{jK_0(\beta y + \gamma z)} \, d\beta \, d\gamma}{\iint_S J(\beta, \gamma) \, d\beta \, d\gamma}. \tag{8.36}$$

The complex degree of coherence is expressed by the normalized Fourier transformation of the energy distribution $J(\beta, \gamma)$ emitted by the source.
Note.
  If M moves into C, $\beta = \gamma = 0$ and, according to (8.32),

$$r_2 - r_1 = -\frac{y^2 + z^2}{2R}; \tag{8.37}$$

ψ_{12} therefore represents the phase difference

$$\psi_{12} = \frac{2\pi}{\lambda_0}(CT_2 - CT_1) \tag{8.38}$$

and ψ_{12} is negligible if $CT_2 - CT_1 \ll \lambda_0$.

8.3   Degree of Coherence of Two Points Illuminated by an Incoherent Uniform Circular Source

The source S is limited by a circular aperture of center C and radius ρ. The normal CO to the plane of the source passes through T_2. We then have

$$\gamma_{12}(0) = \left[\frac{2J_1(Z)}{Z}\right] \exp(j\psi_{12}), \tag{8.39}$$

where $J_1(Z)$ is the Bessel function of the first order of the variable Z defined by

$$Z = \frac{2\pi}{\lambda_0} \frac{\rho}{R}(y^2 + z^2)^{1/2}, \tag{8.40}$$

and

$$\psi_{12} = -\frac{2\pi}{\lambda}\left(\frac{y^2 + z^2}{2R}\right) \tag{8.41}$$

because the Fourier transformation of a circle is given by the classical expression $2J_1(Z)/Z$.
  Figure 8.3 shows the variations of the degree of partial coherence

$$|\gamma_{12}(0)| = \left|\frac{2J_1(Z)}{Z}\right|. \tag{8.42}$$

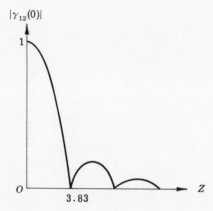

FIG. 8.3   Variation of the degree of partial coherence $|\gamma_{12}(0)|$ as a function of the distance T_1T_2.

as a function of Z. For $Z = 0$ the degree of partial coherence is a maximum equal to 1. If z increases, $|\gamma_{12}(0)|$ decreases and becomes zero for $Z = 3.83$; T_1 and T_2 are therefore completely incoherent if

$$Z = \frac{2\pi}{\lambda_0}\frac{\rho}{R}T_1T_2 = 3.83$$

and   (8.43)

$$T_1T_2 = \frac{1.22\lambda_0}{2\alpha},$$

where $\alpha = \rho/R$ is the angle under which the radius of the source is seen from T_2. If we tolerate a degree of partial coherence equal to 0.88, T_1T_2 must not exceed the value

$$T_1T_2 \leqslant \frac{0.32\lambda_0}{2\alpha}.$$ (8.44)

We can represent this result by tracing the curve $|\gamma_{12}(0)|$ as a function of z (Fig. 8.4). This curve shows the phenomenon of diffraction in amplitude of a point source. In fact, the degree of partial coherence $|\gamma_{12}(0)|$ is given by the Fourier transformation of the source's energy distribution; now, because this distribution is constant, $|\gamma_{12}(0)|$ gives the distribution in amplitude of the diffraction phenomenon produced by a uniform pupil having the form of the source. The two points T_1 and T_2 will be coherent if the distance from T_1 to T_2 (T_2 is the origin) is sufficiently small so that the ordinate relative to T_1 varies as little as possible from the central ordinate.

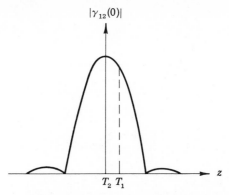

FIG. 8.4 T_1 and T_2 are coherent if the relative ordinates of these two points differ only slightly.

8.4 Contrast of the Fringes in Young's Experiment as a Function of the Degree of Partial Coherence: Case of Quasi-monochromatic Light

We refer again to Young's experiment in Section 8.1 by assuming that the two pinholes T_1 and T_2 are illuminated by an incoherent luminous slit (Fig. 8.5). The normal to the source at its center C passes through the center of $T_1 T_2$. According to Section 8.1 the fringe constant (located, for example, in the plane $y'z'$) is given by (8.15). If the slit is seen from T_1 and T_2 under the angle 2α, we have, according to (8.36),

$$\gamma_{12}(0) = \frac{\sin 2\pi\alpha z/\lambda_0}{2\pi\alpha z/\lambda_0}, \qquad (8.45)$$

where $z = T_1 T_2$. Figure 8.6 shows the variations of $|\gamma_{12}(0)|$ as a function of α.

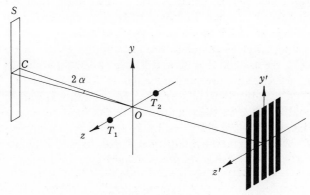

FIG. 8.5 The contrast of fringes is related to the degree of coherence of the two holes T_1 and T_2.

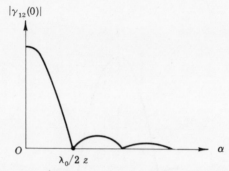

FIG. 8.6   Degree of coherence of T_1 and T_2 as a function of the angular width 2α of the source.

If $\alpha = \lambda_0/2z$, the fringes disappear. They reappear for $\alpha > \lambda_0/2z$ and disappear again for $\alpha = \lambda_0/z$, and so on. Because T_1 and T_2 are symmetrical with respect to O,

$$\psi_{12} = \frac{2\pi}{\lambda_0}(CT_2 - CT_1) = 0,$$

and $\gamma_{12}(0)$ is real. If T_2 coincides with O, we have

$$\psi_{12} = \frac{2\pi}{\lambda_0}(CO - CT_1) \tag{8.46}$$

and

$$\gamma_{12}(0) = \frac{\sin 2\pi\alpha z/\lambda_0}{2\pi\alpha z/\lambda_0} e^{j\psi_{12}} = |\gamma_{12}(0)|e^{j\alpha(0)}. \tag{8.47}$$

The phase difference ψ_{12} produces a lateral displacement of the fringes. If the central fringe is at O' when T_1 and T_2 are symmetrical, it is displaced toward the positive z' when T_2 moves to O ($T_1 T_2$ remains equal to z). The degree of coherence is the modulus of (8.47) and the contrast of the fringes does not change. Let us calculate the distribution of the intensities along $O'z'$ (Fig. 8.7). We assume that T_1 and T_2 are two slits parallel to the source slit. In Fig. 8.7 the slits are perpendicular to the plane of the figure, and the source slit is at the focus of a lens L_1. The two slits T_2 and T_1 are placed after L_1, and we observe the phenomena in the focal plane π' of a second lens L_2. The rays that are diffracted by T_1 and T_2 in an arbitrary direction θ arrive at P'. We calculate the intensity at P' located at a distance z' from the center O'. The slit T_1, if it acted alone, would give an intensity at π' represented by

$$I_1 = \left(\frac{\sin 2\pi\alpha'z'/\lambda_0}{2\pi\alpha'z'/\lambda_0}\right)^2, \tag{8.48}$$

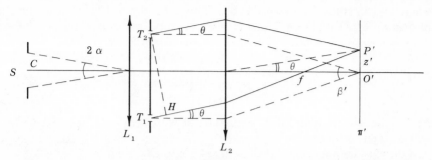

FIG. 8.7   Calculation of intensity distribution in the interference fringes produced by T_1 and T_2.

where $\alpha' = a/f$; $2a$ is the width of the slit T_1 and f is the focal length of the lens L_2. This is a diffraction pattern of the center O'. The same is true for T_2; if T_2 is identical to T_1, we have $I_1 = I_2$. We calculate the phase difference ψ between the vibrations diffracted by T_1 and T_2 which arrive at P'. This difference is represented by $K_0 \cdot T_1 H$. We then have

$$\psi = K_0 \cdot T_1 H = K_0 z \theta. \tag{8.49}$$

Now

$$\theta = \frac{z'}{f},$$

and if

$$\frac{z}{f} = \beta', \qquad (z = T_1 T_2),$$

we have

$$\psi = \frac{2\pi \beta' z'}{\lambda_0}. \tag{8.50}$$

According to (8.16), we have

$$2\pi v_0 \theta = \frac{2\pi \beta' z'}{\lambda_0}.$$

The intensity I at an arbitrary point P' ($O'P' = z'$) (8.16) is given by

$$I = 2\left(\frac{\sin 2\pi\alpha' z'/\lambda_0}{2\pi\alpha' z'/\lambda_0}\right)^2 \left\{1 + \left|\frac{\sin 2\pi\alpha z/\lambda_0}{2\pi\alpha z/\lambda_0}\right| \cos\left[\alpha(0) - \frac{2\pi\beta' z'}{\lambda_0}\right]\right\}. \tag{8.51}$$

If the slits T_1 and T_2 are sufficiently narrow, the light diffracted by them is, for all practical purposes, distributed uniformly in the region of the plane π'

where we can study the variations of I. This is condition 1 listed at the end of Section 8.1. Condition 2 and 3 were already implicitly fulfilled when (8.45) was written. Hence we have, up to a constant factor,

$$I = 1 + \left| \frac{\sin 2\pi\alpha z/\lambda_0}{2\pi\alpha z/\lambda_0} \right| \cos\left[\alpha(0) - \frac{2\pi\beta' z'}{\lambda_0} \right], \qquad (8.52)$$

and, if the slits T_1 and T_2 are symmetrical with respect to the axis CO', $\alpha(0)$ is equal to 0 or π.

If the slits are not symmetrical with respect to CO', we have

$$\psi_{12} = \frac{2\pi}{\lambda_0}(CT_2 - CT_1), \qquad (8.53)$$

and $\alpha(0)$ is equal to ψ_{12} or $\psi_{12} + \pi$. In all cases the bright fringes correspond to

$$\cos\left[\alpha(0) - \frac{2\pi\beta' z'}{\lambda_0} \right] = 2m\pi \qquad (m = 0, \pm1, \pm2, \ldots)$$

and the dark fringes to

$$\cos\left[\alpha(0) - \frac{2\pi\beta' z'}{\lambda_0} \right] = (2m + 1)\pi.$$

The intensities I_{max} and I_{min} of the bright and dark fringes are given by

$$I_{max} = 1 + \left| \frac{\sin 2\pi\alpha z/\lambda_0}{2\pi\alpha z/\lambda_0} \right|, \qquad (8.54)$$

$$I_{min} = 1 - \left| \frac{\sin 2\pi\alpha z/\lambda_0}{2\pi\alpha z/\lambda_0} \right|, \qquad (8.55)$$

from which the contrast of the fringes is obtained with

$$\gamma = \frac{2\left| \dfrac{\sin 2\pi\alpha z/\lambda_0}{2\pi\alpha z/\lambda_0} \right|}{1 + \left| \dfrac{\sin 2\pi\alpha z/\lambda_0}{2\pi\alpha z/\lambda_0} \right|}, \qquad (8.56)$$

a value given directly by (8.15) and (8.45). We can compare this result with that obtained with (2.24). By using $s = 2\alpha\overline{CO} = 2\alpha d$, $z = 2a$, and $m = 2a\pi/\lambda d$ we find (2.24), again.

8.5 Measurement of the Angular Diameter of Stars by Michelson's Method: Application of the Notion of Partial Coherence

The principle of Michelson's method can be explained in a simple manner by use of the notion of partial coherence.

Figure 8.8 is a diagram of the experiment. Light coming from a star, reflected in four mirrors, M_1, M_1', M_2, and M_2', passes through the two slits F_1 and F_2 placed in front of the mirror of the telescope (represented by the objective lens O). The distance F_1F_2 is equal to 114 cm, but it is the distance M_1M_2 of the order of 6 meters between the two mirrors M_1 and M_2 that plays the fundamental role. We observe interference fringes (Young's fringes) in the focal plane of the telescope in S', whose spacing, determined by F_1F_2, is approximately 0.02 mm. To take the measurements, we vary the distance M_1M_2 between the two mirrors, which has no influence on the spacing of the fringes. From the viewpoint of the measurement of the angular diameter it all happens as if the slits were placed at F_1' and F_2'.

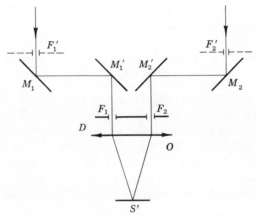

FIG. 8.8 Measurement of the angular diameter of stars by Michelson's method (degree of partial coherence).

Let us set $F_1'F_2' = 2a$ and let f be the focal length of the objective O, that is, of the mirror of the telescope. We assume that the star can be considered as a uniform circular source. According to (8.42), the degree of partial coherence of F_1' and F_2' in quasi-monochromatic light is given by

$$\gamma_{12}(0) = \left| \frac{2J_1(Z)}{Z} \right|, \tag{8.57}$$

with

$$Z = \frac{\pi}{\lambda} 2a\alpha \; ; \tag{8.58}$$

if Z is small, that is, if the distance $2a$ of the two slits is small, the degree of partial coherence is nearly 1 and we can see the fringes very well.

If $2a$ and, consequently, z increase, the degree of partial coherence diminishes and becomes zero for $Z = 3.83$. The slits $F_1{}'$ and $F_2{}'$ are incoherent and the fringes disappear. According to (8.58), we have

$$2a = \frac{1.22\lambda}{2\alpha}. \tag{8.59}$$

By measuring the spacing of the slits $F_1{}'$ and $F_2{}'$; that is, of the two mirrors M_1 and M_2, when the fringes disappear for the first time, we obtain the angular diameter of the star.

For a star of angular diameter $2\alpha = 0.02$ sec, we obtain a distance $2a$ between the mirrors of approximately 7 meters. Considering the rigidity which must be demanded of the mechanical elements of an interferometer, we understand the enormous difficulties encountered by Michelson in the construction of instruments of this dimension. That is why Michelson and Pease had to limit their measurements to a very small number of stars.

8.6 Coherence of Two Points Illuminated by an Extended Source through a Double-refracting Plate

We insert a crystalline double-refracting plate L (Fig. 8.9) between the extended source S and the two points T_1 and T_2. The plate is cut at 45° to the axis, because the fringes at infinity for this inclination are parallel and equidistant straight lines. The plate is oriented so that its principal section is parallel to the plane MT_1T_2, in which M is an arbitrary point of S. A polarizer is mounted in front of L but is not shown in Fig. 8.9. We assume also that T_1 can receive only ordinary rays and T_2, only extraordinary rays.

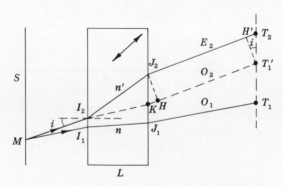

FIG. 8.9   Coherence of two points T_1 and T_2 illuminated by S across a birefringent plate L.

This condition can be easily realized by placing a half-wave plate in front of T_1 (or T_2) and a second polarizer covering T_1 and T_2. In Fig. 8.9 we assume that the shear $T_1'T_2$ produced by the plate L is smaller than the spacing of the points T_1 and T_2.

Let $(MI_2T_2) - (MI_1T_1)$ be the path difference between $MI_2J_2T_2$ and $MI_1J_1T_1$. By adjusting ψ_{12} given by (8.33) equal to zero, we have, according to (8.32),

$$r_2 - r_1 = \beta y + \gamma z = (MI_2T_2) - (MI_1T_1), \qquad (8.60)$$

and the complex degree of coherence is written

$$\gamma_{12}(0) = \frac{\iint_S J(\beta, \gamma) e^{jK_0[(MI_2T_2)-(MI_1T_1)]} \, d\beta \, d\gamma}{\iint_S J(\beta, \gamma) \, d\beta \, d\gamma}. \qquad (8.61)$$

Now

$$(MI_2T_2) - (MI_1T_1) = (MI_2T_2) - (MI_2T_1') + (MI_2T_1') - (MI_1T_1). \qquad (8.62)$$

Let us replace plate L with a polariscope of the type in Fig. 7.8 or by a Savart polariscope (Fig. 7.1). The discussion given above holds good and in the polariscope in Fig. 7.8 the rays remain in the plane of the figure as for the plate L alone. In the Savart polariscope the two rays O and E are no longer in the plane of the figure, and it becomes less simple to represent the phenomenon. The following argument for use of the polariscope in Fig. 7.8 is valid for both instruments.

Equations 7.6 and 7.7 show that

$$(MI_2J_2) - (MI_2H) = \Delta = id = KH. \qquad (8.63)$$

Here $d = T_2T_1'$; therefore

$$(MI_2T_2) - (MI_2T_1') = 0. \qquad (8.64)$$

According to (8.62), we have

$$(MI_2T_2) - (MI_1T_1) = (MI_2T_1') - (MI_1T_1), \qquad (8.65)$$

from which the complex degree of coherence

$$\gamma_{12}(0) = \frac{\iint_S J(\beta, \gamma) e^{jK_0[(MI_2T_1')-(MI_1T_1)]} \, d\beta \, d\gamma}{\iint_S J(\beta, \gamma) \, d\beta \, d\gamma}. \qquad (8.66)$$

The degree of coherence between T_1 and T_2 is equal to that between T_1 and T_1'. The polariscope L increases the degree of coherence between T_1 and T_2

and permits perfect coherence (equal to 1) if T_1 is coincident with $T_1{}'$, that is, if the shear is equal to the distance that separates T_1 and T_2. According to the theory applicable to these polariscopes (Sections 7.2 and 7.3), this result is valid for all wavelengths, and T_1 and T_2 can be illuminated with a source S which emits white light. We can therefore perform the experiment described in Fig. 8.10. T_1 and T_2 consist of two fine slits, and their spacing is equal to the shear produced by the polariscope L, which is placed between two polarizers $\mathscr{P}_1$ and $\mathscr{P}_2$. A half-wave plate, for example, covers the slit T_2. Hence we can observe Young's fringes on the screen E by using an extended source S of white light. The phenomena are the same if we use a Wollaston prism.

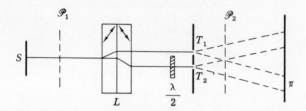

FIG. 8.10   Observation of Young's fringes with a large source.

8.7   Coherence of Two Points Illuminated by a Grating in Incoherent Light

Let us consider an extended incoherent uniform source S (Fig. 8.11) which emits quasi-monochromatic light. In front of it we place a grating R with the lines vertical, and we illuminate the two vertical slits T_1 and T_2 in Young's experiment. In order that the two slits T_1 and T_2 give high-contrast fringes on the observation screen E_2 it is necessary that they be illuminated as coherently as possible. The distribution of coherence in the plane E_1 is given by the Fourier transformation of the energy distribution of the source S. Now, if we place a grating against S, the distribution of the energy is that of the grating. The Fourier transformation in E_1 is shown by the diffraction phenomenon in amplitude, produced by the grating R. We therefore, have, a series of peaks, the central image and the spectra of the grating, whose distances depend on the period of the grating and the distance from R to E_1. It should be noted that these spectra do not exist in the plane E_1, which is uniformly lighted by S and R (S is an extended incoherent source). These fictitious spectra represent the distribution of coherence in the plane E_1.

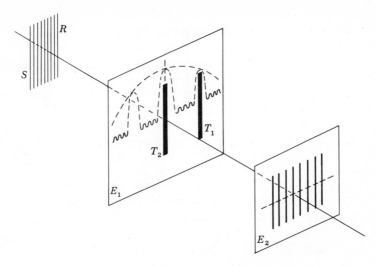

FIG. 8.11   Coherence of T_1 and T_2 illuminated by a grating R.

Let us place "the central image" of coherence on T_2 (it corresponds to what would be the direct image of the source if the grating R were illuminated in coherent light). If T_1 falls on the first peak of coherence, right or left (this would be the position of the first spectrum if the grating were illuminated in coherent light), T_1 and T_2 are coherent because there is little difference in height compared with the peak corresponding to T_2. Under these conditions Young's fringes show high contrast on the screen E_2 and are extremely luminous because they are lighted by a large source.

If we move T_1 closer to T_2, the two slits are no longer coherent because T_1 leaves the peak of coherence. But if we move T_1 away, we obtain coherence when T_1 arrives at the second peak (second coherence spectrum) provided that its height is not too different from that of the peak corresponding to T_2.

Naturally, the spacing of the peaks of coherence depends on the wavelength. Therefore if the distance T_1T_2 produces coherence for a specific wavelength, it will no longer do so for another wavelength because the distance from the peaks to the "central image" will have changed. Hence it is not possible to observe Young's fringes on the screen E_2 with a large source S if the source does not emit quasi-monochromatic light. We refer to Zernike–Vaissala's experiment of the three slits, as done by Maréchal. Figure 8.12 shows the plane E_1 in which the three slits T_1, T_2, and T_3 are located. These three slits, illuminated by the same source (a grating placed against an extended source S), are coherent if their distances are such

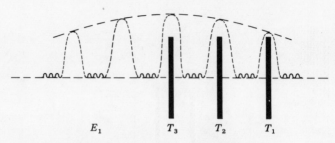

FIG. 8.12   Coherence of three slits T_1, T_2, and T_3 illuminated by a grating.

that T_3 is on the "central image" of coherence and T_1 and T_2 fall on the first two peaks of coherence (on the same side of the central peak). Furthermore, the three peaks must vary very little in height. As in Young's experiment, the three slits are illuminated by a large source of quasi-monochromatic light and the phenomenon becomes much brighter.

Chapter IX

Intensity Interferometer

9.1 The Hanbury-Brown and Twiss Interferometer

To measure the angular diameter of the stars, Hanbury-Brown and Twiss designed an interferometer of a new kind. This instrument does not give the degree of partial coherence $|\gamma_{12}(0)|$ directly, but its square $|\gamma_{12}(0)|^2$.

The principle of the interferometer is outlined in Fig. 9.1. The two photomultipliers PM_1 and PM_2 receive light from the star whose angular diameter is to be measured, and the currents produced are proportional to the star's luminous intensity. The light originating from the star is emitted in the form of wavetrains, and consequently the anodic currents fluctuate.

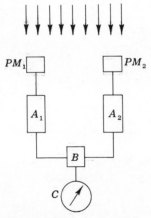

FIG. 9.1   Principle of Hanbury-Brown and Twiss intensity interferometer.

They are amplified by two amplifiers A_1 and A_2, and their product is formed by a linear multiplier B. A device placed in one of the branches of the interferometer introduces a variable delay t_0 which permits the compensation of a difference in the time of arrival of the wavetrains on the photomultipliers. The multiplier is followed by an integrator that measures the correlation of the currents, from which, as we shall see, the square of the modulus

181

of the complex degree of coherence is derived. It should be noted that in reality the two photomultipliers PM_1 and PM_2 do not directly receive the light of the star. To increase the flux, the two photomultipliers are placed at the foci of two mirrors O_1 and O_2 (Fig. 9.2). As in Michelson's experiment, we take the measurements of correlation for different distances $2a$ of the two photomultipliers. The experimental curve obtained in this way approaches the theoretical curve that gives $|\gamma_{12}(0)|^2$ as a function of $2a$, from which we derive $|\gamma_{12}(0)|$, and hence the angular diameter of the star. Because the method of Hanbury-Brown and Twiss is based on measurements of intensity, we call the instrument in Figs. 9.1 and 9.2 an intensity interferometer.

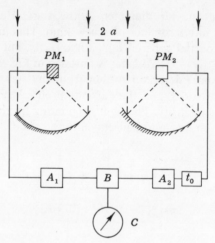

FIG. 9.2   The two photomultipliers of the Hanbury-Brown and Twiss interferometer are placed at the focuses of two mirrors O_1 and O_2.

9.2   Relation between the Intensity Fluctuations and the Degree of Partial Coherence*

Let $I_1(t)$ and $I_2(t)$ be the instantaneous intensities received at P_1 and P_2 where the two photomultipliers PM_1 and PM_2 are located. We have

$$I_1(t) = V_1(t)\, V_1{}^*(t),$$
$$I_2(t) = V_2(t)\, V_2{}^*(t),$$

(9.1)

where $V_1(t)$ and $V_2(t)$ are the analytic signals associated with the real vibrations (see Chapter 1).

* We follow the treatment given by L. Mandel.

Between the complex amplitudes $V_1(t)$ and $V_2(t)$ at P_1 and P_2 is a mutual coherence defined by (1.88):

$$\Gamma_{12}(t_0) = \overline{V_1(t + t_0)\, V_2{}^*(t)}\,;\tag{9.2}$$

this is the mutual coherence at P_1 and P_2 when the vibration at P_1 is considered at a time t_0 later than at P_2; $\Gamma_{12}(t_0)$ represents a correlation of the second order. The mutual coherence $\Gamma_{12}(t_0)$ between the amplitudes in P_1 and P_2 implies a correlation between the fluctuations of the intensity. We now establish this correlation. The cross correlation of the intensities at P_1 and P_2 is defined by

$$\overline{I_1(t + t_0)\, I_2(t)} = \overline{V_1(t + t_0)\, V_1{}^*(t + t_0)\, V_2(t)\, V_2{}^*(t)},\tag{9.3}$$

which is a correlation of the fourth order.

If the wavetrains are emitted at random following Gaussian statistics, which is the case here, it is shown that the correlation of the fourth order $\overline{I_1(t + t_0)\, I_2(t)}$ contains no more information than the correlation of the second order $\overline{V_1(t + t_0)\, V_2{}^*(t)}$. We can deduce the mutual coherence and consequently the degree of partial coherence from these two types of correlations from which we derive the angular diameter of the star, as discussed in Section 8.5.

The study of $\overline{I_1(t + t_0)\, I_2(t)}$ permits us to attack the problem in a new way. This is of considerable interest because it requires a simpler experimental setup. As in Section 1.2 (1.17), we set

$$\begin{aligned}
V_1(t) &= V_1^{(r)}(t) + j\, V_1^{(i)}(t),\\
V_2(t) &= V_2^{(r)}(t) + j\, V_2^{(i)}(t).
\end{aligned}\tag{9.4}$$

The cross correlation of the intensities is written as

$$\begin{aligned}
\overline{I_1(t + t_0)\, I_2(t)} &= \overline{V_1^{(r)2}(t + t_0)\, V_2^{(r)2}(t)} + \overline{V_1^{(i)2}(t + t_0)\, V_2^{(r)2}(t)},\\
&\quad + \overline{V_1^{(r)2}(t + t_0)\, V_2^{(i)2}(t)} + \overline{V_1^{(i)2}(t + t_0)\, V_2^{(i)2}(t)}.
\end{aligned}\tag{9.5}$$

Before calculating the second member of (9.5) we give some relations that will be useful later on.

By using (1.31) and (1.32) we have

$$\overline{V_1(t + t_0)\, V_2(t)} = 0,\tag{9.6}$$

from which, according to (7),(4)

$$\begin{aligned}
\overline{V_1^{(r)}(t + t_0)\, V_2^{(r)}(t)} &= \overline{V_1^{(i)}(t + t_0)\, V_2^{(i)}(t)},\\
\overline{V_1^{(i)}(t + t_0)\, V_2^{(r)}(t)} &= -\,\overline{V_1^{(r)}(t + t_0)\, V_2^{(i)}(t)}.
\end{aligned}\tag{9.7}$$

Let $t_0 = 0$ and $V_1(t) = V_2(t)$. We find

$$\overline{V_1^{(r)2}(t)} = \overline{V_1^{(i)2}(t)} = \tfrac{1}{2}|V_1(t)|^2 \tag{9.8}$$

and

$$\overline{V_1^{(i)}(t)\,V_1^{(r)}(t)} = 0.$$

Hence at the same time t the values of $V_1^{(r)}(t)$ and $V_1^{(i)}(t)$ have no correlation. According to (9.8) and (9.1), we have

$$\overline{V_1^{(r)2}(t)} = \overline{V_1^{(i)2}(t)} = \frac{\overline{I_1}}{2}, \tag{9.9}$$

in which $\overline{I_1}$ is the mean value of $I_1(t)$. Let us expand (9.2) by writing

$$\Gamma_{12}(t_0) = \overline{V_1^{(r)}(t + t_0)\,V_2^{(r)}(t)} + j\,\overline{V_1^{(i)}(t + t_0)\,V_2^{(r)}(t)}$$
$$-j\,\overline{V_1^{(r)}(t + t_0)\,V_2^{(i)}(t)} + \overline{V_1^{(i)}(t + t_0)\,V_2^{(i)}(t)}. \tag{9.10}$$

By using (9.7) we have

$$\Gamma_{12}(t_0) = 2\,\overline{V_1^{(r)}(t + t_0)\,V_2^{(r)}(t)} - 2j\,\overline{V_1^{(r)}(t + t_0)\,V_2^{(i)}(t)}, \tag{9.11}$$

from which

$$\overline{V_1^{(r)}(t + t_0)\,V_2^{(r)}(t)} = \tfrac{1}{2}\,\mathrm{Re}[\Gamma_{12}(t_0)] = \overline{V_1^{(i)}(t + t_0)\,V_2^{(i)}(t)} \tag{9.12}$$

and

$$\overline{V_1^{(r)}(t + t_0)\,V_2^{(i)}(t)} = \tfrac{1}{2}\,\mathrm{Im}[\Gamma_{12}(t_0)] = \overline{V_1^{(i)}(t + t_0)\,V_2^{(r)}(t)}. \tag{9.13}$$

Re and Im mean the real and the imaginary parts of the quantities in brackets.

We can now establish the relation that exists between the cross correlation $\overline{I_1(t + t_0)\,I_2(t)}$ of the intensities and the mutual coherence function $\Gamma_{12}(t_0)$. This relation can be established by means of (9.5), (9.9), (9.12) and (9.13) and by using a theorem valid in Gaussian statistics. Let $X(t)$ and $Y(t)$ be two real functions of time; it can be shown that   *e.g. use (Gaussian moment theorem)*

$$\overline{X^2 Y^2} = \overline{X^2}\ \overline{Y^2} + 2\overline{XY}^2. \tag{9.14}$$

We apply this theorem to the four real expressions of the second member (9.5) and obtain

$$\overline{V_1^{(r)2}(t + t_0)\,V_2^{(r)2}(t)} = \overline{V_1^{(r)2}(t)\,V_2^{(r)2}(t)} + 2\left[\overline{V_1^{(r)}(t + t_0)\,V_2^{(r)}(t)}\right]^2. \tag{9.15}$$

According to (9.9),

$$\overline{V_1^{(r)2}(t + t_0)\,V_2^{(r)2}(t)} = \frac{\overline{I_1}\,\overline{I_2}}{4} + 2\left[\overline{V_1^{(r)}(t + t_0)\,V_2^{(r)}(t)}\right]^2, \tag{9.16}$$

and by using (9.12)

$$\overline{V_1^{(r)2}(t + t_0)\, V_2^{(r)2}(t)} = \frac{\bar{I}_1 \bar{I}_2}{4} + \frac{1}{2}\{\mathrm{Re}[\Gamma_{12}(t_0)]\}^2 . \tag{9.17}$$

Similarly, for the three other terms of (9.5),

$$\overline{V_1^{(i)2}(t + t_0)\, V_2^{(r)2}(t)} = \frac{\bar{I}_1 \bar{I}_2}{4} + \frac{1}{2}\{\mathrm{Im}[\Gamma_{12}(t_0)]\}^2 , \tag{9.18}$$

$$\overline{V_1^{(r)2}(t + t_0)\, V_2^{(i)2}(t)} = \frac{\bar{I}_1 \bar{I}_2}{4} + \frac{1}{2}\{\mathrm{Im}[\Gamma_{12}(t_0)]\}^2 , \tag{9.19}$$

$$\overline{V_1^{(i)2}(t + t_0)\, V_2^{(i)2}(t)} = \frac{\bar{I}_1 \bar{I}_2}{4} + \frac{1}{2}\{\mathrm{Re}[\Gamma_{12}(t_0)]\}^2 . \tag{9.20}$$

By sum, we obtain

$$\overline{I_1(t + t_0)\, I_2(t)} = \bar{I}_1 \bar{I}_2 + |\Gamma_{12}(t_0)|^2 . \tag{9.21}$$

In fact, we measure the fluctuations $\Delta I_1(t)$ and $\Delta I_2(t)$ of the mean values $\bar{I}_1$ and $\bar{I}_2$. The fluctuations $\Delta I_1(t)$ and $\Delta I_2(t)$ show the instantaneous difference between the intensities $I_1(t)$ and $I_2(t)$ with respect to $\bar{I}_1$ and $\bar{I}_2$. We have

$$\Delta I_1(t) = I_1(t) - \bar{I}_1, \qquad \Delta I_2(t) = I_2(t) - \bar{I}_2 \tag{9.22}$$

with

$$\overline{\Delta I_1(t)} = 0, \qquad \overline{\Delta I_2(t)} = 0,$$

from which

$$\overline{I_1(t + t_0)\, I_2(t)} = \overline{[\bar{I}_1 + \Delta I_1(t + t_0)][\bar{I}_2 + \Delta I_2(t)]}$$

$$= \bar{I}_1 \bar{I}_2 + \overline{\Delta I_1(t + t_0)\, \Delta I_2(t)}. \tag{9.23}$$

By comparing (9.21) and (9.23) we obtain finally

$$\overline{\Delta I_1(t + t_0)\, \Delta I_2(t)} = |\Gamma_{12}(t_0)|^2 \tag{9.24}$$

and by normalizing

$$\overline{\Delta I_1(t + t_0)\, \Delta I_2(t)} = \bar{I}_1 \bar{I}_2 \, |\gamma_{12}(t_0)|^2 , \tag{9.25}$$

which is the desired relation between the cross correlation of the fluctuations of intensity and the degree of partial coherence $\gamma_{12}(t_0)$ at P_1 and P_2 (where the photomultipliers are located) when P_1 is delayed by t_0 with respect to P_2.

9.3   Relation between the Signals of the Photomultipliers and the Degree of Partial Coherence

In practice, the photomultipliers do not give currents proportional to the luminous intensities $I_1(t)$ and $I_2(t)$. The currents are proportional to the mean values of $I_1(t)$ and $I_2(t)$ over a short period T, which is the time of resolution of the photomultipliers. The signal produced by the photomultipliers therefore takes the form

$$S(t) = \frac{m}{T} \int_t^{t+T} I(t')\, dt' , \qquad (9.26)$$

where m is a factor characterizing the sensitivity of the photocathode and $I(t')$ is the instantaneous value of the luminous intensity. The multiplier measures the correlation $\overline{S_1(t + t_0)\, S_2(t)}$, where t_0 is a possible delay between the signals transmited by the two branches of the interferometer. We have, by taking $t_0 = 0$;

$$S_1(t)\, S_2(t) = \frac{m^2}{T^2} \int_t^{t+T} \int_t^{t+T} I_1(t')\, I_2(t'')\, dt'\, dt''.$$

We then put

$$u = t' - t, \qquad v = t'' - t$$

and take the mean

$$\overline{S_1(t)\, S_2(t)} = \frac{m^2}{T^2} \int_0^T \int_0^T \overline{I_1(t + u)\, I_2(t + v)}\, du\, dv ,$$

but because the luminous vibration is stationary

$$\overline{S_1(t)\, S_2(t)} = \frac{m^2}{T^2} \int_0^T \int_0^T f(u - v)\, du\, dv , \qquad (9.27)$$

where

$$f(u - v) = \overline{I_1(t + u - v)\, I_2(t)}.$$

We reduce the double integral in (9.27) to a simple integral and set

$$\tau = u - v.$$

We must now consider the integral

$$\int_0^T \left[\int_{u-T}^u f(\tau)\, d\tau \right] du.$$

By changing the order of integration in the domain shown in Fig. 9.3 we have

$$\int_{-T}^{0} f(\tau)\left(\int_{0}^{T+\tau} du\right) d\tau + \int_{0}^{T} f(\tau)\left(\int_{\tau}^{T} du\right) d\tau = \int_{-T}^{T} (T - |\tau|) f(\tau) d\tau$$

and (9.26) becomes

$$\overline{S_1(t) S_2(t)} = \frac{m^2}{T^2} \int_{-T}^{T} (T - |\tau|) \overline{I_1(t + \tau) I_2(t)} d\tau.$$

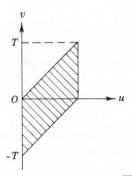

FIG. 9.3   Calculation of the mean $\overline{S_1(t) S_2(t)}$.

According to (9.21)

$$\overline{S_1(t) S_2(t)} = \frac{m^2}{T^2} \int_{-T}^{T} (T - |\tau|)[\bar{I}_1\bar{I}_2 + |\Gamma_{12}(\tau)|^2] d\tau,$$

from which

$$\overline{S_1(t) S_2(t)} = m^2\bar{I}_1\bar{I}_2 + \frac{m^2}{T^2} \int_{-T}^{T} (T - |\tau|) |\Gamma_{12}(\tau)|^2 d\tau. \qquad (9.28)$$

But according to (9.23) we can write

$$\overline{S_1(t) S_2(t)} = \overline{\Delta S_1(t) \Delta S_2(t)} + \bar{S}_1\bar{S}_2. \qquad (9.29)$$

By assuming that the star emits a small spectral range Δv (quasi-monochromatic light) in which m remains constant, (9.26) shows that

$$\bar{S}_1 = m\bar{I}_1, \qquad \bar{S}_2 = m\bar{I}_2. \qquad (9.30)$$

By substituting (9.29) and (9.30) into (9.28) we obtain

$$\overline{\Delta S_1(t) \Delta S_2(t)} = \frac{m^2}{T^2} \int_{-T}^{T} (T - |\tau|) |\Gamma_{12}(\tau)|^2 d\tau$$

or

$$\overline{\Delta S_1(t) \Delta S_2(t)} = \frac{\bar{S}_1 \bar{S}_2}{T^2} \int_{-T}^{T} (T - |\tau|)\, |\gamma_{12}(\tau)|^2 \, d\tau, \qquad (9.31)$$

but by referring again to the definition of γ_{12} (1.88) we have

$$\gamma_{12}(\tau) = \gamma_{12}(0)\, \gamma_{11}(\tau), \qquad (9.32)$$

where $\gamma_{11}(\tau)$ represents the autocorrelation function. By substitution into (9.31)

$$\overline{\Delta S_1(t) \Delta S_2(t)} = \frac{\bar{S}_1 \bar{S}_2}{T^2} |\gamma_{12}(0)|^2 \int_{-T}^{T} (T - |\tau|)|\gamma_{11}(\tau)|^2 \, d\tau. \qquad (9.33)$$

When $t_0 = 0$, we see that (9.33) differs from (9.25) only by the factor

$$\mathscr{A} = \frac{1}{T^2} \int_{-T}^{T} (T - |\tau|)\, |\gamma_{11}(\tau)|^2 \, d\tau. \qquad (9.34)$$

If the time of resolution T of the photomultipliers is long compared with the coherence time $\tau_c = 1/\Delta v$, we can write

$$\mathscr{A} = \frac{1}{T} \int_{-\infty}^{+\infty} |\gamma_{11}(\tau)|^2 \, d\tau. \qquad (9.35)$$

The integral of the second number has the dimensions of time. It is of the order of magnitude of the coherence time τ_c. If C is a coefficient of the order of 1, we have

$$\mathscr{A} = \frac{C\tau_c}{T} \qquad (9.36)$$

and (9.33) is written

$$\overline{\Delta S_1(t) \Delta S_2(t)} = \bar{S}_1 \bar{S}_2 \frac{\tau_c}{T} |\gamma_{12}(0)|^2. \qquad (9.37)$$

This expression of the first member of (9.37) is measured by the multiplier followed by an integrator. Hence we can deduce the degree of partial coherence $|\gamma_{12}(0)|$ and thus the angular diameter of the star according to (8.57) and (8.59).

Figure 9.4 shows the result of the measurements by Hanbury–Brown and Twiss on Sirius A. The abscissae indicate the spacing of the photomultipliers in meters and the ordinates the measured normalized correlation. The curve in heavy line shows the theoretical variations of the correlation, that is, $|\gamma_{12}(0)|^2$ if we calculate for $2\alpha = 0.0069$ seconds of arc (relation 8.59). The

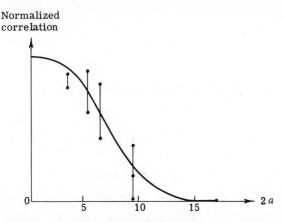

Fig. 9.4   Results of measurements done by Hanbury-Brown and Twiss on Sirius A.

precision obtained is greater than with Michelson's method and the intensity interferometer is an instrument much simpler to build. Unfortunately, a short-coming of the intensity interferometers is that the correlation $\overline{\Delta S_1(t)\,\Delta S_2(t)}$ is proportional to the square of the degree of partial coherence. Now we know that the degree of partial coherence represents the Fourier transform of the energy distribution on the source, that is, on the star. Hence, the correlation is proportional to the square of the intensity, and the method is limited to bright stars. On the other hand, the atmospheric scintillation has only a small influence on the measurements.

Chapter X

Interferences with Lasers

10.1 Introduction

Light emitted by a laser has a remarkable quality in spatial and temporal coherence, which allows experimental work that is impractical with thermal light sources.

The cavity of a ruby laser is shown schematically in Fig. 10.1. The plane waves oscillate between the two plane faces A and B; face B is semi-transparent. The laser beam passes through this face. We assume that all the vibrations emitted by different points of an emerging plane wave in coincidence with B have the same amplitude. Under these conditions the radiance is the same as that of a plane wave limited by a diaphragm of diameter D (the diameter of the ruby). It appears as if the light came from a diffraction pattern at infinity with an angular radius $\alpha = 1.22\lambda/D$. This means that by placing a lens O behind the laser (this lens must have an aperture larger than D) we observe at the focus of O a diffraction pattern of the angular radius α.

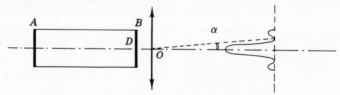

FIG. 10.1 Radiation of a laser.

For $D = 1$ cm and $\lambda = 0.6\,\mu$, which are current values, we have $\alpha = 7 \times 10^{-5}$ radian, a large spatial coherence. Naturally, we can also obtain large spatial coherence with thermal sources but with an incomparably weaker intensity. In addition, the temporal coherence of lasers is considerably larger than that of thermal sources. For the most monochromatic thermal light sources the coherence time is of the order of 10^{-8} sec. In lasers the coherence times are much longer, for example, of the order of 10^{-2} sec, and experiments may be attempted during the span of one wavetrain.

10.2   Nelson and Collin's Experiment Demonstrating the
Spatial Coherence of a Laser

This is Young's experiment, with a laser as the source (Fig. 10.2). The two slits T_1 and T_2 are placed against the exit face B of the ruby and the fringes are observed on a screen π placed at a certain distance from the ruby.

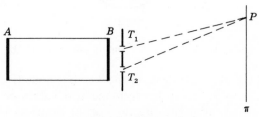

FIG. 10.2   Spatial coherence of a laser.

The results show that the position and the structure of the fringes are in perfect agreement with classical theory. In Nelson and Collins' experiment the width of each slit is 7.5 μ and their center-to-center distance is equal to 0.0541 mm. The screen π is at 324 mm from the slits, and the receiver is a photographic film. We can conclude that the ruby utilized gives perfect coherence at a distance equal to the spacing of the slits, which here is 0.0541 mm. To show that the spatial coherence is due to the laser effect, Nelson and Collins repeated the experiment, using the fluorescence of the ruby. All points of the crystal emitted incoherent vibrations. The luminous intensity produced on one or the other of the slits by any of these points is inversely proportional to the square of the distance between the point under consideration and the slits. Consequently, the intensity at T_1 and T_2 is due to those parts of the ruby that are closest to the slits.

We find that there are no fringes on the screen π; hence the slits T_1 and T_2 are incoherent. It is the laser effect that produces the spatial coherence and the appearance of the interference fringes.

The experiments are easier to perform with gas lasers, which are continuous sources. The slits are placed against the exit face of the laser, as in the preceding experiment. It is known that by disturbing slightly the adjustment of the surfaces of the interferometer that form the cavity of the laser, we can give the electrical field different orientations in different regions of the emerging wave. A certain "spatial mode" corresponds to a given distribution of the electrical field. Spatial modes are designated by the three letters, TEM (transverse electromagnetic), with indices characterizing the mode. The mode of the lowest order is TEM_{00}, characterized by a constant phase on the wavefront (Fig. 10.3). In Fig. 10.3 the arrow indicates the

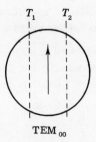

FIG. 10.3 Young's experiment with the mode TEM$_{00}$.

orientation of the electrical field. In the TEM$_{01}$ mode (Fig. 10.4) a phase difference equal to π occurs between the two halves of the wavefront. The two arrows indicating the directions of the electrical field in these two regions form an angle of 180° between them one to the other. Let us assume that the laser operates in the TEM$_{00}$ mode and place the two slits T_1 and T_2 according to Fig. 10.3. These slits are indicated by dotted lines. The results are the same as before, T_1 and T_2 appear to be illuminated by a source seen under a very small angle, and the fringes are easily observed.

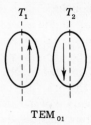

FIG. 10.4 Young's experiment with the mode TEM$_{01}$.

Let us consider the TEM$_{01}$ mode (Fig. 10.4). The two slits T_1 and T_2 still act as two coherent sources, but because of the distribution of the electrical field in the two regions occupied by the two slits the vibrations emitted by T_1 and T_2 have a phase difference of π. In fact, we find a displacement of the fringes equal to one half the interval separating two bright fringes (or two dark fringes).

10.3 Interference of the Beams Emerging in Opposite Directions from a Laser

Kisliuk and Walsh performed the experiment shown in Fig. 10.5. The two reflectors A and B of the laser are semireflecting, and two beams can

emerge from the laser in two opposite directions. One is reflected in the
mirror M_1 and the other in the mirror M_2. These two mirrors play a purely
geometrical role by directing the two beams to an observation screen π.

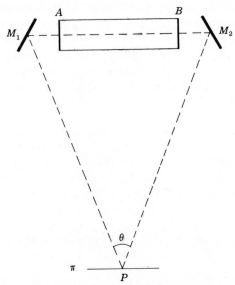

FIG. 10.5   Kislink and Walsh experiment.

The geometric arrangement is such that the angle θ is small. Under these
conditions, the vibrations which arrive at any point on the screen can be
considered parallel. These vibrations are coherent, and we observe interference fringes at π. The waves that emerge from the faces A and B are
indeed coherent, for a system of stationary waves is established between A
and B in the laser. This is equivalent to a point source S (Fig. 10.6) placed

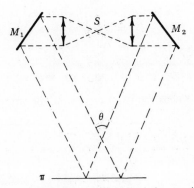

FIG. 10.6   Analogy of the Kislink and Walsh experiment with a point source.

at the focus of two identical objectives O_1 and O_2. The distance separating
two bright or two dark fringes is equal to $\lambda/2\theta$. This kind of experiment
cannot be performed with thermal light sources for practical reasons. In
fact, a source S, even though small (Fig. 10.7), contains a considerable
number of atoms. The path difference at an arbitrary point P between the
vibrations originating at atom A_i and reflected by M_1 and M_2 is not the
same as the path difference between the vibrations from atom A_j. Let OM
be the axis of symmetry of the instrument: we set $A_iM = x$ and $OP = y$.
The path difference between the vibrations at P, having traveled along the
paths A_iM_1P and A_iM_2P, is

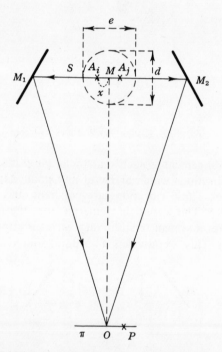

FIG. 10.7   Kislink and Walsh experiment with an extended source.

The intensity at P is proportional to

$$\cos^2 \frac{2\pi}{\lambda}\left(x - \frac{y}{\theta}\right). \qquad (10.2)$$

Let us assume that the width d of the source in a direction perpendicular to $M_1 M_2$ is negligible. We integrate with respect to x, assuming that all the sources A_i, A_j,... are uniformly distributed on a length e ($e/2$ on each side of M). The intensity at P is given, to a constant factor K, by the expression

$$I_P = K \left(e + \frac{\lambda}{2\pi} \sin \frac{2\pi e}{\lambda} \cos \frac{4\pi y}{\theta} \right), \tag{10.3}$$

from which the contrast of the fringes is

$$\gamma = \frac{\lambda/\pi \sin 2\pi e/\lambda}{e + \lambda/2\pi \sin 2\pi e/\lambda}, \tag{10.4}$$

This is equal to zero and the fringes disappear if $e = \lambda/2$. To observe the fringes, we must use an extremely flat source whose thickness e is small compared with the wavelength.

10.4   Beats Produced by Optical Frequencies Given by the Lasers

Figure 10.8 is a diagram of this experiment. The beams emitted by two lasers are detected by a photomultiplier PM and a receiver R. The mirror M_2 is semireflecting. The experiment performed by Jaseja, Javan, and Townes in 1963 had as its objective the study of the stability of the frequency of the oscillations of gas lasers for the wavelength $1.153\ \mu$. Let us assume that the vibrations received by the PM and coming from laser No. 1 have an amplitude of $\sqrt{I_1} \cos(2\pi v_1 t + \Phi_1)$ and that the amplitude of the vibration due to laser No. 2 is $\sqrt{2} \cos(2\pi v_2 t + \Phi_2)$. The current produced by the photomultiplier is given by

$$I(t) = A + B + C + \sqrt{I_1}\sqrt{I_2} \cos[2\pi(v_1 - v_2)t + \Phi_1 - \Phi_2], \tag{10.5}$$

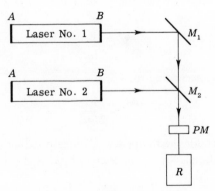

FIG. 10.8   Beats produced by two lasers.

where A, B, and C are terms that do not appear in the experiment because they contain v_1, v_2, or $v_1 + v_2$ and their variations cannot be detected by the photomultiplier. If Φ_1, Φ_2 are constant, we see, according to (10.5), that the current will fluctuate at the frequency $v_1 - v_2$. We therefore have beats, and in the experiment performed by Jaseja, Javan, and Townes the frequency was of the order of 1700 cps. The results have shown that the frequency variations were approximately 20 cps for one or the other of the two lasers. According to (1.64), the monochromaticity of the radiations emitted by the lasers corresponds to a coherence length of approximately 15,000 km. It should be noted that in this experiment great precautions must be taken to avoid all vibrations that could modify the distance separating the mirrors in the lasers. These variations, in fact, would cause frequency changes in the oscillations of the lasers.

We can also observe the phenomenon of beating with only one laser by using the frequencies that correspond to two different axial modes. Let us consider a laser with plane reflectors: let L be the distance between the two reflectors and n, the index of the medium separating them. Let us take the simplest spatial mode (i.e., the TEM_{00} mode). We then have a plane wave of uniform phase. The resonance condition for the wavelength λ_1 is

$$L = K\frac{\lambda_1}{2n}, \tag{10.6}$$

where K is an integer. For the ruby lasers K varies between 200,000 and 800,000. We can write (10.6) in the form

$$\frac{1}{\lambda_1} = \frac{K}{2Ln}. \tag{10.7}$$

Resonance for another wavelength λ_2 such that $\lambda_2 = \lambda_1 - \Delta\lambda$ will occur with

$$\frac{\Delta\lambda}{\lambda_1{}^2} = \frac{1}{2Ln}, \tag{10.8}$$

which we can write, according to (1.56),

$$\frac{\Delta v}{c} = \frac{1}{2Ln}. \tag{10.9}$$

If there is resonance for the frequency v_1 corresponding to λ_1 there will be resonance for the frequency v_2, so that $v_2 = v_1 + \Delta v$. For a gas laser, in which $L = 1$ meter, we have

$$\Delta v = 150 \text{ Mc}. \tag{10.10}$$

Receiving the beam sent from a laser on a photomultiplier (Fig. 10.9) we can observe the beats produced by the frequencies due to these axial modes as done by Herriott. By referring to Fig. 1.17, we see that the value Δv, given by (10.10), corresponds to the peak $v_2 - v_1$.

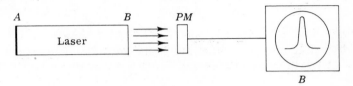

FIG. 10.9   Beats produced by two different axial modes given by a laser.

10.5   Interferences Produced with Two Lasers

Interference fringes by the superposition of vibrations originating from two lasers were observed by Magyar and Mandel in 1963. Beams emerging from the two lasers are received by two slits T_1 and T_2 (Fig. 10.10). Two mirrors m_1 and m_2 inclined at 45° allow the superposition of the vibrations on the detector R. The polarizer $\mathscr{P}$ renders the vibrations parallel. If the two lasers are replaced by two ordinary thermal sources, a large number of wavetrains arrive on R during the time of one observation. Under these conditions the vibrations originating at T_1 and T_2 are incoherent, but after passing through $\mathscr{P}$ they are parallel though still incoherent. There is no interference phenomenon observable at R. With lasers things are

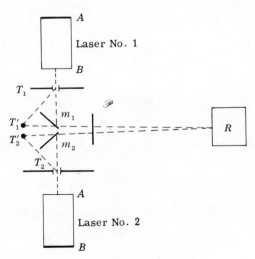

FIG. 10.10   Interference with two lasers.

different; because of the considerable temporal coherence we can perform one observation in the time of one wavetrain, that is, during the coherence time. If there are fringes, they must be spaced according to (2.12):

$$l = \frac{\lambda D}{2a},$$

where D is the distance from T_1' and T_2' (T_1' and T_2' are the images of T_1 and T_2 by reflection on m_1 and m_2) to R and $2a$ is the distance separating T_1' and T_2'. We apply (8.5):

$$V(t) = K_1 V_1(t - \theta_1) + K_2 V_2(t - \theta_2),$$

where $K_1 V_1(t - \theta_1)$ and $K_2 V_2(t - \theta_2)$ are the vibrations received by R and $V(t)$, the resulting vibration. The vibrations $V_1(t)$, $V_2(t)$, and $V(t)$ are complex vibrations (analytic signals). To simplify, we set $K_1 = K_2 = 1$, and with $\theta = \theta_1 - \theta_2$ we write the resulting vibration on the detector R in the form

$$V(t) = V_1\left(t - \frac{\theta}{2}\right) + V_2\left(t + \frac{\theta}{2}\right). \tag{10.11}$$

The instantaneous intensity is given by

$$I(t) = V(t) V^*(t). \tag{10.12}$$

By setting

$$I_1\left(t - \frac{\theta}{2}\right) = V_1\left(t - \frac{\theta}{2}\right) V_1^*\left(t - \frac{\theta}{2}\right),$$

$$I_2\left(t + \frac{\theta}{2}\right) = V_2\left(t + \frac{\theta}{2}\right) V_2^*\left(t + \frac{\theta}{2}\right), \tag{10.13}$$

we have, according to (8.7),

$$I(t) = I_1\left(t - \frac{\theta}{2}\right) + I_2\left(t + \frac{\theta}{2}\right) + 2\mathscr{R}\left[V_1^*\left(t - \frac{\theta}{2}\right) V_2\left(t + \frac{\theta}{2}\right)\right]. \tag{10.14}$$

We consider the case of quasi-monochromatic light and assume that the frequencies v_1 and v_2 emitted by the two lasers are different. According to Section 1.4, we can write the complex vibration in the form

$$V_1(t) = a_1(t) \exp\{j[2\pi v_1 t + \varphi_1(t)]\}, \tag{10.15}$$

$$V_2(t) = a_2(t) \exp\{j[2\pi v_2 t + \varphi_2(t)]\}. \tag{10.16}$$

With

$$a_1(t) = |V_1(t)| = \sqrt{I_1(t)},$$
$$a_2(t) = |V_2(t)| = \sqrt{I_2(t)}.$$

(10.17)

In quasi-monochromatic light we have seen that the variations of $a_1(t)$, $a_2(t)$, $\varphi_1(t)$, and $\varphi_2(t)$ are slow compared to those of $\sin 2\pi vt$ and $\cos 2\pi vt$. We can consider $a_1(t)$, $a_2(t)$, $\varphi_1(t)$, and $\varphi_2(t)$ as constants if $\theta \ll \tau$ where τ is the coherence time. We then have

$$I_1\left(t - \frac{\theta}{2}\right) \simeq I_1(t),$$

$$I_2\left(t + \frac{\theta}{2}\right) \simeq I_2(t),$$

and

$$V_1^*\left(t - \frac{\theta}{2}\right) V_2\left(t + \frac{\theta}{2}\right) = [I_1(t) I_2(t)]^{1/2}$$
$$\times \exp\{j[2\pi(v_2 - v_1)t + \pi(v_2 + v_1)\theta + \varphi_2(t) - \varphi_1(t)]\},$$

(10.18)

from which

$$I(t) = I_1(t) + I_2(t) + 2[I_1(t) I_2(t)]^{1/2}$$
$$\times \cos[2\pi(v_2 - v_1)t + \pi(v_2 + v_1)\theta + \varphi_2(t) - \varphi_1(t)].$$

(10.19)

The observation, however, is not instantaneous, and if T is the time necessary to perform one observation the received signal according to (9.26) is

$$S(t) = \frac{1}{T}\int_t^{t+T} I(t')\, dt'.$$

(10.20)

If T itself is much shorter than the coherence time τ, we can assume that $I_1(t)$ and $I_2(t)$ will remain constant during the time T and the integral will be extended only over the cosine function in (10.19):

$$S(t) = S_1(t) + S_2(t)$$
$$+ 2[S_1(t) S_2(t)]^{1/2}\int_t^{t+T} \cos[2\pi(v_2 - v_1)t + \pi(v_2 + v_1)\theta + \varphi_2(t) - \varphi_1(t)]\, dt.$$

(10.21)

We obtain

$$S(t) = S_1(t) + S_2(t) + 2[S_1(t) \, S_2(t)]^{1/2} \cos \left[\pi(v_2 + v_1)\theta \right.$$

$$\left. + \varphi_2 - \varphi_1 + 2\pi(v_2 - v_1)\left(t + \frac{T}{2}\right) \right] \frac{\sin \pi(v_2 - v_1)T}{\pi(v_2 - v_1)T}. \tag{10.22}$$

This expression is valid if $\theta \ll \tau$ and $T \ll \tau$. It shows that $S(t)$ varies with θ, that is, with the position of the point under consideration on the detector R. The time difference θ is, in fact, directly linked with the path difference δ by the relation $\theta = \delta/c$ (Section 1.11). The intensity $S(t)$ is a sinusoidal function of θ. We can therefore assume that there are interference fringes on the detector R. Let us calculate their contrast. We have

$$S_{\max} = S_1(t) + S_2(t) + 2[S_1(t) \, S_2(t)]^{1/2} \left| \frac{\sin \pi(v_2 - v_1)T}{\pi(v_2 - v_1)I} \right|,$$

$$\tag{10.23}$$

$$S_{\min} = S_1(t) + S_2(t) - 2[S_1(t) \, S_2(t)]^{1/2} \left| \frac{\sin \pi(v_2 - v_1)T}{\pi(v_2 - v_1)} \right|,$$

from which the contrast

$$\gamma = \frac{S_{\max} - S_{\min}}{S_{\max}} = \frac{4[S_1(t) \, S_2(t)]^{1/2} \left| \dfrac{\sin \pi(v_2 - v_1)T}{\pi(v_2 - v_1)T} \right|}{S_1(t) + S_2(t) + 2[S_1(t) \, S_2(t)]^{1/2} \left| \dfrac{\sin \pi(v_2 - v_1)T}{\pi(v_2 - v_1)T} \right|}.$$

$$\tag{10.24}$$

If

$$T \ll (v_2 - v_1)^{-1} \tag{10.25}$$

we then have

$$\gamma = \frac{4[S_1(t) \, S_2(t)]^{1/2}}{S_1(t) + S_2(t) + 2[S_1(t) \, S_2(t)]^{1/2}}, \tag{10.26}$$

which is just (1.130) or (8.14) with $\gamma_{12}(0) = 1$. The contrast of the fringes is a maximum and equal to 1 if $I_1 = I_2$. It should be noted that the phenomenon will be visible only if the two wavetrains are emitted simultaneously by the two lasers. For each new simultaneous emission of two wavetrains the phases $\varphi_1(t)$ and $\varphi_2(t)$ take random values, and we can never predict the position of the fringes on the screen.

Chapter XI

Interferential Study of Wavefronts

Let us place a luminous point source in the focus of an objective corrected for infinity. The emerging wave is plane if the aberrations of the objective are properly corrected. Study of the wavefront permits us to recognize and characterize these defects.

To determine the form of a wavefront we make it interfere with a known reference wave. On the basis of the observed interference fringes we can derive the exact form of the wavefront furnished by the objective.

11.1   The Twyman–Green Interferometer

The Twyman–Green method is based on the utilization of Michelson's interferometer. The plane mirror M_2 of Fig. 4.2 is replaced by the system under study associated with a suitable reference surface (Fig. 11.1). Let us

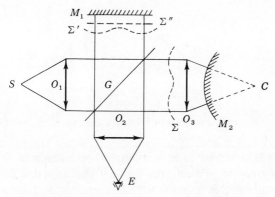

FIG. 11.1   Twyman–Green interferometer.

take the case of a photographic objective O_3. We place behind O_3 a convex mirror M_2 whose center of curvature C coincides sensibly with the focus of the objective under study.

Because the objective O_3 has numerous aberrations, the emerging wave Σ is deformed; the eye, placed at F, detects fringes of equal thickness between the plane reference wave Σ'' furnished by the plane mirror M_1 and the wave under study Σ'. If the objective O_3 is perfect, Σ is a plane wave and there is uniform illumination. The path difference between Σ' (symmetrical to Σ with respect to G) and Σ'' is constant, for Σ and Σ' are planes parallel to Σ''. By modifying the orientation of M_1, we observe rectilinear and equidistant fringes.

It should be noted that the objective O_3 is traversed twice by the luminous rays; the deformations of the wave are therefore twice as large as the deformations to be measured.

11.2   The Martin–Watt–Weinstein Interferometer

The Martin–Watt–Weinstein interferometer was derived from the Twyman–Green instrument. A luminous point source S (Fig. 11.2) illuminates the objective O with the help of the beamsplitter G. It also illuminates a spherical concave mirror M_1, whose center coincides with S.

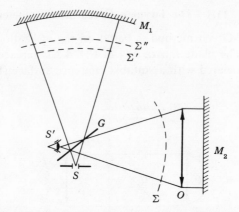

FIG. 11.2   Martin, Watt, and Weinstein interferometer.

The objective O is placed so that its focus coincides with S, and an autocollimation mirror M_2 reflects the light. If the objective O is perfect, the emerging wavefront Σ is a sphere with its center at S'. It interferes with the spherical wavefront Σ'', given by M_1, and we have a flat color, just as if fringes of equal thickness between Σ'' and Σ' symmetrical to Σ with respect to G had been observed. If the objective O shows aberrations, the wavefront Σ is deformed, and its interference with Σ'' produces fringes which the eye at S' can observe.

11.3   Michelson's Method

In Michelson's method we place in front of the objective O two parallel slits T_1 and T_2, whose heights are small compared with the diameter of O (Fig. 11.3). The slit T_2 is fixed, and the distance between T_1 and T_2 can vary. For an arbitrary position of T_1 we observe in the plane F conjugate to the source a system of Young's interference fringes. If the objective O is perfect, the path difference $(T_1F) - (T_2F)$ is zero in F, the center of the spherical wave Σ, whatever the position of T_1. The central fringe of the fringe system is fixed and located in F. If the wavefront Σ is not spherical, that is, if the objective O has aberrations, the path difference $(T_1F) - (T_2F)$ is no longer zero in F, and the central fringe is displaced by a distance $y = [(T_1F) - (T_2F)]/\alpha$. From the measurement of this displacement we can derive the form of the wavefront and consequently the defects of the objective. This method is not easy to apply, for, when T_1 is moved away from T_2, the distance λ/α between the fringes becomes very small and it is difficult to follow the displacement of the central fringe.

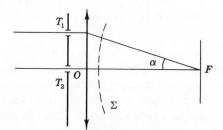

FIG. 11.3   Michelson's method.

11.4   Application of Polarization Interferometers to the Study of Aberrations

The objective O_1 is illuminated in linearly polarized light coming from a point source, not shown in Fig. 11.4. The distance between the source and the objective O_1 is fixed by the conditions under which we must study the aberrations of the objective. The image S' of the source is picked up by an auxiliary objective O_2 whose object focus coincides with S'. The light

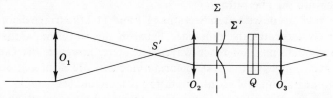

FIG. 11.4   Measurement of aberrations with the help of a polarization interferometer.

emerging from O_2 forms a parallel beam, which passes through a Savart polariscope Q and an auxiliary objective O_3. A polarizer (not shown) is placed behind Q.

The combination O_2O_3 is a telescope of low magnification with which we can focus on the objective O_1 itself. The eye is focused on the objective O_3, where the image of the source is formed, and the field appears uniformly illuminated. The focal length of the objective O_2 is small compared with that of the objective O_1 and, therefore, its aberrations can be neglected. If the objective O_1 is perfect, the wave after traversing O_2 is a plane wave Σ. The polariscope forms two waves OE and EO (Fig. 11.5) from the incoming wave, whose mutual distance Δ (path difference between the two waves) in the propagation direction is fixed by the inclination of the polariscope.

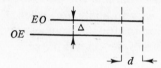

FIG. 11.5   Disposition of two wavefronts when the objective is perfect.

If the objective O_1 is not perfect, the incident wave Σ' (Fig. 11.4) is no longer plane. After passing through the polariscope these two waves are displaced with respect to one another (Fig. 11.6), their mutual displacement (path difference) is no longer constant, and the field is no longer uniformly illuminated. The variations in brightness are evidence of the deformations of the wave Σ', this is, the aberrations of the system.

FIG. 11.6   Disposition of two wavefronts when the objective is imperfect.

We can also place the polariscope Q near S', in which case the fringes appear (fringes at infinity of the polariscope) and their deformation permits us to measure the aberrations.

In the methods described in Sections 11.1 and 11.2 the fringe deformation immediately indicates the difference between the wavefront under study and the nondeformed reference wavefront. Here, however, the two interfering wavefronts have the same deformation; they are displaced only with respect to one another. The interpretation is therefore less simple.

As an example, we shall examine a third-order spherical aberration.

The difference between the real wavefront Σ' (Fig. 11.4) and the reference wavefront Σ is given by

$$\Delta_0 = aH^4,$$

where H is the height of incidence, that is the distance from the axis to the region where the difference between Σ and Σ' has the value Δ_0. The constant a depends on the magnitude of the aberration.

We calculate the lines of equal path difference Δ between the two wavefronts OE and EO. Figure 11.7 shows the phenomena projected on the plane Σ in Fig. 11.4; O_1 and O_2 are the projections of the wave centers of the waves OE and EO produced by the doubling of the polariscope. The distance $d = O_1O_2$ is fixed by the thickness of the plates of the polariscope.

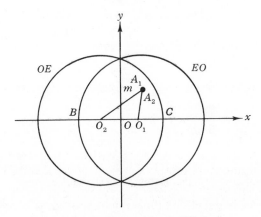

FIG. 11.7   Calculation of path difference.

We choose as coordinate axes the axis Ox which passes through O_1 and O_2, the axis Oy which passes through the center O of O_1O_2, and the axis Oz which is perpendicular in O to the plane xOy (Oz is not shown in Fig. 11.7). Let us consider a point m on the plane Σ (Fig. 11.7) and calculate its distances to the two waves OE and EO. The distance to the wave OE is given by $\overline{mA_2} = a\overline{O_2m}^4$; A_2 is the intersection with OE of the perpendicular to the plane Σ through m. Similarly, the distance $\overline{mA_1}$ from point m to EO is $\overline{mA_1} = a\overline{O_1m}^4$, in which the difference Δ between OE and EO at m is

$$\Delta = \overline{mA_2} - \overline{mA_1} = a(\overline{O_2m}^4 - \overline{O_1m}^4).$$

If x and y are the coordinates of the point m, we obtain

$$\Delta = 4a\,dx\left(\frac{d^2}{4} + x^2 + y^2\right); \qquad (11.1)$$

Δ is an uneven function of x and an even function of y. The lines of equal path difference Δ are therefore symmetrical curves with respect to Oy and Ox (Fig. 11.8).

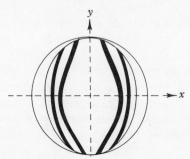

FIG. 11.8   Form of fringes in presence of spherical aberration of the third order.

If the waves are perfectly spherical, we have

$$\Delta = \frac{xd}{R}, \tag{11.2}$$

where R is the radius of curvature of the waves. The fringes are rectilinear and parallel and are oriented perpendicularly to the direction of shearing.

11.5   Bates' Interferometer

As in the preceding method, the wave to be studied interferes with itself, and the device used is a modified Mach–Zehnder interferometer (Fig. 11.9). The wave under study is a convergent wave that emerges from an optical instrument not shown in Fig. 11.9. The plates L_1 and L_2 and the mirrors M_1 and M_2 are parallel, and we assume that the two paths IM_2L_2 and IM_1L_2 are identical.

We also assume that the center of the wave Σ is at S' on L_2 for the rays that followed the path IM_2L_2, as it is for the rays that followed the path IM_1L_2. The two virtual waves corresponding to the two paths IM_2L_2 and IM_1L_2 also overlap in Σ'. The eye at L_2 observes a uniform field.

Let us turn L_2 around a vertical axis which passes through S'. The two waves Σ_1' and Σ_2' (Fig. 11.10) corresponding to the two paths are no longer coincident. These two waves interfere in their common part and we are led back to Section 11.4. If Σ is a sphere (no aberration), the field is uniform in the part common to the two waves Σ_1' and Σ_2'. If there are aberrations Σ_1' and Σ_2' have the same deformation, but because of their displacement the path difference changes and the field is no longer uniform. As in Section

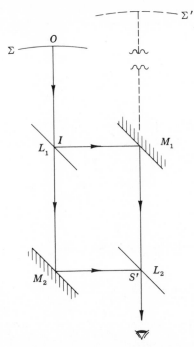

FIG. 11.9   A Bates interferometer.

11.4, if the displacement is small, we obtain the angular aberration. To render the measurements easier, we can turn L_1 and M_2 together around OI. Instead of having only one image of the source at S', we will have two images slightly displaced in a direction perpendicular to the plane of Fig. 11.10.

We therefore have two wavefronts whose displacement is due to (a) a rotation of L_2 which produces a vertical displacement, (b) a translation caused by the rotation of L_1 and M_2.

If the two waves are spherical (no aberration), we have a system of rectilinear parallel fringes (Section 11.4). These fringes are not modified by the angular displacement due to the rotation of L_2. In the presence of aberrations the fringes are modified, and from them we can deduce the deformation of the incident wave.

11.6   Ronchi's Method

In Ronchi's method we use a grating R with a small number of lines per millimeter (Fig. 11.11), which is placed near the focus of the objective O.

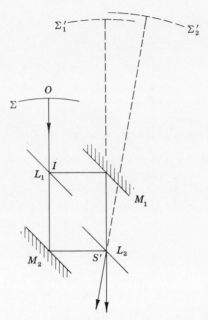

FIG. 11.10 Doubling produced in a Bates interferometer.

The objective is illuminated by a point source at infinity, and the eye is focused on the image of the source. By observing O through R we see several images of the objective. A central image S_0' (Fig. 11.12) and several lateral images S_1', S_1'', S_2', S_2'', etc., which correspond to the spectra. These images are overlaid, as shown in Fig. 11.12, and they interfere because we know that the direct image of the source and the spectra are in phase. In the common parts we observe rectilinear parallel fringes if the wave emerging from the objective O is spherical. If there are aberrations, the fringes are deformed and from them we can derive the form of the wavefront.

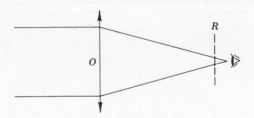

FIG. 11.11 The Ronchi method.

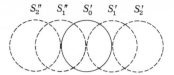

$$S_2'' \quad S_1'' \quad S_0' \quad S_1' \quad S_2'$$

FIG. 11.12   Disposition of waves in the Ronchi method.

11.7   Burch's Interferometer

The diagram of Burch's interferometer appears in Fig. 11.13. At S' on the spherical mirror we form an image of a point source S by means of an objective O; D_1 and D_2 are two identical diffusing replicas, obtained from the same diffusing surface. The replica D_1 is placed so that C is at the center of curvature of M. Near C is a semireflecting plate G inclined at 45°.

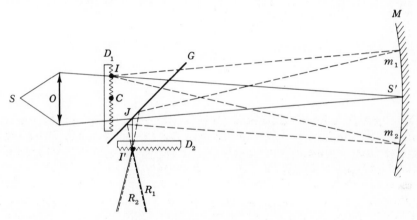

FIG. 11.13   Burch's diffusion interferometer.

The replica D_2 coincides with the virtual image of D_1 and is mounted so that each point at D_1 coincides with a corresponding point of D_2. We con-consider an incident ray arriving at I on the diffusing surface of D_1: one part of the energy is diffused and forms a cone that covers the mirror M at $m_1 m_2$. The other part of the energy is in the ray IS' which passes through D_1 as if there were no diffusing surface. After reflection in S' the ray follows the path $S'JI'$ and arrives at I' on the diffusing surface of the replica D_2. Because I' corresponds exactly to I, a cone of diffused rays R_1 (heavy line) originates at I' and is identical to the one originating at I. The cone of diffused rays coming from I covers the surface of the mirror M and after reflection on M and on G converges on the point I'. One part of the energy traverses D_2 as if there were no diffusing surface: this is the cone of rays R_2 (dotted lines). We can therefore consider two coherent beams emerging from D_2:

1. One beam diffused in I which traverses D_2 without being diffused again. A spherical wave reflected on M, if the mirror is perfect, corresponds to this beam.

2. A beam that traverses D_1 but is diffused by D_2. A spherical wave which originates at I' corresponds to this beam; it is the reference wave. We can indeed assume that the rays which form this wave have been reflected in S' on a very small surface of the mirror M and therefore are not affected by eventual defects of M.

The eye placed at D_2 to observe the surface at M sees a uniform field if the mirror is perfect (we do not speak of the small bright image at S' which consists of the reference light). If there are aberrations, the field is no longer uniform and the aberration is described here according to the methods of Sections 11.1 and 11.2.

Chapter XII

Interferometric Measurement of the Transfer Function of an Optical Instrument—Noncoherent Illumination

12.1 Introduction

The classical notion of the limit of resolution is based on the possibilities, given by the optical instrument, of separating two point sources. In fact, we consider two luminous points of the same intensity whose images are two diffraction patterns. When the distance between the two diffraction patterns is sufficient, the eye sees two distinct images. If the two patterns are too close, the eye sees only one image. The limit of resolution is therefore given by the distance (angular or linear) of the two point sources at the moment at which the eye can no longer distinguish the presence of two images.

This notion of the limit of resolution is fairly subjective and is a poor representation of the properties of an optical instrument. Appreciation of the resolution or nonseparation of two images can vary with the observer. A preferred method of characterizing the qualities of an optical instrument utilizes the "transfer function." The optical instrument is considered as a true filter, which transmits or cuts off certain details of an object. The object chosen for this test is incoherent and consists of a sinusoidal test pattern of variable period. We consider, in general, the spatial frequency, the inverse of the spacing of the test pattern. The instrument acts, as we shall see, as a true filter of the spatial frequencies. It is obvious that it allows the low frequencies to pass more easily (test pattern with a large spacing) than the high frequencies (test pattern with close spacing). It is also a low-pass filter. The curve characterizing the manner in which each frequency is transmitted constitutes the transfer function. Before studying this function, which is of great practical importance, it is necessary to specify in detail certain notions indispensable to the comprehension of the principle involved in the methods of measurement.

We consider an objective illuminated by a point source S at infinity (Fig. 12.1); Σ represents the wavefront limited by the exit pupil of the objective.

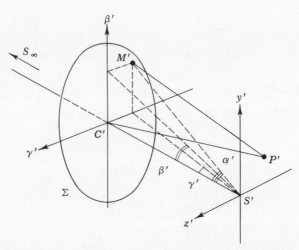

FIG. 12.1   Diffracted amplitude at P' by a spherical wave with circular contour.

We take two axes, $C'\beta'$ and $C'\gamma'$, which pass through the intersection C' of the axis of the objective and the wavefront Σ. The coordinates β', γ' represent the angles. We take two axes, $S'y'$ and $S'z'$, which pass through the image S' of S. The plane $y'S'z'$ is normal to the axis $C'S'$ of the objective. Let us characterize the distribution of the amplitudes on the wavefront by the function $g(\beta', \gamma')$. If the objective is not uniformly transparent, its transparency is specified by $g(\beta', \gamma')$, which is real if the aberrations of the objective have been corrected (no phase variation on the wavefront Σ). If the objective is uniformly transparent but not corrected, $g(\beta', \gamma')$ is purely imaginary. In the general case $g(\beta', \gamma')$ is complex. The Fourier transform permits the calculation of the amplitude at an arbitrary point P', which we assume is located in the plane $y'S'z'$. To calculate the amplitude at P' we calculate the amplitude at an arbitrary point of the diffraction phenomenon which is the image of the point source S. If $U(y'z')$ is the amplitude at P', the Fourier transform can be written

$$U(y', z') = \iint g(\beta', \gamma')e^{-jK(\beta'y' + \gamma'z')}\, d\beta'\, d\gamma',$$

$$g(\beta', \gamma') = \iint U(y', z')e^{jK(\beta'y' + \gamma'z')}\, dy'\, dz'.$$

$$(12.1)$$

The exponent $K(\beta'y' + \gamma'z')$ represents the phase difference at P' between the vibrations originating from an arbitrary point $M'(\beta', \gamma')$ of the wavefront and the center C':

$$K(\beta'y' + \gamma'z') = \frac{2\pi}{\lambda}(M'P' - C'P').$$

$$(12.2)$$

The functions $g(\beta', \gamma')$ and $U(y'z')$ are Fourier transforms of the functions $U(y', z')$ and $g(\beta', \gamma')$.

When the wavefront Σ is limited by a circular contour (objective of circular contour) and the objective is perfect, we know that

$$U(y'z') = \frac{2J_1(Z)}{Z}. \tag{12.3}$$

$J_1(Z)$ is the Bessel function of the first order of the variable Z, defined by $Z = K\alpha_m'(y'^2 + z'^2)^{1/2}$, where α_m' is the maximum value of the angle $\alpha' = \widehat{M'S'C'}$, that is, when M' reaches the edges of the wavefront.

12.2 Fundamental Theorem

The filtering of spatial frequencies and the transfer function can be studied with the help of the following theorem:

The Fourier transform of the image of an incoherent object is equal to the product of the object transform and the transform of the image of an isolated luminous point.

The image of an isolated point produced by an optical instrument is a diffraction pattern. If the instrument is perfect, this image is Airy's disk, given by $[2J_1(Z)/Z]^2$. The Fourier transform of the image of an isolated point is the Fourier transform of diffraction in intensity.

In the study of the transfer function of an optical instrument the test object chosen is a sinusoidal test pattern with a variable period. If we call ω the Fourier transform of the object, that is, of a sinusoid, and Ω, the Fourier transform of the image of an isolated luminous point, we have

Fourier transform of the image $= \omega \times \Omega$.

Hence, to know the image, we must determine the transform Ω which characterizes the instrument. The transform ω does not involve the properties of the instrument but only the structure of the object itself. Consequently, it is important to know the transform Ω. We shall see later that this constitutes the transfer function.

12.3 Fourier Transform of the Image of a Luminous Point

The intensity at a point $y'z'$ of the diffraction phenomenon of the image of the point source S is given by $|U(y'z')|^2$.

Let us calculate the Fourier transform of this expression:

$$E(y', z') = |U(y', z')|^2 = U(y', z')\, U^*(y', z'), \tag{12.4}$$

because $U(y', z')$ is a complex function in the general case. We introduce two new variables μ' and ν', which are spatial frequencies of the form

$$\mu' = \frac{\beta'}{\lambda}, \qquad \nu' = \frac{\gamma'}{\lambda}. \tag{12.5}$$

The Fourier transform of $E(y'z')$ can be written

$$\Omega(\mu', \nu') = \iint E(y', z')e^{j2\pi(\mu'y' + \nu'z')}\, dy'\, dz'. \tag{12.6}$$

This is the Fourier transform of the image of an isolated point. Using (12.4) we may write

$$\Omega(\mu', \nu') = \iint U(y', z')\, U^*(y', z')e^{j2\pi(\mu'y' + \nu'z')}\, dy'\, dz'. \tag{12.7}$$

Now, according to (12.1),

$$U^*(y', z') = \iint g^*(\beta', \gamma')e^{jK(\beta'y' + \gamma'z')}\, d\beta'\, d\gamma'. \tag{12.8}$$

We therefore have

$$\Omega(\mu', \nu') = \iint U(y', z')e^{j2\pi(\mu'y' + \nu'z')}\left[\iint g^*(\beta', \gamma')e^{jK(\beta'y' + \gamma'z')}\, d\beta'\, d\gamma'\right] dy'\, dz'. \tag{12.9}$$

By reversing the order of the integration

$$\Omega(\mu', \nu') = \iint g^*(\beta', \gamma')\left\{\iint U(y', z')e^{jK[(\beta' + \lambda\mu')y' + (\gamma' + \lambda\nu')z']}\, dy'\, dz'\right\} d\beta'\, d\gamma'. \tag{12.10}$$

Now

$$g(\beta' + \lambda\mu', \gamma' + \lambda\nu') = \iint U(y', z')e^{jK[(\beta' + \lambda\mu')y' + (\gamma' + \lambda\nu')z']}\, dy'\, dz'. \tag{12.11}$$

Hence

$$\Omega(\mu', \nu') = \iint g^*(\beta', \gamma')g(\beta' + \lambda\mu', \gamma' + \lambda\nu')\, d\beta'\, d\gamma'. \tag{12.12}$$

Obviously, we also have

$$\Omega(\mu', \nu') = \iint g(\beta', \gamma')\, g^*(\beta' - \lambda\mu', \gamma' - \lambda\nu')\, d\beta'\, d\gamma'. \tag{12.13}$$

Equation 12.13 shows that the function $\Omega(\mu', \nu')$ represents the autocorrelation function of $g(\beta', \gamma')$, that is, the distribution of the amplitudes on the wavefront. The function $g(\beta', \gamma')$ is zero outside the contour of the pupil:

$$g(\beta', \gamma') = 0 \quad \text{if} \quad \beta'^2 + \gamma'^2 > \alpha_m'^2.$$

Inside the contour of a perfectly transparent pupil $(\beta'^2 + \gamma'^2 \leqslant \alpha_m'^2)$ we have

$$g(\beta', \gamma') = e^{jK\Delta(\beta', \gamma')}, \tag{12.14}$$

in which $\Delta(\beta', \gamma')$ represents the aberration of the objective in the form of an optical path. This is the deviation between the surface of the real wave and a reference sphere. Similarly, $g^*(\beta' - \lambda\mu', \gamma' - \lambda v')$ is zero outside a second contour identical to that of the pupil, but displaced by a length $\lambda(\mu'^2 + v'^2)^{1/2}$. These contours, shown in Fig. 12.2, are circumferences if we consider an

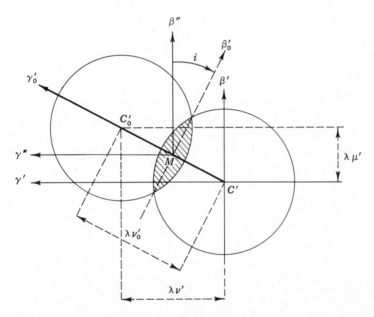

FIG. 12.2   The transformation of the image of a point source (transfer function) is represented by the shaded region.

objective limited by a circular contour. The circumference with its center at C' corresponds to $g(\beta', \gamma')$, and $g^*(\beta' - \lambda\mu', \gamma' - \lambda v')$ corresponds to a circumference with its center at C_0'. Equation 12.13 shows that $\Omega(\mu', v')$ is zero outside the region held by the two circles in common (cross-hatched region in Fig. 12.2). Let us effect a translation of the axes and take as the origin of the coordinates M the center of $C'C_0'$:

$$\beta' = \beta'' + \frac{\lambda\mu'}{2},$$

$$\gamma' = \gamma'' + \frac{\lambda v'}{2}.$$

We then have

$$\Omega(\mu', v') = \iint g\left(\beta'' + \frac{\lambda\mu'}{2}, \gamma'' + \frac{\lambda v'}{2}\right) g^*\left(\beta'' - \frac{\lambda\mu'}{2}, \gamma'' - \frac{\lambda v'}{2}\right) d\beta'' \, d\gamma''. \quad (12.15)$$

We rotate the axes $M\beta''\gamma''$ through an angle i and thus obtain a new set of axes $M\beta_0'\gamma_0'$. By putting

$$\beta_0' = \beta'' \cos i + \gamma'' \sin i,$$
$$\gamma_0' = \gamma'' \cos i - \beta'' \sin i \qquad (12.16)$$

where

$$v_0' = (\mu'^2 + v'^2)^{1/2}, \qquad (12.17)$$

we obtain

$$\Omega(0, v_0') = \iint g\left(\beta_0', \gamma_0' + \frac{\lambda v_0'}{2}\right) g^*\left(\beta_0', \gamma_0' - \frac{\lambda v_0'}{2}\right) d\beta_0'\, d\gamma_0'. \quad (12.18)$$

In the following we always consider the axes $M\beta_0'\gamma_0'$ and to simplify the writing we suppress the indices 0; that is, we utilize Fig. 12.3, and the relation (12.18) is replaced by the following:

$$\Omega(v') = \iint g\left(\beta', \gamma' + \frac{\lambda v'}{2}\right) g^*\left(\beta', \gamma' - \frac{\lambda v'}{2}\right) d\beta'\, d\gamma'. \qquad (12.19)$$

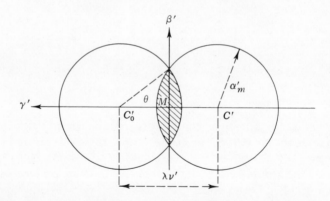

FIG. 12.3   Calculation of the Fourier transformation of a point-source.

12.4   Fourier Transformation of the Image of a Luminous Point in a Perfect Instrument

If the instrument is stigmatic, the Fourier transformation $\Omega(v')$ takes a very simple form. In fact, because the instrument is perfect, $g(\beta', \gamma' + \lambda v'/2)$ is real and constant inside the contour of the pupil, as is $g^*(\beta', \gamma' - \lambda v'/2)$. Consequently, the function $\Omega(v')$ is represented by the surface S, which the two circles of Fig. 12.3 (cross-hatched region) have in common. We can normalize $\Omega(v')$ and write

$$\Omega(v') = \frac{\iint g(\beta', \gamma' + \lambda v'/2)\, g^*(\beta', \gamma' - \lambda v'/2)\, d\beta'\, d\gamma'}{\iint g(\beta', \gamma')\, g^*(\beta', \gamma')\, d\beta'\, d\gamma'}\; ; \qquad (12.20)$$

that is,

$$\Omega(v' = 0) = 1.$$

If S_m is the maximum value of the surface S, we have

$$\Omega(v') = \frac{S}{S_m}. \qquad (12.21)$$

Let α_m' (Fig. 12.1) be the maximum value of α'. We then have

$$S_m = \pi R^2 \alpha_m'^2,$$

where R is the radius of curvature $C'S'$ (Fig. 12.1) of the wavefront.

We can easily calculate S:

$$S = 2R^2 \alpha_m'^2 (\theta - \sin\theta \cos\theta),$$

from which we obtain

$$\Omega(v') = \frac{2}{\pi}(\theta - \sin\theta \cos\theta). \qquad (12.22)$$

Figure 12.3 shows the relation between θ and the spatial frequency v'. We then have

$$\cos\theta = \frac{\lambda v'}{2\alpha_m'}. \qquad (12.23)$$

The curve of Fig. 12.4 shows the variations of $\Omega(v')$ as a function of $\cos\theta$.

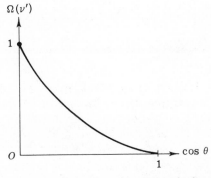

FIG. 12.4 $\Omega(v')$ as a function of $\cos\theta$ (transfer function).

12.5   Filtering of the Spatial Frequencies by a Perfect Optical Instrument: Transfer Function

We represent the test object (transmission grating of contrast 1) not in the object plane but in the image plane. We characterize it by a frequency v_0' (this would be the frequency of the geometrically perfect image of the object) and give the distribution of intensity by

$$O(z') = \frac{1}{2}(1 + \sin 2\pi v_0' z') = \frac{1}{2} - \frac{j}{4}(e^{j2\pi v_0' z'} - e^{-j2\pi v_0' z'}). \quad (12.24)$$

This is the function that represents the object. The Fourier transform of the object is therefore

$$\omega(v') = \frac{1}{2} - \frac{j}{4}(e^{j2\pi v_0' z'}e^{j2\pi v' z'} - e^{-j2\pi v_0' z'}e^{j2\pi v' z'})$$

or

$$\omega(v') = \frac{1}{2} - \frac{j}{4}[e^{j2\pi(v_0' + v')z'} - e^{-j2\pi(v_0' - v')z'}]. \quad (12.25)$$

Hence it is represented by the three amplitude terms $1/2$, $-j/4$, and $+j/4$, which correspond, respectively, to $v' = 0$, $v' = -v_0'$ and $v' = +v_0'$. Let us take $\omega(v')$ as the ordinate (Fig. 12.5) and $\lambda v'$ (which is an angle) as abscissas. We have shown only the term $v = v_0'$ of the amplitude $j/2$ because the

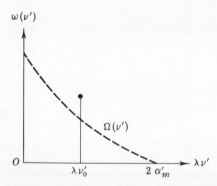

FIG. 12.5   Filtering of spatial frequencies for an optical instrument.

first term of $\omega(v')$ is real and cannot be shown on the same figure. The function $\Omega(v')$ of Fig. 12.4 is shown here by dotted lines. Its limit, on the abscissa, corresponds to $\cos \theta = 1$, that is, according to (12.23), to $\lambda v' = 2\alpha_m'$. According to the fundamental theorem (Section 12.2), the image of the test object (transmission grating) is given by the product $\omega(v')\Omega(v')$. According to (12.20), we see that $\Omega(v' = 0) = 1$, as the function $\Omega(v')$, is normalized.

We have therefore, as intensity distribution in the image of the transmission grating,

$$I(z') = \frac{1}{2} - \frac{j}{4}(e^{j2\pi v_0'z'} - e^{-j2\pi v_0'z'}) \; \Omega(v_0'), \qquad (12.26)$$

where $\Omega(v_0')$ is normalized. We can write

$$I(z') = \tfrac{1}{2}[1 + \Omega(v_0')\sin 2\pi v_0'z']. \qquad (12.27)$$

The image is a sinusoid with a contrast smaller than 1. We have in fact

$$\gamma = \frac{2\Omega(v_0')}{1 + \Omega(v_0')}. \qquad (12.28)$$

Equation 12.27 and Fig. 12.5 show that a sinusoidal transmission grating of frequency v_0' and contrast 1 is transmitted by a perfect instrument if $\lambda v_0' < 2\alpha_m'$, but the contrast of the image is smaller than 1 and is given by (12.28). The optical instrument performs a filtering of the spatial frequencies. It passes all frequencies below $2\alpha_m'/\lambda$ and cuts off all higher frequencies. The function $\Omega(v')$ constitutes the filter and characterizes the optical instrument; $\Omega(v')$ is called the transfer function. Near the frequency $2\alpha_m'/\lambda$ the values of $\Omega(v_0')$ are small, and we have $\gamma \simeq 2\Omega(v_0')$.

12.6 Imperfect Optical Instrument

In the general case in which the instrument is imperfect the transfer function $\Omega(v')$ is no longer given by the surface common to the two circles of Fig. 12.3. We can say only that it is zero for all points located outside the common region (cross-hatched). The transfer function $\Omega(v')$ is given by (12.19). Let us return to the sinusoidal test object $O(z)$ of Section 12.5. The Fourier transform $\omega(v')$ of the object obviously remains unchanged, and the amplitude terms $1/2$, $-j/4$, and $j/4$ must be multiplied by the function $\Omega(v')$, which is unknown and in which v' takes the values 0, $-v_0'$, and v_0'. According to (12.26), the image is

$$I(z') = \frac{1}{2} - \frac{j}{4}[\Omega(-v_0')e^{j2\pi v_0'z'} - \Omega(v_0')e^{-j2\pi v_0'z'}]$$

because the function $\Omega(v')$ is normalized and $\Omega(v' = 0) = 1$. But $E(y', z')$ is real and (12.6) shows that $\Omega(-v_0') = \Omega^*(v_0')$. Let us write

$$\Omega(v_0') = \Omega_1 + j\Omega_2 = |\Omega(v_0')|\exp(j\psi). \qquad (12.29)$$

We then have

$$\Omega(-v_0') = \Omega^*(v_0') = \Omega_1 - j\Omega_2,$$

from which

$$I(z') = \frac{1}{2} - \frac{j}{4}[(\Omega_1 - j\Omega_2)e^{j2\pi v_0'z'} - (\Omega_1 + j\Omega_2)e^{-j2\pi v_0'z'}]$$

$$I(z') = \frac{1}{2} + \frac{\Omega_1}{2}\sin 2\pi v_0'z' - \frac{\Omega_2}{2}\cos 2\pi v_0'z',$$

but, according to (12.29),

$$\Omega_1 = |\Omega(v_0')|\cos\psi, \qquad \Omega_2 = |\Omega(v_0')|\sin\psi \qquad (12.30)$$

and

$$\tan\psi = \frac{\Omega_2}{\Omega_1},$$

from which

$$I(z') = \frac{1}{2} + \frac{|\Omega(v_0')|}{2}\sin(2\pi v_0'z' - \psi). \qquad (12.31)$$

Hence the contrast is given by

$$\gamma = \frac{2|\Omega(v_0')|}{1 + |\Omega(v_0')|}. \qquad (12.32)$$

If the instrument is perfect, $\Omega(v_0')$ is real, and we again have (12.28). We see that the measurement of the contrast γ of the image of the sinusoidal test object gives the modulus $|\Omega(v_0')|$ of the transfer function:

$$|\Omega(v_0')| = \frac{\gamma}{2 - \gamma}. \qquad (12.33)$$

The phase change ψ represents a lateral shift of the image of the test object. The real image of the grating is shifted by ψ with respect to its perfect geometrical image. The phase change ψ appears only in the presence of dissymmetrical aberrations such as coma. In a spherical aberration or astigmatism $\Omega(v_0')$ is real.

12.7   Principle of the Interferometric Measurement of the Transfer Function

According to (12.20), (12.29), and (12.33), the transfer function is given by

$$\Omega(v') = \frac{\iint g(\beta', \gamma' + \lambda v'/2)\,g^*(\beta', \gamma' - \lambda v'/2)\,d\beta'\,d\gamma'}{\iint g(\beta', \gamma')g^*(\beta', \gamma')\,d\beta'\,d\gamma'} = |\Omega(v')|\exp(j\psi), \quad (12.34)$$

$$\Omega(v') = \frac{\gamma}{2 - \gamma}\exp(j\psi). \qquad (12.35)$$

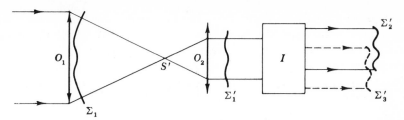

FIG. 12.6 Principle of the interferential measurement of the transfer function of an optical instrument.

We assume that the deformed wave Σ_1 (Fig. 12.6) is collimated after traversing the objective O_1 by a perfect system O_2. We obtain the wave Σ'_1, which would have to be plane if the objective O_1 were perfect. An interferometer I, of a not yet specified nature shears the wave Σ'_1. At the exit of the system we find the two waves Σ'_2 and Σ'_3 identical to Σ'_1, but longitudinally and laterally shifted. The longitudinal shift between the two waves Σ'_2 and Σ'_3 (Fig. 12.7)

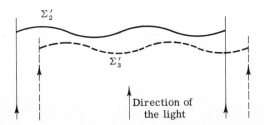

FIG. 12.7 Disposition of two wavefronts emanating from an interferometer.

shows the variable path difference between Σ'_2 and Σ'_3. The lateral shift d is produced by the interferometer. In agreement with Fig. 12.3, we can assume that the two waves limited by the two circumferences are laterally shifted by $d/2$ in opposite directions, M being in the center of $C'C_0'$. If φ is the phase difference between Σ'_2 and Σ'_3 at point M, the intensity in an arbitrary point of the two waves Σ'_2 and Σ'_3 is

$$\left| g\left(\beta', \gamma' + \frac{\lambda v'}{2}\right) + g\left(\beta', \gamma' - \frac{\lambda v'}{2}\right) \exp(j\varphi) \right|^2 . \tag{12.36}$$

The functions $g(\beta', \gamma' + \lambda v'/2)$ and $g(\beta', \gamma' - \lambda v'/2)$ are complex, and the terms that determine the phase difference between the two waves (when $\varphi = 0$) are contained in the expression $g(\beta', \gamma' + \lambda v'/2)$ and $g(\beta', \gamma' - \lambda v'/2)$. The flux that emerges from the interferometer is then given by

$$B(\varphi) = \int\int \left| g\left(\beta', \gamma' + \frac{\lambda v'}{2}\right) + g\left(\beta', \gamma' - \frac{\lambda v'}{2}\right) \exp(j\varphi) \right|^2 d\beta'\, d\gamma'. \tag{12.37}$$

The quantity $B(\varphi)$ gives the total flux, that is, the flux that traverses not only the region common to the two waves but also corresponds to the regions that do not cover one another. We expand

$$B(\varphi) = \iint \left| g\left(\beta', \gamma' + \frac{\lambda v'}{2}\right) \right|^2 d\beta' \, d\gamma' + \iint \left| g\left(\beta', \gamma' - \frac{\lambda v'}{2}\right) \right|^2 d\beta' \, d\gamma' + A + B,$$

where

$$A = \iint g\left(\beta', \gamma' - \frac{\lambda v'}{2}\right) g^*\left(\beta', \gamma' + \frac{\lambda v'}{2}\right) \exp(j\varphi) \, d\beta' \, d\gamma',$$

$$B = \iint g\left(\beta', \gamma' + \frac{\lambda v'}{2}\right) g^*\left(\beta', \gamma' - \frac{\lambda v'}{2}\right) \exp(-j\varphi) \, d\beta' \, d\gamma'.$$

Now

$$A + B = 2\mathscr{R}\left[\exp(j\varphi) \iint g\left(\beta', \gamma' + \frac{\lambda v'}{2}\right) g^*\left(\beta', \gamma' - \frac{\lambda v'}{2}\right) d\beta' \, d\gamma'\right],$$

where $\mathscr{R}[\;\;]$ means the real part of the expression in brackets because

$$g_1 g_2{}^* + g_2 g_1{}^* = 2\mathscr{R}[g_1 g_2{}^*] = 2\mathscr{R}[g_1{}^* g_2],$$

and

$$B(\varphi) = \iint \left| g\left(\beta', \gamma' + \frac{\lambda v'}{2}\right) \right|^2 d\beta' \, d\gamma' + \iint \left| g\left(\beta', \gamma' - \frac{\lambda v'}{2}\right) \right|^2 d\beta' \, d\gamma'$$

$$+ 2\mathscr{R}\left[\exp(j\varphi) \iint g\left(\beta', \gamma' + \frac{\lambda v'}{2}\right) g^*\left(\beta', \gamma' - \frac{\lambda v'}{2}\right) d\beta' \, d\gamma'\right]. \qquad (12.38)$$

If we normalize this expression, the first two integrals of the second member of (12.38) represent the energy traversing the pupil. According to (12.34):

$$2\mathscr{R}\left[\exp(j\varphi) \iint g\left(\beta', \gamma' + \frac{\lambda v'}{2}\right) g^*\left(\beta', \gamma' - \frac{\lambda v'}{2}\right) d\beta' \, d\gamma'\right] = 2|\Omega(v')| \cos(\varphi + \psi),$$

from which, up to a constant factor,

$$B(\varphi) = 1 + |\Omega(v')| \cos(\varphi + \psi), \qquad (12.39)$$

where $|\Omega(v')|$ is normalized.

Equation 12.39 shows that if we vary the phase difference φ between two waves shifted with respect to one another the transmitted flux $B(\varphi)$ varies sinusoidally (Fig. 12.8). The difference between the maxima and the minima gives the modulus $|\Omega(v')|$ of the transfer function. The phase ψ is given by the

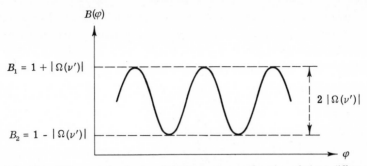

FIG. 12.8   Flux $B(\phi)$ emanating from an interferometer as a function of phase difference ϕ.

shift between the curve representing (12.39) and the curve $1 + \cos\varphi$ which corresponds to the perfect instrument (Fig. 12.9).

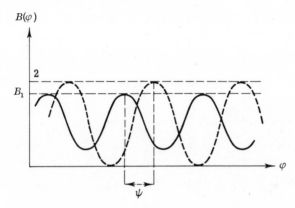

FIG. 12.9   Measurement of phase ψ of the transfer function.

Therefore the measurements consist of the determination of two values for each value of v':

$$B_1 = 1 + |\Omega(v')|,$$
$$B_2 = 1 - |\Omega(v')|,$$

from which

$$|\Omega(v')| = \frac{B_1 - B_2}{2}. \tag{12.40}$$

By determining B_1 and B_2 for different values of v' we can trace the curve that represents variations of $|\Omega(v')|$ as a function of v', that is, the transfer function. Instead of considering Σ_2' and Σ_3' in Fig. 12.6, we can search their virtual images in the pupil of the objective O_1 under study. The wavefront Σ_1, located at the exit pupil of the objective is therefore replaced by the two wavefronts, virtual images of Σ_2' and Σ_3'. We now consider the shear d of the two waves at the exit pupil shown as $d = C'C_0'$ in Fig. 12.10.

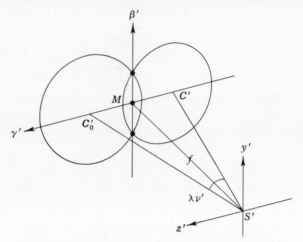

FIG. 12.10   Doubling of the wavefront in the exit pupil.

According to (12.5), which defines v', we have (Fig. 12.10):

$$\frac{d}{f} = \lambda v',$$

where f is the focal length of the objective. Hence we have

$$v' = \frac{d}{\lambda f}, \tag{12.41}$$

which permits us to calculate the spatial frequency v'.

Consequently, in the interferometric measurement of the transfer function corresponding to a frequency v' no sinusoidal test object is used. The autocorrelation function characterizing the transfer function is measured directly. The autocorrelation function appears due to the shearing of the incident wave produced by the interferometer.

Measurements so performed give the transfer function which could have been obtained by the classical method if we had used a sinusoidal test pattern of the frequency v'. It is the shearing produced by the interferometer that fixes the frequency v'. Thus to trace the curve that represents the transfer function it is necessary that the interferometer provide variable shearing.

12.8 Interferometric Device by H. H. Hopkins and Kelsall for the Measurement of the Transfer Function

Hopkins was the first to measure a transfer function with an interferometer. Figure 12.11 is a diagram of the instrument constructed by Kelsall.

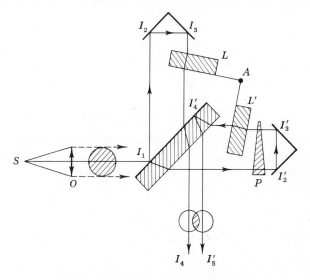

FIG. 12.11   Hopkins and Kelsall interferometer.

The basis is that of Michelson's interferometer. The two mirrors are replaced by two reflecting dihedrals at an angle of 90°. We then have the two paths

$$I_1 I_2 I_3 I_4 \quad \text{and} \quad I_1 I_2' I_3' I_4' I_5'.$$

The interferometer is illuminated by a monochromatic beam of parallel rays originating from the objective O. Because this beam is narrow the incident beams reflected by the same dihedral do not cover each other. Two identical plane-parallel plates L and L' are then positioned so that L is traversed by the returning beam $I_3 I_4$ and L', by the returning beam $I_3' I_4'$. The two plates are maintained perpendicular to each other by the same arm which can turn around point A. This allows the two waves to shift laterally [d in (12.41)]. To produce the phase variations φ we oscillate a prism with a very small angle in front of one of the dihedrals. The motion of P, which is perpendicular to the light beam, varies the path difference in an order of 25 wavelengths per second. Furthermore, if the rotation of L and L' around A is slow enough, we can measure the values B_1 and B_2 (Fig. 12.8) continuously at a determined frequency (characterized by the displacement of the two waves) to derive $|\Omega(v')|$. The measurements are performed by capturing the flux emerging from the interferometer on a photomultiplier. This signal is amplified and sent to a recorder, on which the curve representing the modulus of the transfer function is directly registered. To obtain the phase we allow a second beam to penetrate into the interferometer. This beam, which originates at a perfect objective and serves as a reference, must follow the same optical path exactly. We can then compare the displacement ψ between the two curves of Fig. 12.9 and derive from them the phase of the transfer function. These measurements can be made automatically.

12.9   Device by Hariharan and Sen

Figure 12.12 is a diagram of the interferometer by Hariharan and Sen. The objective under study is at O_1 and is illuminated by a small source S placed at the focus. The wave emitted by O_1 is divided into two by a plate G inclined at 45° and having one semireflecting surface AB. We consider

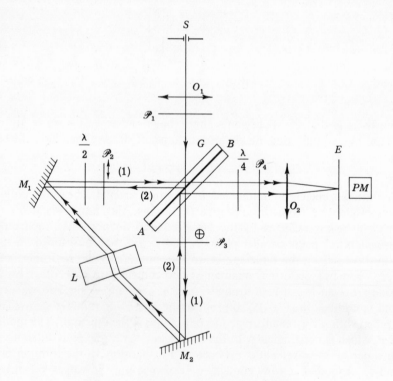

FIG. 12.12   Hariharan and Sen interferometer.

the path (1), represented by double arrows, along which the wave passes
through AB, is reflected successively on the two plane mirrors M_2 and M_1,
and again passes through AB. On the other path the wave is reflected on
AB, then successively on M_1 and M_2, and again on AB. This path is marked
by single arrows. The two waves traverse an auxiliary objective O_2; their
luminous rays are concentrated in the focus of O_2 on a diffusing screen E
placed in front of a photomultiplier PM. When the interferometer is
adjusted, the superimposition of the two waves is exact and there is no
phase difference. To produce a lateral shift between them a plane-parallel
plate L is introduced which shifts them in opposite directions; L produces
the shift d which appears in (12.41). Hariharan and Sen use a polarization
device to generate a phase shift between the two waves.

The incident wave originating at O_1 is polarized by a polarizer $\mathscr{P}_1$ whose
principal section is 45° to the plane of the figure. We interpose two other
polarizers $\mathscr{P}_2$ and $\mathscr{P}_3$; $\mathscr{P}_2$ passes the vibrations oriented in the plane of the
figure and $\mathscr{P}_3$, those perpendicular to it.

Between $\mathscr{P}_2$ and M_1 we place a half-wave plate with its axes at 45° to the
plane of the figure. Just before they pass through a quarter-wave plate,
interposed between AB and a fourth polarizer $\mathscr{P}_4$, the vibrations of path
(1) are in the plane of the figure and those of path (2) are perpendicular to it.

If the axes of the quarter-wave plate are at 45° to the plane of the figure,
the vibrations corresponding to paths (1) and (2) become circular. When
the direction of the vibrations passing through $\mathscr{P}_4$ form an angle $\varphi/2$ with
the plane of the figure, the two waves corresponding to paths (1) and (2)
have a phase difference of φ. By turning $\mathscr{P}_4$ we can vary the phase between
0 and 2π.

12.10   Tsuruta's Polarization Interferometer for the Measurement of the Transfer Function

A simplified diagram of Tsuruta's instrument is given in Fig. 12.13. The
monochromatic beam of parallel rays originating from the objective O_1
under study traverses a Savart polariscope and a Sénarmont compensator

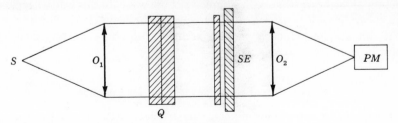

FIG. 12.13   Tsuruta interferometer.

SE. The beam is then sent through the lens O_2 on a photomultiplier *PM*. The shearing of the initial wave into two waves (Fig. 12.14) is produced by

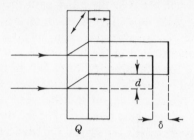

FIG. 12.14   Doubling of the wavefront produced by a Savart polariscope.

the Savart polariscope Q. The shift d is given by (7.5) and the path difference by (7.3). In fact, in order to produce a variable shearing, the Savart is replaced by the three polariscopes Q_1, Q_2, and Q_3 of Fig. 12.15. The polariscopes Q_1 and Q_2 are those that have been described in Section 7.5.

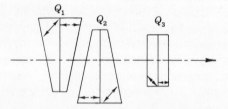

Fig. 12.15   Polariscope of variable doubling (Tsuruta).

They are followed by a Savart polariscope Q_3 of the classical type which, suitably oriented, can cancel the shearing produced by Q_1 and Q_2 at its smallest value. Oriented at 90° of the preceding position, Q_3 adds its shear to that of Q_1 and Q_2.

If we use quartz elements, the shearing is always weak and we can interpose an afocal system between O_1 and Q which strongly reduces the cross section of the beam, that is, the diameter of the wave. In this way we increase the shearing with respect to the diameter of the wave. It should be noted that this system, which is placed before the double-refracting elements, must be perfectly corrected.

12.11   Curves Showing the Transfer Function

Figure 12.16 shows the influence of a defect of focus on the transfer function when the instrument has no aberration. Curve 1 corresponds to a

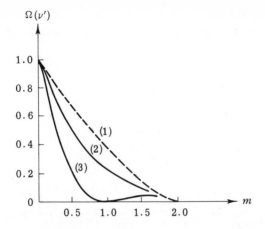

FIG. 12.16   Out-of-focus transfer curves after H. H. Hopkins.

perfect adjustment (this is the curve of Fig. 12.4). Curve 2 is the result of a defect of focus characterized as follows: in agreement with Fig. 12.18 we call O the objective under study, α' is its aperture, and δx is the defect of focus, that is, the distance between the plane passing through the perfect image S' (center of the spherical wave) and the plane passing through S''. We set

$$\varphi_d = \frac{\pi\alpha'^2}{\lambda}\,\delta x\,; \qquad (12.42)$$

φ_d is the phase difference in S'' between the vibrations emanating from C' (wave center) and M' (edge of the wave). In Fig. 12.16 curve 1 corresponds to $\varphi_d = 0.64\pi$ and curve 2 to $\varphi_d = 1.28\pi$. We take as abscissa the parameter m related to the spatial frequency ν' by the equation

$$m = \frac{\alpha'}{\lambda'}\nu'\,. \qquad (12.43)$$

For $\alpha' = 0.10$, $\lambda = 0{\cdot}5\,\mu$, we have $\nu' = 200m$; that is, $\nu' = 20$ lines per millimeter if $m = 0.10$.

These curves show that a small defect of focus causes a rapid decrease in the high frequencies (fine detail).

Figure 12.17, curve 2, shows the influence of spherical aberration on an objective open to $f/4$ with $\lambda = 0.5\,\mu$.

The spherical aberration is characterized here as follows (Fig. 12.19): the plane of adjustment passes through C at equal distances from the

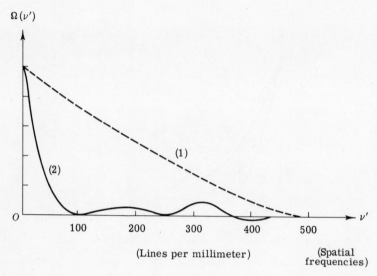

FIG. 12.17   Effects of primary spherical aberration on the transfer function after E. H. Linfoot.

paraxial focus F_p and the marginal focus F_m. The maximum distance between the real wavefront Σ and a sphere centered at C is given by

$$\varphi_a = -\frac{\pi\alpha'^2}{8\lambda}\,\delta x',\tag{12.44}$$

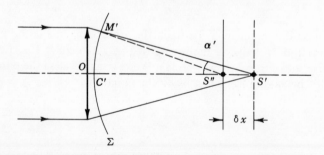

FIG. 12.18   Characterization of the defect of focus.

where $\delta x' = \overline{F_p F_m}$ represents the longitudinal spherical aberration. In Fig. 12.17, curve 2, we have $\varphi_a = \pi$. The abscissas give directly the number of lines per millimeter. Curve 1 corresponds, as in Fig. 12.16, to a perfectly adjusted instrument. In the regions of 400 lines per millimeter the curve has negative values of $\Omega(\nu')$, which indicates an inversion of contrast.

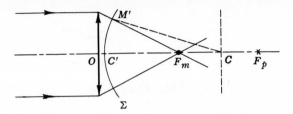

FIG. 12.19   Characterization of spherical aberration.

Chapter XIII

Thin Films

13.1 Thin Films: Antireflection Coatings

When a light beam passes through an optical instrument, one part of it is reflected on the surfaces of the lenses and returns in the direction of the source; it can be considered lost for the image formation. A fraction of this light can be reflected again and returned toward the image to form a parasitic halo. The reflection on the surfaces of the lenses of an optical instrument reduces the image brightness and increases the parasitic halo. We are interested therefore in reducing as much as possible the light reflected by the surfaces of the instrument's optical elements.

Let L be a surface of glass of index N to be treated (Fig. 13.1). We deposit on it a thin transparent film of thickness e and index n.

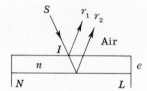

FIG. 13.1   Interference produced by a thin film.

We take as the unit of amplitude the amplitude of the incident ray SI. The amplitudes reflected by the thin film are (Fresnel's formulas)

$$r_1 = \frac{1-n}{1+n}, \qquad r_2 = \frac{n-N}{n+N}. \tag{13.1}$$

Let φ be the phase difference between the two reflected rays. By assuming $n < N$ we have

$$\varphi = \frac{2\pi\delta}{\lambda} = \frac{4\pi n e}{\lambda}. \tag{13.2}$$

The reflected intensity is

$$I = r_1^2 + r_2^2 + 2r_1 r_2 \cos\varphi. \tag{13.3}$$

For the wavelength λ there will be a minimum of the reflected light if

$$\varphi = (2K + 1)\pi,$$

from which

$$ne = (2K + 1)\frac{\lambda}{4}, \tag{13.4}$$

and the intensity becomes

$$I = (r_1 - r_2)^2. \tag{13.5}$$

We are interested in using film of the smallest possible thickness so that the variations of the phenomena with λ may be as small as possible. Without the thin film the reflectance R of the glass N alone would be

$$R = \left(\frac{1 - N}{1 + N}\right)^2. \tag{13.6}$$

After the treatment, that is, the deposition of the film n, R, according to (13.1) and (13.5), becomes

$$R' = I = \left[\frac{2(N - n^2)}{(n + 1)(n + N)}\right]^2. \tag{13.7}$$

TABLE 13.1

N Glass to be treated	1.40	1.50	1.60	1.70
R Reflectance before treatment	0.028	0.040	0.053	0.067
R' Reflectance after treatment ($n = 1.35$)	0.015	0.008	0.003	0.001

The reflectance is only slightly diminished for low indices, but for high indices the reduction is large.

In order to have complete extinction of the reflection in monochromatic light of wavelength λ, we must first fulfill the condition $r_1 = r_2$.

According to (13.1), we have

$$n = \sqrt{N}. \tag{13.8}$$

For optical glasses the indices are between 1.5 and 1.8; hence the square root varies between 1.22 and 1.34. Because there are no usable substances for the fabrication of films with indices lower than 1.34, the condition $r_1 = r_2$ cannot be practically realized. When we observe a glass plate treated for the wavelength λ_0 in white light, this radiation is almost absent in the reflected light whose spectral composition is modified. Because we cannot realize the reduction of the reflection in the same fashion for all wavelengths of the spectrum, it is advantageous to choose as λ_0 that wavelength for which the detector has the maximum of sensitivity. For example, for the eye, λ_0 would be the wavelength for yellow, and in reflection the plate would appear purple. If $ne = \lambda/4$ ($K = 1$), we have purple of the first order. In the preceding example the glass of index N has been covered with only one thin film. It is possible to use several superimposed films and further reduce the losses by reflection.

13.2   Formulas for Transparent Thin Films: Multiple Reflections

The results of Section 13.1 were obtained by taking into account only two reflected rays. The approximation is sufficient in many cases, but it may be interesting to have the complete formulas. Let us calculate the reflected amplitude (Fig. 13.2).

$$r_1 = \frac{n_0 - n_1}{n_0 + n_1}, \qquad r_2 = \frac{n_1 - n_2}{n_1 + n_2}, \qquad \varphi = \frac{4\pi n_1 e}{\lambda}. \qquad (13.9)$$

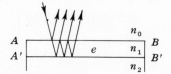

FIG. 13.2   Multiple rays in a thin film.

Because the media are transparent, the reflected amplitude is given by

$$U = r_1 + (1 - r_1{}^2)r_2 e^{-j\varphi} - (1 - r_1{}^2)r_2{}^2 r_1 e^{-j2\varphi} + \cdots, \qquad (13.10)$$

the reflectance in amplitude of the medium n_1 on the medium n_0 being $-r_1$. For an infinite number of beams we obtain

$$U = \frac{r_2 + r_1 e^{j\varphi}}{r_1 r_2 + e^{j\varphi}}, \qquad (13.11)$$

whose intensity (or reflectance R) is

$$I = U_1 U^* = R = \frac{r_1{}^2 + r_2{}^2 + 2r_1 r_2 \cos \varphi}{1 + 2r_1 r_2 \cos \varphi + r_1{}^2 r_2{}^2}. \tag{13.12}$$

We study the variation of the reflectance R as a function of φ. In taking the derivative of (13.12), we obtain

$$\frac{dR}{d\varphi} = \frac{4r_1 r_2 \sin \varphi (r_1{}^2 + r_2{}^2 - r_1{}^2 r_2{}^2 - 1)}{(1 + r_1{}^2 r_2{}^2 + 2r_1 r_2 \cos \varphi)^2}. \tag{13.13}$$

We consider only the numerator $dR/d\varphi$ and replace r_1 and r_2 with their values (13.9). We have, up to a constant (positive) factor,

$$-n_0 n_1{}^2 n_2 \frac{(n_0 - n_1)(n_1 - n_2)}{(n_0 + n_1)(n_1 + n_2)} \sin \varphi. \tag{13.14}$$

The derivative is zero for $\varphi = K\pi$. Equation 13.14 shows that $dR/d\varphi < 0$ if $\varphi < \pi$, and, when $n_0 < n_1 < n_2$,

$$
\begin{array}{c|cccc}
\varphi & 0 & \pi & 2\pi & 3\pi \\
\hline
dR/d\varphi & - & + & - & \\
R & \searrow & \nearrow & \searrow &
\end{array}
. \tag{1}
$$

When $n_0 < n_1 > n_2$, we have

$$
\begin{array}{c|ccc}
\varphi & \pi & 2\pi & 3\pi \\
\hline
dR/d\varphi & + & - & + \\
R & \nearrow & \searrow & \nearrow
\end{array}
. \tag{2}
$$

The maximum values of (1) are

$$\varphi = 2K\pi, \qquad R_0 = \left(\frac{r_1 + r_2}{1 + r_1 r_2}\right)^2 = \left(\frac{n_0 - n_2}{n_0 + n_2}\right)^2, \qquad n_1 < n_0 < n_2, \tag{13.15}$$

which correspond to a glass of index n_2 not covered by the thin film. The minimum values are

$$\varphi = (2K + 1)\pi, \qquad R_1 = \left(\frac{r_1 + r_2}{1 - r_1 r_2}\right)^2 = \left(\frac{n_0' n_2 - n_1{}^2}{n_0 n_2 + n_1{}^2}\right)^2, \qquad n_1 < n_0 < n_2, \tag{13.16}$$

which correspond to a glass of index n_2 covered with a thin film of optical thickness

$$n_1 e = (2K + 1)\frac{\lambda}{4}.$$

The maximum values of (2) are

$$\varphi = 2K\pi, \quad R_0 = \left(\frac{r_1 + r_2}{1 + r_1 r_2}\right)^2 = \left(\frac{n_0 - n_2}{n_0 + n_2}\right)^2, \quad n_0 < n_1 > n_2, \quad (13.17)$$

which correspond to a glass of index n_2 not covered by a thin film.

The maximum values are

$$\varphi = (2K + 1)\pi, \quad R_2 = \left(\frac{r_1 - r_2}{1 - r_1 r_2}\right)^2 = \left(\frac{n_0 n_2 - n_1^2}{n_0 n_2 + n_1^2}\right)^2, \quad n_0 < n_1 > n_2,$$

$$(13.18)$$

which correspond to an increase in the reflection of a glass of index n_2 covered by a thin film of optical thickness

$$n_1 e = (2K + 1)\frac{\lambda}{4}.$$

We can sum up these results by saying that the value

$$\varphi = (2K + 1)\pi \tag{13.19}$$

corresponds to a reflectance

$$R = \left(\frac{r_1 - r_2}{1 - r_1 r_2}\right)^2 = \left(\frac{n_0 n_2 - n_1^2}{n_0 n_2 + n_1^2}\right)^2 \tag{13.20}$$

which is maximum or minimum, depending on the values of n_1 with respect to n_0 and n_2:

$$\text{if} \quad n_0 < n_1 < n_2, \quad R \text{ is minimum,}$$

$$\text{if} \quad n_0 < n_1 > n_2, \quad R \text{ is maximum.}$$

The curves of Fig. 13.3 show the variations of R. For $n_0 < n_1 < n_2$ we have curve 1 whose minima have the value R_1 (13.16). For $n_0 < n_1 > n_2$ we have curve 2 with the maximum values R_2 (13.18).

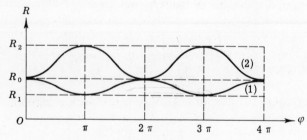

FIG. 13.3   The reflectance R as a function of the phase difference ϕ.

13.3 Increase of Reflectance of Glass Surfaces

In certain instruments, for example, in the Fabry–Perot interferometer, it is important to increase the reflectance of the glass surfaces and to maintain simultaneously a good transmission. The reflectance of a glass surface can be strongly increased by depositing on it a thin transparent film of high index and of optical thickness $\lambda/4$, which follows immediately from (13.18).

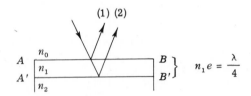

FIG. 13.4   Increase in reflectance by a thin film.

The phenomenon is easily understood (Fig. 13.4): because $n_1 > n_0$, we must add to the path difference $2 \times \lambda/4$ of the two rays (1) and (2) an additional delay equal to $\lambda/2$. The total path difference is equal to λ. The reflected waves on the two interfaces AB and $A'B'$ are in phase and the reflectance is maximum. We can obtain still better results by means of multiple transparent thin films.

13.4 Transmission Interference Filters

We have already given the theory of transmission interference filters in Chapter 6 (Section 6.9). We limit ourselves here to some supplementary indications. In their most simple form transmission interference filters consist of a transparent thin film bounded by two thin semitransparent metallic films, all of which have uniform thickness.

We refer again to the example in Section 6.9 and consider the filter which produces bright bands for wavelengths $\lambda = 1.09\,\mu$, $\lambda = 0.546\,\mu$, and $\lambda = 0.364\,\mu$. This filter transmits green only. Equation 6.54 shows that for a reflectance $R = 0.9$ we have a bandwidth $d\lambda = 84\,\text{Å}$ in the region of $\lambda = 0.546\,\mu$. Filters of this type have transmittances of the order of 10 to 40 per cent with bandwidths of 50 to 300 Å.

Transparent multiple thin films allow us to obtain high reflectances almost without introducing absorption. This is the reason why their use is particularly recommended for the construction of interference filters. With a filter made of 15 transparent thin films we can obtain bandwidths of the order of 20 Å in the violet with a transmittance of nearly 0.70 (Fig. 13.5).

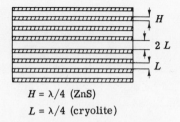

$H = \lambda/4$ (ZnS)

$L = \lambda/4$ (cryolite)

FIG. 13.5   Interference filter by transmission formed of 15 films.

13.5   Reflection Interference Filters

In their simplest form reflection interference filters (Fig. 13.6) consist of a perfectly reflecting mirror (1) on which a thin film of transparent material (2) is deposited. This film is itself covered with a thin semireflecting metallic

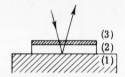

(1) Opaque metal
(2) Dielectric
(3) Semitransparent metal

FIG. 13.6   Interference filter by reflection.

film (3). The thicknesses of (2) and (3) are adjusted in such a way that the waves reflected by the two metallic surfaces are in phase. We must add to the optical thickness of (2) the path difference equivalent to the phase changes produced at the metal-dielectric interfaces. The whole must equal $\lambda/2$. The optical paths are doubled by reflection, and the path difference is equal to λ, the wavelength for which we need the reflection filter.

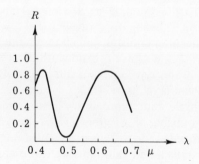

FIG. 13.7   Variation of reflectance of a filter with wavelength.

The curve of Fig. 13.7 shows the reflectance of a filter of opaque aluminum plus a thin film of MgF_2 plus a semitransparent film of aluminum. We can increase the selectivity of the filter by increasing the number of films. The curve in Fig. 13.8 shows the result when the filter in Fig. 13.9 is used. There are two films of MgF_2 and two semitransparent films of aluminum in (a) and (b). The aluminum film in (c) is opaque.

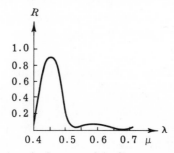

FIG. 13.8   Variation of reflectance of the filter represented in Fig. 13.9.

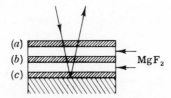

FIG. 13.9   Interference filter by reflection formed of five films.

13.6   The Turner Frustrated Total Reflection Filter

In this system we replace the reflection of the semitransparent metallic films of the preceding filters with the frustrated total reflection on the hypotenuse face of two total reflecting prisms (Fig. 13.10). Light falls on

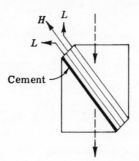

FIG. 13.10   The Turner frustrated total reflection filter.

the films at an angle of incidence superior to the angle of total reflection. It is known that because of the penetration of the evanescent wave in the medium of the lower index a fraction of the incident light escapes through the films if they are sufficiently thin. We have a Fabry–Perot-type interference filter with a high transmittance and no absorption. Illuminated with natural light, the filter transmits two bands which are polarized at a right angle. The transmittance is 0.5 for each band. In polarized light and for a suitable orientation of the incident vibration the transmission factor is maximum and equal to 1 for each band.

13.7   Thin Films in the Infrared and the Ultraviolet

In the infrared region the thin films are also useful for the fabrication of antireflecting films and for transmission and reflection filters. As for antireflecting thin films utilized in the visible spectrum, the films used in the infrared permit the increase of energy transmitted by the optical system by reducing the losses by reflection and consequently parasitic light.

The materials used in the infrared often have a very high index of refraction and the losses due to reflection therefore are considerable (see Fig. 13.11). The ordinates represent the reflectance in normal incidence on the

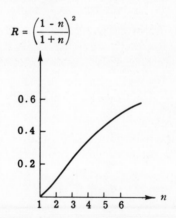

FIG. 13.11   Reflectance of the surface of a plate of refractive index n placed in air.

surface of index n (the medium is air); the abscissas represent the index n. For example, for germanium, whose index is $n = 4$, we have $R = 0.36$. The transmittance is only 0.47 (germanium is transparent in the infrared). For many applications a simple antireflecting film is sufficient, and the reflectance is given by (13.20). The index n_1 is given by (13.9) if $n_0 = 1$. We take the example of germanium whose index is $n_2 = 4.1$ for $\lambda = 2\,\mu$ and $n_2 = 3.94$ for $\lambda = 10\,\mu$. We cover the germanium with a film of SiO ($n_1 = 1.9$) of an optical thickness $\lambda/4$. The results appear in Fig. 13.12. The transmittance

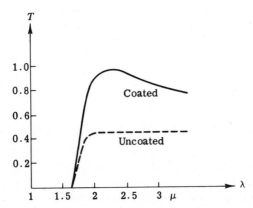

FIG. 13.12   Transmittance T of a germanium plate, treated and nontreated, as a function of wavelength λ.

of the germanium plate passes from 0.46 to more than 0.90, beginning with $\lambda = 2\,\mu$. Infrared transmission interference filters are obtained by the customary techniques of multiple films.

Because of the existence in the infrared of transparent substances with high indices, such as germanium, interference filters are somewhat easier to obtain in the infrared than in the visible spectrum, in which such substances are not known.

Figures 13.13 and 13.14 show two filters made of thin films of germanium

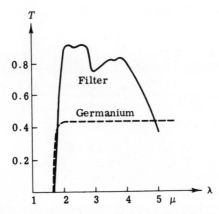

FIG. 13.13   Interference filter by transmission for infrared (11 films).

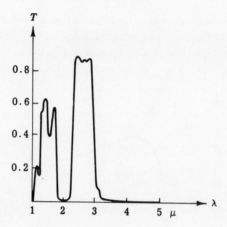

FIG. 13.14   Interference filter by transmission for infrared (five films).

and cryolite. The first (Fig. 13.13) consists of 11 films all of which have optical thicknesses equal to $\lambda/4$, except the two extremes:

$$\text{transparent} \quad \left| H \right| \; L H L H L H L H L \; \left| H \right| \; \text{air}$$
$$\text{substrate} \quad \left| \frac{\lambda}{8} \right| \qquad\qquad\qquad\quad \left| \frac{\lambda}{8} \right|$$

H is germanium and L cryolite. The second (Fig. 13.14) consists of three films of germanium and two of $\lambda/4$ (cryolite):

$$\text{transparent} \quad \left| H L H L H \right| \; \text{air}$$
$$\text{substrate}$$

It is frequently advantageous to use surfaces that are highly reflecting in the infrared and weakly reflecting in the visible. These reflection filters are useful for the reduction of parasitic light in the infrared spectrographs. Figure 13.15 shows a combination of three films. The silicon monoxide and

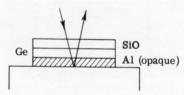

FIG. 13.15   Surface of high reflectance in infrared and a low reflectance in the visible spectrum.

the germanium films have a thickness of approximately one quarter wavelength and the aluminum film is just thick enough to be opaque. The
germanium absorbs the visible strongly, but not the infrared. Because of the
SiO film, the reflection of the system becomes almost zero for the visible.
The reflectance, equal to 0.80 for $\lambda = 1\,\mu$ and 0.90 for $\lambda = 1.2\,\mu$, remains
high for longer wavelengths. The reflectance in the visible is of the order of
0.02.

On the other hand, there are mirrors which reflect the visible and trans-
mit the infrared radiations without absorbing them (cold mirrors). These
mirrors are also obtained by the use of multiple films. Figure 13.16 shows

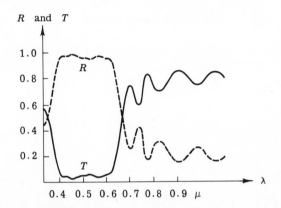

Fɪɢ. 13.16 Surface of high reflectance in the visible spectrum and low reflectance in infrared
(cold mirror).

the reflectance R and the transmittance T of a mirror of this type. Cold
mirrors are useful in high intensity projectors in which the elimination of
heat becomes an important problem.

In the ultraviolet region also we seek to reduce parasitic light and to
improve the reflection of mirrors and gratings by using thin films. In
instruments designed for this purpose, it is advantageous to use surfaces
with high reflectance in the ultraviolet and low reflectance in the unused
areas. Figure 13.17 shows the reflectance of a glass surface on which a
germanium film with a reflectance $R = 0.50$ for $\lambda = 0.4\,\mu$ has been evaporated, followed by a film of zinc sulfide until, because of interference, the
reflection becomes zero for this wavelength.

Another important result is the increase of the reflectance of aluminum by
a thin film of magnesium fluoride. Figure 13.18 shows the high increase of
the reflectance in the far infrared.

Finally, we want to point out the improvement in reflectance of gratings
in the far ultraviolet. The aluminized gratings obtained as replicas lack

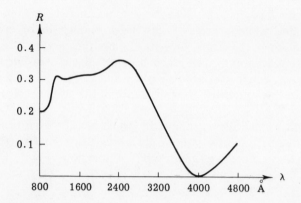

FIG. 13.17 Variation of reflectance R of a glass surface on which a film of germanium and a film of zinc sulphide has been deposited.

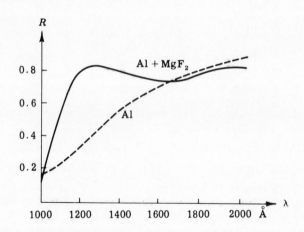

FIG. 13.18 Increase in reflectance of aluminum by depositing a thin film of magnesium fluoride.

good reflectance in the far ultraviolet, but it is considerably improved by covering them with another aluminum film evaporated in a second or two (flash coating). Figure 13.19 shows the results. The grating has a blaze near 1200 Å. These results are still further improved by adding a film of magnesium fluoride.

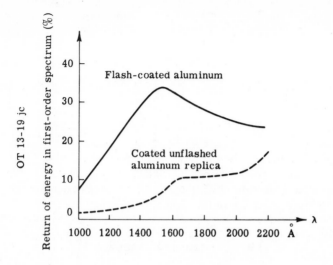

FIG. 13.19   Increase in reflectance of aluminum by depositing another film of aluminum by rapid evaporation.

13.8   Note on the Calculation of a Stack of Transparent Thin Films

When we have to deal with a stack of thin films, matrix calculus is particularly convenient. Each thin film is represented by an elementary matrix, and the lumped properties of the combination of films is represented by a matrix obtained as the product of elementary matrices. A transparent thin film in normal incidence can be characterized by the matrix

$$
\begin{pmatrix} m_{11} & m_{12} \\ m_{21} & m_{22} \end{pmatrix} = \begin{pmatrix} \cos\dfrac{\varphi}{2} & j\dfrac{\sin\varphi/2}{n_1} \\ jn_1 \sin\dfrac{\varphi}{2} & \cos\dfrac{\varphi}{2} \end{pmatrix} ; \qquad (13.21)
$$

n_1 is the index of the film and φ is given by (13.9). From matrix (13.21) we can derive two expressions in which the squares of the moduli give the reflectance R and transmittance T:

$$
R = \left| \frac{n_0(m_{11} + n_s m_{12}) - (m_{21} + n_s m_{22})}{n_0(m_{11} + n_s m_{12}) + (m_{21} + n_s m_{22})} \right|^2, \qquad (13.22)
$$

$$
T = \left| \frac{2n_0}{n_0(m_{11} + n_s m_{12}) + (m_{21} + n_s m_{22})} \right|^2. \qquad (13.23)
$$

We have replaced the index n_2 with the general index n_s so that the preceding formulas can be applied to multiple thin films; n_s is the index of the last medium. If we have an arbitrary number of films, we can write

$$\begin{pmatrix} m_{11} & m_{12} \\ \\ m_{21} & m_{22} \end{pmatrix} = \begin{pmatrix} \cos\dfrac{\varphi_1}{2} & j\dfrac{\sin\varphi_1/2}{n_1} \\ \\ jn_1\sin\dfrac{\varphi_1}{2} & \cos\dfrac{\varphi_1}{2} \end{pmatrix} \begin{pmatrix} \cos\dfrac{\varphi_2}{2} & j\dfrac{\sin\varphi_2/2}{n_2} \\ \\ jn_2\sin\dfrac{\varphi_2}{2} & \cos\dfrac{\varphi_2}{2} \end{pmatrix}.$$

By taking the product of the matrices of the second member we obtain a matrix that permits us to express the values of m_{11}, m_{12}, m_{21}, and m_{22}. By carrying them over into (13.22) and (13.23) we can calculate the reflectance and the transmittance of the ensemble of films.

13.9   Fabrication of Thin Films

The method used in particular is the evaporation in vacuo. It can be applied to a large number of substances and permits us to obtain deposits as extended as we would wish. The substance to be evaporated can be heated in several ways: it is placed in direct contact with a wire or a metallic plate through which an electric current passes. We can also place the substance in a refractory boat formed on the heating filament.

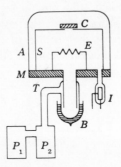

FIG. 13.20   Principle of the method of vacuum evaporation of a thin film.

Figure 13.20 is the diagram of a device for the evaporation of thin films. The evacuated recipient consists of a plate M on which a removable belljar (in glass or metal) can be placed. The evacuation is done with a primary pump P_1 and a diffusion pump P_2, which are connected to the belljar by the tubing T on which a liquid air trap B is mounted. The plate on which we want to deposit the thin film, for example, is at C on a support S. The substance to be evaporated is placed in contact with the filament F heated by transmission of an electric current. The vacuum meter is in general an ionization gauge.

The fabrication of antireflecting and high reflectance films, interference filters, and polarizers has led several experimenters to develop methods of fabrication of superposed thin films, each of which has a determined thickness and index. The fabrication of these multiple films necessitates strict control of the thickness of each film during its deposition. Furthermore, a multiple film must be prepared in one single operation, that is, without breaking the vacuum in between.

Chapter XIV

Interference Spectroscopy

14.1 Introduction

Interference spectroscopy, originating from the works of Michelson, Fabry, and Lummer, has been highly developed because of thin film research and the use of physical detectors.

The principle of the interferential methods is to analyze light by means of a double-beam or multiple-beam interferometer. In a multiple beam interferometer of the Fabry–Perot type we allow the light to be analyzed to pass through the interferometer and study the interference fringes that appear. If the incident light is formed by monochromatic radiation, we observe a single system of fringes. If the source emits two monochromatic radiations, we observe two distinct fringe systems. Instead of separating the different radiations of a spectrum with a prism or grating, we separate the fringes in the interferometer produced by the monochromatic radiations under study. Thus we can analyze the fine structure of a line and measure the wavelengths with high precision.

Two-beam interferometers of the Michelson type are also used in interferometric spectroscopy. When, for example, a Michelson interferometer is illuminated by a complex source, the flux emerging from it is a function of the path difference and the spectral composition of the source. By measuring the flux as a function of the path difference we can derive the spectral composition of the source.

14.2 Interferential Spectroscopy with a Fabry–Perot Interferometer Associated with a Spectrograph

Figure 14.1 outlines the principle of the apparatus. The source whose emission lines we want to study is in S at the focus of the objective O_1. Behind this is placed a Fabry–Perot interferometer or an interferometric etalon in I whose fringes at infinity are in the focal plane of the objective O_2. Because of the complex structure of the source, the rings caused by the diverse radiations are superposed, and to separate them we use a spectrograph M. The slit F of the spectrograph is oriented to the diameter of one

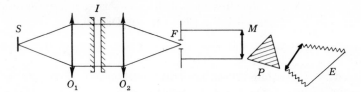

FIG. 14.1   A Fabry–Perot interferometer associated with a spectrograph.

ring, and on the plate E we obtain as many distinct images of the slit F as there are different radiations. Each image (Fig. 14.2) describes that part of the ring system which is contained in the slit F and corresponds to a determined radiation. If the slit F is narrow, each image will consist of a

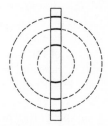

FIG. 14.2   Image of the slit of the spectrograph.

series of bright points. In a line without fine structure the image appears as shown in Fig. 14.3a. Because of the fineness of the rings exhibited by the Fabry–Perot interferometer, we can recognize the structure of a line. A double line appears as shown in Fig. 14.3b.

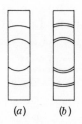

(a)   (b)

FIG. 14.3   Image of the slit of the spectrograph in a single line (a) or a double line (b).

The spectrograph only separates the lines from one another, but the Fabry–Perot interferometer permits us to detect in each image of the slit the fine structure of the line under study.

14.3   Interferometric Spectroscopy with a Fabry–Perot Interferometer Connected to a Photoelectric Detector

In the interferometric method which has just been described data are simultaneously collected on a photographic plate. In another instrument, conceived by P. Jacquinot, which operates on the same principle, the spectral line whose structure is under study is first isolated by a monochromator. The luminous beam is then sent to a Fabry–Perot inteferometer, and we observe the luminous rings in the focal plane of its objective. A ring-shaped diaphragm centered on the rings is placed in the focal plane to isolate a small fraction of them. Beyond the diaphragm is a photomultiplier connected with an amplifier and a readout instrument. We assume that the spacing of the interferometer plates is modified: the rings become larger or smaller, and the phenomenon passes in front of the ring-shaped diaphragm. The variations of the luminous intensity are recorded by a photomultiplier, and we obtain a curve that gives the structure of the line. In reality, a Fabry–Perot etalon is used. The variations of the optical path are not obtained by a displacement of the plates, which would be much too coarse, but by a variation of the pressure in the housing of the etalon. Because of the pressure variations, the index of air changes and so, consequently, does the path difference. The rings pass in front of the ring-shaped diaphragm as if the spacing of the plates had changed, but the motion remains perfectly regular and precise.

The methods of interferometric spectroscopy are not limited to the study of emission lines. They are also applied to the study of absorption lines and can be employed in the ultraviolet and the infrared regions. These methods have found their applications in astronomy, notably in the study of the spectra of stars and nebulae.

14.4   Interferometric Spectroscopy by Fourier Transformation: Principle of the Method

We now consider a two-beam interferometer, for example, a Michelson interferometer, illuminated by a complex source (Fig. 14.4).

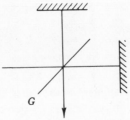

FIG. 14.4   Use of the Michelson interferometer in spectroscopy by Fourier transformation.

We can describe the spectral composition of the source by a function $B(\sigma)$ which gives the variation of intensity as a function of the wavenumber σ. We call $B(\sigma)$ the intensity per wavenumber unit. In a small spectral interval $d\sigma$ the intensity of the source is characterized by $B(\sigma)\,d\sigma$. Let δ be the path difference produced by the interferometer. If the interferometer is illuminated only by the spectral interval $d\sigma$, the intensity at the exit is

$$B(\sigma)(1 + \cos 2\pi\sigma\delta)\,d\sigma. \tag{14.1}$$

The variable part is

$$I(\delta) = B(\sigma)\cos 2\pi\sigma\delta\,d\delta. \tag{14.2}$$

If the interferometer is illuminated by a spectrum that ranges between σ_1 and σ_2, we have

$$I(\delta) = \int_{\sigma_1}^{\sigma_2} B(\sigma)\cos 2\pi\sigma\delta\,d\delta. \tag{14.3}$$

$I(\delta)$ is called the interferogram. If the radiation is rigorously monochromatic, the interferogram (Fig. 14.5) is a sinusoid of constant amplitude (14.3).

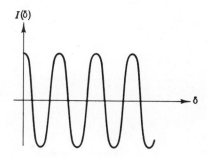

FIG. 14.5   Variable part of the flux emanating from the interferometer (interferogram).

If the radiation is not monochromatic, the amplitude of the sinusoid decreases when δ increases (Fig. 14.6). For a broad spectrum, the different

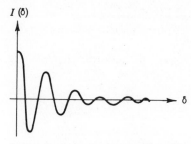

FIG. 14.6   An interferogram in nonmonochromatic radiation.

sinusoids corresponding to the different frequencies are in phase only for the path difference zero, and the interferogram is reduced to fringes near this position.

Spectroscopy by Fourier transformation permits reconstruction of the spectrum $B(\sigma)$ from the interferogram $I(\delta)$. To determine $I(\delta)$ we vary the path difference δ progressively and record the intensity variations of the emerging beam [i.e., $I(\delta)$], for example, with a photocell. We then pass from the interferogram $I(\delta)$ to the spectrum $B(\sigma)$ by applying the Fourier transformation. Let us consider the following transformations:

$$f(x) = \int_{-\infty}^{+\infty} g(u)e^{j2\pi ux}\,du,$$

$$g(u) = \int_{-\infty}^{+\infty} f(x)e^{-j2\pi ux}\,dx.$$

(14.4)

We assume that the two curves representing the functions $f(x)$ and $g(u)$

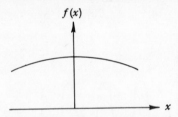

FIG. 14.7   A function $f(x)$ represented by a curve symmetrical to the ordinate axis.

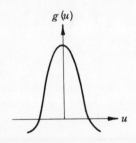

FIG. 14.8   Fourier transformation of the function $f(x)$ in Fig. 14.7.

are symmetrical with respect to the ordinate axis (Fig. 14.7 and 14.8): We then write

$$f(x) = \int_{-\infty}^{+\infty} g(u) \cos 2\pi ux\,du,$$

$$g(u) = \int_{-\infty}^{+\infty} f(x) \cos 2\pi ux\,dx.$$

(14.5)

To apply the Fourier transformation to (14.3) we consider the function $B(-\sigma)$ to be symmetrical to $B(\sigma)$ (Fig. 14.9) with respect to the ordinate

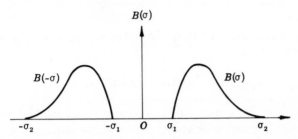

FIG. 14.9 A symmetrical profile $B(-\sigma)$ is associated with the profile $B(\sigma)$ of the radiation.

axis (the negative order numbers have obviously no physical reality). We then have

$$B_p(\sigma) = \tfrac{1}{2}[B(\sigma) + B(-\sigma)]. \qquad (14.6)$$

The determination of $B(\sigma)$ gives the spectrum, and (14.3) can therefore be written

$$I(\delta) = \int_{-\infty}^{+\infty} B_p(\sigma) \cos 2\pi\sigma\delta \, d\sigma. \qquad (14.7)$$

Similarly, we consider the curve $I(\delta)$ symmetrical with respect to the ordinate axis (Fig. 14.10).

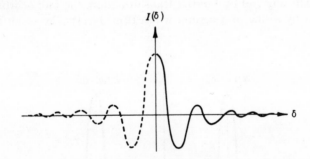

FIG. 14.10 A symmetrical interferogram associated with the original interferogram.

Under these circumstances we can write

$$I(\delta) = \int_{-\infty}^{+\infty} B_p(\sigma) \cos 2\pi\sigma\delta \, d\sigma,$$

$$B_p(\sigma) = \int_{-\infty}^{+\infty} I(\delta) \cos 2\pi\sigma\delta \, d\delta. \qquad (14.8)$$

RESOLVING POWER

In reality, δ does not vary from zero to infinity (or from $-\infty$ to $+\infty$ since we consider a symmetrical function) but from zero to a finite limited value.

The calculated value of $B_p'(\sigma)$ for a determined value σ is no longer the correct value $B_p(\sigma)$:

$$B_p'(\sigma) = \int_{-\Delta}^{+\Delta} I(\delta) \cos 2\pi\sigma\delta \, d\delta. \qquad (14.9)$$

It is Δ that limits the resolving power of the method. Indeed, let us assume that the spectrum reduces to a single spectral line of the wave number σ_0. According to (14.2) and by taking intensity equal to unity

$$I(\delta) = \cos 2\pi\sigma_0\delta, \qquad (14.10)$$

from which

$$B_p'(\sigma) = \int_{-\Delta}^{+\Delta} \cos 2\pi\sigma_0\delta \cos 2\pi\sigma\delta \, d\delta \qquad (14.11)$$

and, up to a constant factor,

$$B_p' = \frac{\sin 2\pi \, \Delta(\sigma + \sigma_0)}{2\pi \, \Delta(\sigma + \sigma_0)} + \frac{\sin 2\pi \, \Delta(\sigma - \sigma_0)}{2\pi \, \Delta(\sigma - \sigma_0)},$$
$$B_p'(\sigma) = B'(\sigma + \sigma_0) + B'(\sigma - \sigma_0). \qquad (14.12)$$

After analyzing $I(\delta)$ by Fourier transformation, the monochromatic line is replaced by a line of a certain width (Fig. 14.11). The result is already

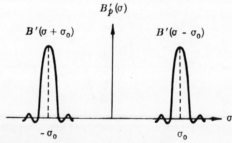

FIG. 14.11   A single spectral line σ_0 gives rise, on coming out of the interferometer, to a spectral line that is not infinitely narrow.

known: the interrupted sinusoid (14.11) produces a line proportionally larger as Δ becomes smaller. In Fig. 14.11 $B_p'(\sigma)$ has negative values, but we must not forget that $I(\delta)$, according to (14.2), represents the variable part of (14.1) and that it can have negative values.

In (14.12) it is sufficient to consider

$$B'(\sigma - \sigma_0) = \frac{\sin 2\pi \, \Delta(\sigma - \sigma_0)}{2\pi \, \Delta(\sigma - \sigma_0)}, \qquad (14.13)$$

which is an instrument function.

The first zero of (14.13) is given by

$$\sigma - \sigma_0 = \pm \frac{1}{2\Delta}.$$

The monochromatic radiation is therefore replaced by a line of the width $d\sigma$ (Fig. 14.12):

$$d\sigma = \frac{1}{\Delta}. \qquad (14.14)$$

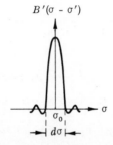

FIG. 14.12 An incident monochromatic radiation gives rise, on coming out of the interferometer, to a radiation of width $d\sigma$ (function of the instrument).

Two lines are separated if their distance is $1/2\Delta$ (Fig. 14.13):

$$\frac{d\sigma}{2} = d\left(\frac{1}{\lambda}\right) = \frac{1}{2\Delta},$$

$$\frac{d\lambda}{\lambda^2} = \frac{1}{2\Delta}, \qquad d\lambda = \frac{\lambda^2}{2\Delta}, \qquad (14.15)$$

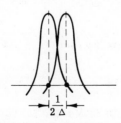

FIG. 14.13 Calculation of resolving power by Fourier transformation.

from which a resolving power

$$\mathscr{R} = \frac{\lambda}{d\lambda} = \frac{2\Delta}{\lambda}. \tag{14.16}$$

FUNCTION $B_p{'}(\sigma)$ WHEN INCIDENT RADIATION IS NOT MONOCHROMATIC AND WHEN THE PATH DIFFERENCE δ VARIES BETWEEN $-\Delta$ AND $+\Delta$

The path difference can vary from $-\Delta$ to $+\Delta$ only, and if the incident radiation is monochromatic the Fourier transformation produces a line of width $d\sigma = 1/\Delta$. Instead of obtaining the real function $B_p(\sigma)$, which would be an infinitely fine incident line, we find $B_p{'}(\sigma)$ given by (14.12).

If the incident radiation is an arbitrary spectrum $B_p(\sigma)$, what will happen? Instead of finding the real spectrum $B_p(\sigma)$, we find a spectrum $B_p{'}(\sigma)$ and calculate it by writing the limitation due to the path difference δ in a form different from (14.9):

$$B_p{'}(\sigma) = \int_{-\infty}^{+\infty} I(\delta)\, D(\delta) \cos 2\pi\sigma\delta \, d\sigma, \tag{14.17}$$

with

$$D(\delta) = 1 \quad \text{if} \quad -\Delta < \delta < \Delta,$$

$$D(\delta) = 0 \quad \text{if} \quad \delta < -\Delta \quad \text{or} \quad \delta > \Delta.$$

The curves representing the functions $I(\delta)$ and $D(\delta)$ are symmetrical. According to (14.8), by calling σ' the variable of the integration, we have

$$I(\delta) = \int_{-\infty}^{+\infty} B_p(\sigma') \cos 2\pi\sigma'\delta d\sigma',$$

$$B_p{'}(\sigma) = \int_{-\infty}^{+\infty} D(\delta) \cos 2\pi\sigma\delta \left[\int_{-\infty}^{+\infty} B_p(\sigma') \cos 2\pi\sigma'\delta \, d\sigma' \right] d\delta.$$

We reverse the order of integration.

$$B_p{'}(\sigma) = \int_{-\infty}^{+\infty} B_p(\sigma') \left[\int_{-\infty}^{+\infty} D(\delta) \cos 2\pi\sigma\delta \cos 2\pi\sigma'\delta \, d\delta \right] d\sigma'.$$

Now

$$\int_{-\infty}^{+\infty} D(\delta) \cos 2\pi\sigma\delta \cos 2\pi\sigma'\delta \, d\delta = \int_{-\Delta}^{+\Delta} \cos 2\pi\sigma\delta \cos 2\pi\sigma'\delta \, d\delta.$$

According to (14.12), we have

$$B_p{'}(\sigma) = \int_{-\infty}^{+\infty} B_p(\sigma') \left[\frac{\sin 2\pi \Delta(\sigma + \sigma')}{2\pi \Delta(\sigma + \sigma')} + \frac{\sin 2\pi \Delta(\sigma - \sigma')}{2\pi \Delta(\sigma - \sigma')} \right] d\sigma'; \tag{14.18}$$

$B_p'(\sigma)$ approaches the real spectrum $B_p(\sigma)$ or $B_p(\sigma')$ as the function of the instrument becomes finer; that is, we can explore a larger path difference.

CALCULATION OF THE FOURIER TRANSFORM $B_p'(\sigma)$

To calculate the integral (14.17) we write

$$B_p'(\sigma) = 2\int_0^L I(\delta) \cos 2\pi\sigma\delta \, d\delta. \qquad (14.19)$$

This calculation can be done with interpolation formulas, and it is sufficiently in order to consider a certain number of equidistant values taken from an interferogram. We replace (14.19) with

$$B_p'(\sigma) = h[I_0 + 2I_h \cos 2\pi\sigma h + \cdots + 2I_{nh} \cos 2\pi\sigma nh], \qquad (14.20)$$

where $I_0, I_h, I_{2h}, \ldots, I_{nh}$ are the values of the interferogram for the values $O, h, 2h, \ldots, nh$ of the path difference. These calculations are done by modern calculating machines.

Chapter XV

Application of Interferences for the Measurement of Lengths

The application of interferences to the measurement of lengths determines the unknown length as a certain number of wavelengths of known radiation. We pass then from this number to the value in ordinary units (meters, centimeters) with all the desired precision.

The standards of length to be determined are of two kinds: end and line. End standards, defined by the distance of two surfaces, occur naturally in the measurement of the dimensions of objects. These determinations are currently employed in industry, for example, in the verification of gages or calipers. Line standards, defined by the distance of two fine lines traced on a polished surface, are used in the construction of fundamental standards of length. The precision with which the length can be defined depends on the fineness and regularity of the lines.

15.1   Measurement of the Thickness of a Transparent Plate

When the thickness of a plate is not too great, we measure the angular diameters of the rings at infinity. Let us consider an air plate bounded by two semimetallized plane parallel glass surfaces.

If p is the order of interference corresponding to the first ring, the order of interference at the center of the rings is $p + \varepsilon$. Let us take the Nth ring: the order of interference to which it corresponds is $p - (N - 1)$. We measure the angular diameters α and β of these two rings. Neglecting the phase changes at reflection, we can write (6.21) for the first ring

$$p = \frac{2e \cos i'}{\lambda} = (p + \varepsilon) \cos i' = (p + \varepsilon) \cos \frac{\alpha}{2}. \qquad (15.1)$$

For the Nth ring we will have

$$p - (N - 1) = (p + \varepsilon) \cos \frac{\beta}{2}. \qquad (15.2)$$

We have two equations with two unknowns p and ε, from which

$$p = \frac{2e}{\lambda} = \frac{\cos \alpha/2}{\cos \alpha/2 - \cos \beta/2}(N - 1). \qquad (15.3)$$

15.2   Measurement of End Standards in the General Case

The length to be measured is given by the thickness AB of a solid body V (Fig. 15.1) which can be opaque. In order that the solid may represent a

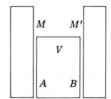

FIG. 15.1   Measurement of an end standard.

precise length, we assume that the end faces A and B are well polished and parallel. We set A on a plane mirror M and B on another, M'. The faces M and M' are semireflecting and their parallelism is adjusted by images of multiple reflection. The adjustment is perfected by observing the rings at infinity of the air plate between M and M'. If the rings at infinity remain immobile when different parts of this plate are in use, the adjustment is correct. The measurement of the thickness of the solid body between its faces A and B is then reduced to the determination of the order of inter-ference of the air plate between M and M' at the center of its rings at in-finity. Obviously the air plates between A and M on one side and between B and M' on the other must be taken into consideration. The thickness of these plates is measured by fringes of superposition and an auxiliary wedge. For the measurement of the thickness AB we operate in the following manner: let p be the order of interference corresponding to the first ring, beginning from the center. The order of interference of the air plate between M and M' at the center of its rings at infinity is

$$p + \varepsilon = \frac{2e}{\lambda}.$$

To obtain the true thickness it will be sufficient to add the thickness of the air plates AM and BM to the value e given by this expression. The measurement then consists in the determination of the integral part p of the order of interference and of the fractional part ε. The angular radius α of the Nth ring is

$$p - (N - 1) = (p + \varepsilon)\cos\alpha.$$

Because α is small, we can write

$$\varepsilon = p\frac{\alpha^2}{2} - (N - 1). \tag{15.4}$$

Therefore, if the integral part of the interference is known, the fractional part can be derived immediately by measuring the angular diameter of an arbitrary ring.

The precise measurement of the integral part p of the order of interference is very important. It can be achieved by different methods, whose principles we discuss next.

15.3   Measurement of the Integral Part of the Order of Interference by the Method of Excess Fractions

The plate between the planes M and M' is illuminated by a monochromatic radiation of wavelength λ. The order of interference at the center of the rings at infinity is

$$p + \varepsilon = \frac{2e}{\lambda},$$

from which

$$e = (p + \varepsilon)\frac{\lambda}{2}.$$

If we illuminate the system with a second monochromatic radiation of wavelength λ' we have

$$e = (p' + \varepsilon')\frac{\lambda'}{2}.$$

By using several radiations $\lambda\lambda'\lambda''\ldots$ we can write the following equalities:

$$p' + \varepsilon' = (p + \varepsilon)\frac{\lambda}{\lambda'}$$

$$p'' + \varepsilon'' = (p + \varepsilon)\frac{\lambda}{\lambda''}$$

$$\ldots\ldots\ldots\ldots\ldots\ldots$$

We can determine $\varepsilon, \varepsilon', \varepsilon''$ by measuring the diameters of some of the rings in each system. On the other hand, we always know beforehand the approximate value of the length to be measured by mechanical means. Therefore we already have the value of p to a certain approximation and can calculate the quantities $(p + \varepsilon)(\lambda/\lambda')$, $(p + \varepsilon)(\lambda/\lambda'')$, ...; that is, $p' + \varepsilon'$, $p'' + \varepsilon''$, ... In this way we obtain the fractional parts ε', ε'', ε''', ..., which we compare with the same fractional parts obtained experimentally. Let us consider the following example: we use the cadmium lines whose wavelengths in Ångstroms are

red line	6438, 4696,
green line	5085, 8220,
blue line	4799, 9088,
violet line	4678, 1500.

The measurement of the diameter of the rings at infinity corresponding to the plate under study gives the following values:

red line	$\varepsilon = 0.82$
green line	$\varepsilon' = 0.00$
blue line	$\varepsilon'' = 0.79$
violet line	$\varepsilon''' = 0.93$.

By mechanical means we know that the order of interference at the center of the red ring is in the neighborhood of $p = 31,050$. Table 15.1 assigns different values to p in the neighborhood of 31,050, and we calculate the quantities:

$$p' + \varepsilon' = (p + \varepsilon)\lambda/\lambda' \qquad \text{(green line)}$$
$$p'' + \varepsilon'' = (p + \varepsilon)\lambda/\lambda'' \qquad \text{(blue line)}$$
$$p''' + \varepsilon''' = (p + \varepsilon)\lambda/\lambda''' \qquad \text{(violet line)}$$

TABLE 15.1

Red Line $p + \varepsilon$	Green Line $(p + \varepsilon)\lambda/\lambda'$	Blue Line $(p + \varepsilon)\lambda/\lambda''$	Violet Line $(p + \varepsilon)\lambda/\lambda'''$
31,051.82	39,310.50	41,652.08	42,736.17
52.82	11.76	53.42	37.54
53.82	13.03	54.77	38.92
54.88	14.30	56.11	40.30
55.82	15.56	57.45	41.67

Among these calculated values we see that $p + \varepsilon = 31{,}053.82$ provides orders of interference for other lines whose fractional parts correspond to the experimental values. These are the values that must be chosen. This method can be adapted to dual-beam as well as to multiple-beam interferences, and the principle of fringes of equal thickness can also be used.

15.4   Measurement of the Integral Part of the Order of Interference by the Method of Coincidences

We illuminate a Fabry–Perot interferometer with two different radiations, λ and λ'. We know that by varying the thickness we can observe the coincidences and the discordancies of rings corresponding to λ and λ'. The period of the discordancies is $L = \lambda\lambda'/(\lambda' - \lambda)$; that is, the thickness changes by $L/2$ when we pass from one discordancy to the next. Let us assume that at a given position of the interferometer there is discordancy at the center of the two plates. The spacing e of the interferometer is a multiple m of the length L plus a semiperiod, for there is coincidence and not discordancy when $e = 0$. We then have

$$e = \left(m + \frac{1}{2}\right)\frac{\lambda\lambda'}{\lambda - \lambda'}. \tag{15.5}$$

By calculating beforehand

$$\Delta_1 = \frac{\lambda\lambda'}{\lambda - \lambda'}, \qquad \Delta_2 = 2\,\frac{\lambda\lambda'}{\lambda - \lambda'}, \qquad \Delta_3 = 3\,\frac{\lambda\lambda'}{\lambda - \lambda'}, \dots$$

We compare these values with the value of e, already known to a good approximation, which gives m without ambiguity. For example, let us consider a plate illuminated by the two blue and green radiations of cadmium. We obtain

$$\frac{\lambda\lambda'}{\lambda - \lambda'} = 158.6\,\mu. \tag{15.6}$$

The mechanical measurement gives the value $e = 15.9$ mm with a precision of 0.1 mm. We calculate the multiples of the period in the neighborhood of the thickness 15.9, according to (15.5).

$$
\begin{aligned}
m &= 99, & e &= 15.7807 \\
m &= 100, & e &= 15.9393 \\
m &= 101, & e &= 16.0979.
\end{aligned}
$$

Hence there is no uncertainty with respect to the number m, which is equal to 100; the exact thickness is 15.9393 mm. This method demands only the simple examination of the appearance of the fringes.

Let us assume that the thickness e corresponds neither to a coincidence nor to a discordance. The mechanically measured thickness, for example, still gives 15.9 mm, but the rings show neither discordance nor coincidence at the center. An increase in the spacing of the interferometer brings the rings closer together. We increase the thickness until we obtain discordance. Let us assume that thirty fringes are transmitted during the operation. Hence the spacing will have been increased by 30 $\lambda/2 = 0^{\mu}.2885 \times 30 = 8^{\mu}.6$. The observed discordance still corresponds to $m = 100$ and the exact thickness is $e = 15.9393$ mm $- 0.0086 = 15.9307$ mm.

15.5   Measurement of the Integral Part of the Order of Interference by the Method of Superposed Fringes

We can use a standard wedge plate and observe the superposed fringes between the plate to be studied and the standard wedge. Observation of the white central fringe makes it possible to determine the thickness ratio immediately. As we already know, the thickness to be measured to a good approximation, it will be easy to find this ratio without ambiguity and to achieve the desired result. We can also utilize the Fabry–Perot interferometer by adjusting its spacing to the thickness measured by mechanical means. We mount the two plates perpendicularly to the optical axis of a telescope V focused on infinity (Fig. 15.2) and illuminated in white light.

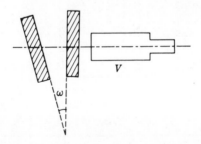

FIG. 15.2   Application of the fringes of superposition to the measurement of length.

By inclining the thicker plate we see the fringes in white light at a certain angle. We move the central white fringe ($\delta = 0$) on the reticle. Let us consider two air plates. According to Section 6.11, for this fringe we have (Fig. 15.3):

$$i_1 = r_1 = 0, \qquad i_2 = r_2 = \omega \qquad (n = 1), \tag{15.7}$$

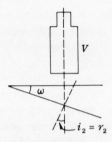

FIG. 15.3   Calculation of the thickness of a plate under study.

and (6.68) becomes

$$\delta = 2e_1 - 2e_2 \cos \omega, \tag{15.8}$$

$$e_1 = e_2 \cos \omega \qquad (\delta = 0). \tag{15.9}$$

15.6   Measurement of the International Meter in Wavelengths by Michelson

The first experimental determination of the length of the meter in wavelengths was done in 1892 at the Bureau International des Poids et Mesures by Michelson, who established a series of nine standards formed by reflecting surfaces (Fig. 15.4). The length l of a standard is the distance separating the two mirrors M_1 and M_2.

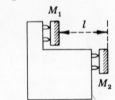

FIG. 15.4   A Michelson length standard.

TABLE 15.2

Standard	1	2	3	4	5	6	7	8	9
Length in mm	0.39	0.7	1.5	3.1	6.2	12.5	25	50	100

The operations are the following:

1. Direct measurement of the length of the standard 1 in wavelengths.

2. Measurement of the length of the standard 9 by successive comparison of the standards.

3. Direct comparison of the standard 9 with the international meter.

DIRECT MEASUREMENT OF STANDARD 1 IN WAVELENGTHS

Standard 1 (mirrors M_1 and M_2) is installed in Michelson's interferometer (Fig. 15.5). Mirror M_3 is very slightly inclined so that its image M_3',

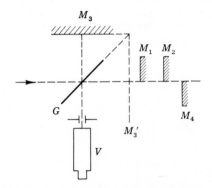

FIG. 15.5   Disposition of standards on a Michelson interferometer.

with respect to G, forms a small angle with M_1 and M_2. When M_1 cuts M_3' we see the fringes in white light. The black fringe is set on a grid engraved on M_3. Let us move M_3 parallel to itself until M_3' cuts M_2 and the black fringe occupies the same position. Mirror M_3 has been moved by a distance exactly equal to the length of the standard. In order to count the number of fringes that have passed, we observe at infinity the rings of the air plate between M_3' and an auxiliary mirror M_4, strictly parallel to M_3'. At the same time we can see the rings at infinity and the grid ruling, that is, the fringes localized in the neighborhood of M_3', by inserting a small diaphragm in front of the telescope V used for observing the grid ruling. The appearance of the field of observation is described in Fig. 15.6. It is divided in three areas

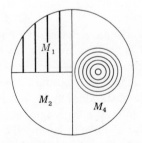

FIG. 15.6   Appearance of the field of observation in an interferometer.

which correspond to the three mirrors, M_1, M_2, and M_3. In Fig. 15.6 mirror M_3 is mounted so that fringes of equal thickness in white light appear on the mirror M_4. We illuminate them in monochromatic light with radiation whose wavelength is comparable to the length of standard 1. We count the number of passing rings until the white light shows fringes of equal thickness on the mirror M_2; the central black fringe occupies the same position on the grid ruling as it does when we focus on M_1. The number of the rings is very large. It is a whole number and a fractional part. The integral part is verified by the method of excess fractions by studying the rings produced by several radiations.

COMPARISON OF STANDARDS

To compare standard 1 (mirrors $M_1 M_2$) with standard 2 (mirrors $M_1' M_2'$) we place them side by side (Fig. 15.7). Standard 1 rides on a mobile carriage

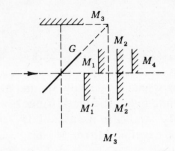

FIG. 15.7   Comparison of standards in an interferometer.

and its faces are parallel to those of standard 2; M_3 is oriented so that its image M_3' forms a small angle with the four mirrors M_1, M_2, M_1', and M_2'. By moving M_3 and standard 1 along their axes, we cut M_1 and M_1' simultaneously by M_3'; fringes then appear in white light, and the black fringe visible on M_1 and M_1' coincides with a line on the ruled grid. We then move M_3 parallel to itself so that M_3' cuts M_2', and white-light fringes appear once again. The position of M_3' is adjusted exactly so that the black fringe falls on the line. We now move standard 1 parallel to itself so that M_1 takes the place of M_2, and M_3 is moved so that its image M_3' intersects M_2, always under the same conditions. M_3' is thus displaced by a distance exactly equal to twice the length l of standard 1. Because standard 2 is not exactly equal to the double of standard 1, M_2 not being in exactly the same plane as M_2', the small difference in length between the two standards remains to be measured. We observe at infinity the rings of plate $M_3'M_4$ by removing standard 1; mirror M_4 is strictly parallel to M_3'. The passing rings are counted when M_3' is moved to a position that allows the fringes to appear in white light with M_2'. At the moment that the black fringe appears on the line in M_2' there is contact between M_3' and M_2'. The plate

$M_3'M_4$ has decreased slightly in thickness and the number of rings which have disappeared in the center gives the difference between standard 2 and two standard 1's. The length of standard 2 is therefore known as a function of the wavelength utilized for the observation of rings at infinity. Thus we arrive step by step at standard 9, whose length is thereby determined.

COMPARISON OF STANDARD 9 WITH THE INTERNATIONAL METER

A fine line a', engraved on the edge of standard 9 (Fig. 15.8), coincides with the extension of the line that limits the length of the meter standard. This operation is performed under a microscope (comparator). By the procedure

FIG. 15.8   Measurement of the international meter.

of optical contacts already described standard 9 is moved a distance ten times its length, and line a' appears opposite line b. The short distance that separates them is measured on a comparator.

RESULTS OF THE MEASUREMENTS

The radiation chosen by Michelson was a red cadmium line. He has defined the standard of the wavelength as the wavelength in dry air at 15°C, and under normal pressure, of the red radiation emitted by a tube with cadmium vapor. The number of fringes corresponding to the meter standard has been determined to an error not larger than two fringes, that is, one wavelength, for displacement by one fringe corresponds to a length equal to $\lambda/2$. Michelson found that the length of the meter standard, expressed as the number of wavelength of the red cadmium line, had the value N:

$$N = 1,553,165.3,$$

$$\lambda = 6,438.472 \text{ Å},$$

with a relative error in the value of the wavelength smaller than one millionth.

15.7   Measurement of the International Meter in Wavelengths by Benoit, Fabry, and Perot

In 1913 Benoit, Fabry, and Perot measured the meter standard by a different method based on the phenomenon of multiple beam interferences produced by silvered plates. The principle of this method is to build an optical line standard and to compare it with the length of a standard ruler (by means of a comparator) precisely known with respect to the international prototype. The optical standard consists of two plane semireflecting mirrors with good parallelism. On their upper edges two fine lines have been engraved, parallel to the mirrors, and it is the distance between these two lines [approximately one meter (99.92 cm)] that determines the length of the optical standard. The measurements are performed in three steps.

1. The measurement, as a function of the meter, of the distance between the two lines of the optical standard.

2. The measurement of the number A of the half-wavelengths in the two distances between the two lines and the respective end mirrors.

3. The measurement in wavelengths of the distance between the two end mirrors.

The first operation is carried out on a comparator. To determine A (second operation) we proceed in the following manner: By displacing the two mirrors of the optical standard we build up successively two standards such that the distance between the lines of the one is equal to twice the distance between the lines of the other. If p_1 and p_2 are the orders of interference of these two standards, we have $A = 2p_2 - p_1$.

The third operation remains; that is, the measurement in wavelengths of the distance between the faces of the plates in the two standards. At the time when Benoit, Fabry, and Perot completed their measurements no known radiation was fine enough to permit obtaining a path difference of one meter. Benoit, Fabry, and Perot were forced to perform a certain number of intermediate steps in constructing four optical standards analogous to the one for 99.92 cm:

$$6.25 \text{ cm}, \qquad 12.49 \text{ cm}, \qquad 24.98 \text{ cm}, \qquad 49.96 \text{ cm}.$$

The standard of 6.25 cm permits observation at infinity of the rings of the red radiation of cadmium used for these measurements. We can therefore measure its thickness precisely by one of the methods already described. We then compare the standard of 6.25 cm with 12.5 cm by superposition. For this purpose we adjust two standards so that the faces are parallel and illuminate with white light (Fig. 15.9).

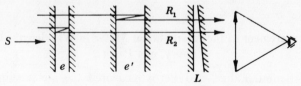

FIG. 15.9   Comparison of two lengths e and e' by the fringes of superposition method.

Let us consider a ray R_1 which passes directly through the standard $e = 6.25$ cm and undergoes two reflections in the standard $e' = 12.5$ cm. A ray such as R_2 is reflected four times in e and passes directly through e'. The path difference between R_1 and R_2 is

$$\delta = 2e' - 4e. \tag{15.10}$$

In spite of the small difference that exists between the standard e' and the thickness $2e$, it is still too large to allow an observation of the fringes in white light. We place a standard wedge L behind the two plates e and e' and move L in its plane. For a certain position of L we obtain a system in which the white fringe indicates the locus of the points at which the thickness e_1 of L is equal to the difference of the thickness of the two standards; that is,

$$2e' - 4e = e_1. \tag{15.11}$$

In this way we obtain the exact length of the 12.5-cm standard. We pass on to 24.98, then to 48.96, and finally to 99.92 by the same measurements. Benoit, Fabry, and Perot found the length of the meter, expressed in wavelength of the red radiation of cadmium, to be

$$N = 1,553,164.13.$$

15.8   New Determination of the Meter in Wavelengths

To obtain a path difference of the order of 1 meter and to compare the meter standard with a wavelength we must use a radiation of a high coherence length. The red line of cadmium used by Michelson and by Benoit, Fabry, and Perot does not have a sufficiently high coherence length. Therefore, it is not possible to compare its length directly with the meter.

Because of the progress realized in the construction of sources, direct measurements have become possible. To obtain a very narrow line, we must use a gas under low pressure and temperature and choose an element with a high atomic weight. Ernst Engelhard perfected a source that meets these conditions—a source that emits the orange radiation of Krypton 86, whose wavelength is 0.6056 μ. The small variations in the wavelength of this line as a function of the conditions of utilizing the lamp, were measured independently by Engelhard at the Physikalisch–Technische Bundesantalt and by J. Terrien at the Bureau International des Poids et Mesures. An extrapolation of the results to zero pressure has permitted the determination of the wavelength for immobile, unperturbed atoms. This wavelength is a natural-length standard fifty times more precise than the prototype in platinum–iridium. The Comité International des Poids et Mesures has defined the meter as the length equal to 1,650,763.73 wavelengths in vacuo of the radiation corresponding to the transition between the levels $2p_{10}$ and $5d_5$ of the Krypton 86 atom.

Chapter XVI

Diverse Applications of Interference

16.1 Measurement of the Refractive Index of a Gas

Interference methods are particularly suitable for the measurement of the refractive index and dispersion of a gas. In fact, the refractive index of a gas is so close to unity that it can be measured by the ordinary methods of refractometry.

METHOD OF LORD RAYLEIGH

The apparatus is the same as that in Young's experiment. Two chambers C_1 and C_2 are placed in front of the slit T_1 and T_2 (Fig. 16.1). To start with,

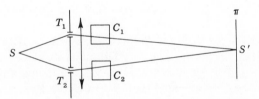

FIG. 16.1 Rayleigh interferometer for measuring the refractive index of a gas.

the chambers are evacuated and the central fringe is brought to S'. The gas under study, with refractive index n, is admitted to one chamber. Let e be the length of the chambers. The path difference, according to (2.34), is

$$\delta = \frac{2ay}{D} - (n - 1)e,$$

which is equal to zero at S' (central fringe) when there is no gas and to $(n - 1)e$ if gas is present. As the path difference changes from zero to $(n - 1)e$ at S', we observe $p = [(n - 1)e]/\lambda$ fringes crossing the field. If gas is admitted to the chamber slowly, it is easy to count the number of fringes without error. If length e is known, index n can be deduced.

When one of the chambers is filled with gas, the source S is replaced by a white-light source. The slit of a spectroscope is placed at a point on the

271

plane π and a channeled spectrum is observed. For wavelength λ, used for previous measurements, the order of interference is $p = [(n - 1)e]/\lambda$. If p is an integer, the wavelength λ corresponds to a maximum in the spectrum. The maxima that follow from the violet side are given by

$$(n_1 - 1)e = (p + 1)\lambda_1, \qquad (n_2 - 1)e = (p + 2)\lambda_2, \ldots .$$

p having been measured, we can deduce the refractive indices of the gas for different wavelengths, that is, the dispersion of the gas. In addition, p can be measured directly from the channeled spectrum. Let us intersect with a cross-wire a maximum corresponding to an order p and wavelength λ and evacuate the chamber. The maxima cross the field of view. They are displaced toward the violet region and are spaced farther apart. In fact, for any maximum $[(n_i - 1)e]/\lambda_i$ remains constant. As the pressure decreases, n_i decreases and for $(n_i - 1)/\lambda_i$ to remain constant, λ_i decreases, the maxima are displaced toward the violet region, and p maxima are observed crossing the point of reference that corresponds to wavelength λ.

USE OF OTHER TYPES OF INTERFEROMETERS

We can use a Michelson interferometer in which the interfering beams are completely separated. This can be an advantage in certain cases, but the risks produced by unequal temperatures in distant regions of the instrument can be great.

The refractive index of a gas can also be measured with a Fabry–Perot interferometer of spacing e. The interferometer is placed in an enclosure that is evacuated. The gas is admitted slowly and the path difference $2ne$ at the center, increases. Each time that $2ne$ increases by λ a ring appears. If the spacing e is known, n can be deduced. It is not necessary to know e if only comparative measurements are to be made. Jamin's interferometer has also been used for measuring the refractive index of a gas.

16.2   Studies in Wind-tunnel Aerodynamics

Research in wind-tunnel aerodynamics makes use of interference measurements of refractive indices for studying the air flow around an obstacle; for example, a model of a wing of an airplane. In fact, the problem is to determine the pressure distribution around the obstacle. Now the refractive index of air is a function of the pressure P according to the relation

$$n = 1 + 0.0003 \frac{P}{H}; \tag{16.1}$$

H is the atmospheric pressure. A study of pressure can therefore be made by studying the distribution of the refractive index (the thickness of air is known and constant) with the help of an interferometer.

In general, we use the Mach–Zehnder interferometer in which the region of fringe localization is quite unrestricted (Fig. 16.2). If M_1 and L_2 are

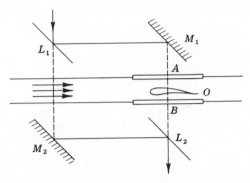

FIG. 16.2   Use of the Mach–Zehnder interferometer in wind-tunnel aerodynamics.

suitably oriented the region of localization is found between them, and it is here that we place the air jet of a wind tunnel. The obstacle O around which the pressure is to be studied is placed in the air jet. The observations are made across two windows A and B formed by two plane-parallel glass plates of high quality.

16.3   Control of the Homogeneity of a Glass Plate

The faces of the plate need be neither polished nor perfectly parallel. An enclosure is made with two glass plates having semireflecting faces, AB, and

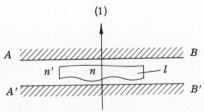

FIG. 16.3   Study of the defects of homogeneity in a glass plate.

$A'B'$ (Fig. 16.3). The plate to be studied is placed between AB and $A'B'$ and a small quantity of a liquid of refractive index n' is applied to its faces and to AB and $A'B'$, which are parallel; the distance between them is e. AB and $A'B'$ are almost in contact with the faces of the plate l. Thus there are two films of refractive index n' and of variable thicknesses e_1 and e_2 if the parellelism of l is not good. For the ray (1) the optical path length between AB and $A'B'$ is

$$nl' + (n' - n)(e_1 + e_2). \qquad (16.2)$$

The index n' is kept close to n and the thicknesses e_1 and e_2 are very small. The term $(n' - n)(e_1 + e_2)$ can therefore be neglected. Let us observe the whole setup by transmission (Fig. 16.4). The image of the source is projected on the hole T placed at the focus of the objective O_1. The plates AB,

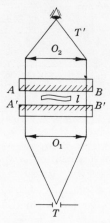

FIG. 16.4 Experimental setup for the study of the homogeneity of a glass plate.

$A'B'$, and l are illuminated in normal incidence. The eye is placed at the focus T' of the objective O_2 which serves at the same time to bring the plate l into focus.

The diameter of the hole T is adjusted as a function of the thickness at l. If n varies, the fringes are localized on l. These fringes give, practically, the variations of n, for those of the term $(n' - n)(e_1 + e_2)$ are negligible.

16.4 Thickness Measurement of a Thin Film

A thin film l is deposited on the plane face of a glass plate AB (Fig. 16.5) (for example by evaporation under vacuum). If the thickness is not too

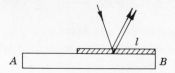

FIG. 16.5 Measurement of a thin transparent plate.

great, the phenomenon can be observed by reflection in white light. As a result of interference in the thin film, a coloration is observed which immediately gives the optical thickness of the film. Let the refractive index of the film be less than that of the support AB. The path difference is $\delta = 2ne$. If the color is purple of the first order, for example, Newton's scale of colors (scale with a white center) yields $2ne = 0.281\ \mu$, from which the thickness can be deduced if n is known. Multiple-beam interference can also be employed (Fig. 16.6). AB and l are covered with a metallic film of uniform thickness.

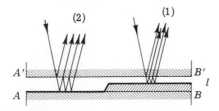

FIG. 16.6   Use of multiple-beam interference for measuring a thin plate.

This operation can easily be done by evaporation in vacuum. A glass plate $A'B'$, whose face in contact with AB is quite plane and semireflecting, is placed on AB. As a result of dust particles, which are always present, an air wedge is formed between AB and $A'B'$. Thus in reflection we observe the fringes formed between AB and $A'B'$. A shift of fringes occurs when we pass from region (1) occupied by the thin film to region (2) in which there is no film. The shift $\delta = 2e$ provides the thickness e of the thin film (Fig. 16.7).

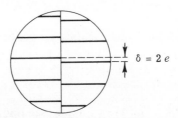

FIG. 16.7   The shift of fringes $\delta = 2e$ shows the thickness e of a thin plate.

16.5   Study of the Flatness of a Surface

In studying the flatness of a surface, we place the surface on a flat standard and examine the fringes of equal thickness of the air film between them; the whole assembly is illuminated by monochromatic light. A wedge is placed between the surface and the standard, and the fringes become more crowded as the thickness of the wedge increases. If the surface under test is perfect, the fringes will be straight and equidistant: otherwise they will be curved and the distance between them will vary. Suppose that the wedge is at E (Fig. 16.8) and let AB be the line of maximum slope of the surface under test with respect to the plane of the standard.

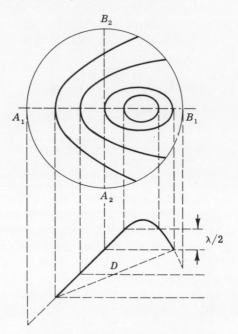

FIG. 16.8   Study of a flat surface.

Let us study the form of the surface along the diameter $A_1 B_1$. The abscissas of the points of intersection of fringes with $A_1 B_1$ are measured and plotted on the x-axis of a graph. Points at equal intervals of $\lambda/2$ are plotted on the y-axis. The thickness varies by $\lambda/2$ as we pass from one fringe to the next. By joining the two extreme fringes by a straight line (D) we obtain the deviations with reference to the plane of the standard. There is a small ambiguity at the extremities of diameter $A_1 B_1$ because the order of interference at these points is not known. We can either extrapolate or relate the deviations to the extreme fringes. The surface can be studied along any other diameter in the same manner. The measurements made along the diameter $A_2 B_2$ (when the wedge is at B_1) furnishes the deviations from the standard plane, but the number of points becomes small if the surface is not too bad. To study the surface along the diameter $A_2 B_2$ it is therefore better to place the wedge at either A_2 or B_2. If the defects are larger than a fringe, a rapid examination with the unaided eye is quite satisfactory. Let us suppose that the pattern of fringes is as shown in Fig. 16.9. The surface can

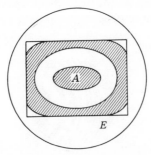

FIG. 16.9 Appearance of the fringes on a concave or convex surface; the defect is of the order of one fringe.

be either concave or convex. The extent of concavity or convexity is represented by the sag or rise at point A. If the sag or rise is of the order of $\lambda/2$, we say that the surface is flat to one fringe. To determine whether the surface is concave or convex, light pressure is exerted with the finger. The fringes spread out displacing themselves from the region where surfaces are in contact toward the regions where the separation increases. If by pressing the edges of the surface the fringes are displaced from the centre toward the edge, the surface is convex. If by pressing at the center of the surface the fringes draw toward the center, the surface is concave. If the air film between the surface under test and the standard is thin, fringes may be observed in white light. The order of succession of the colors is an immediate sign of the defect; however, it must be remembered that the thickness of the air film increases in the direction of the sequence of colors, violet, blue, yellow, and red—that is, in the direction of increasing wavelengths.

16.6 Test of Parallelism of a Transparent Plate

The test of parallelism can be made in two ways: by using fringes of equal thickness or of equal inclination. In the first method we study the fringes of equal thickness produced between the two faces of the plate (Fig. 3.32, for example). Observations are made by reflection in order to provide good contrast. If the faces are strictly parallel and the index of refraction is constant, a uniform coloration is obtained. If the plate has defects, a certain number of fringes will appear characterizing the quality of the plate. In this experiment care should be taken to work in normal incidence and to have the angular diameter of the source proportionately smaller as the thickness of the plate increases. The adjustment for normal incidence of the light beam on the plate can be made by examining the circular fringes at infinity produced by the plate. A source of large angular diameter is taken and its image, as furnished by the instrument, examined. If we use the setup in Fig. 3.33, it is sufficient to observe the image at T', for the slit at T is considerably widened. The rings at infinity will appear as shown in Fig. 16.10.

Fɪɢ. 16.10   Appearance of the rings at infinity when the plate under examination is not normal to the axis of collimation.

We adjust the orientation of the plate under test with respect to the light beam in order to center the rings at infinity on T', the image of T (Fig. 16.11).

Fɪɢ. 16.11   Centering the hole T of the collimator on the rings at infinity.

The diameter of the hole at T is then suitably reduced in order to satisfy (3.49). The parallelism of a plate can also be tested by means of the arrangement in Fig. 3.30. The eyepiece of the telescope is provided with a fine retricule wire, and we displace the plate in its own plane. If the varied thickness of the plate replaces one ring with the next in front of the fine wire, the path difference will change by λ and the thickness by $\lambda/2n$, that is, by approximately 0.18 μ.

16.7   Study of Polishing Defects of a Surface

The measurements in Section 16.5 give defects of flatness for the surface as a whole, but they are not suitable for determining the small local defects produced by polishing. Let us suppose that the wavefront reflected by the surface under test has form (1) (Fig. 16.12). In the study made in Section 16.5 we brought to light the general form (2) of the wavefront, but its small irregularities (1) were not observable. However, the method of multiple-beam

FIG. 16.12   Section of a wavefront reflected by an imperfect surface.

interference reveals them. The surface AB is covered with a reflecting deposit (Fig. 16.13). A glass plate $A'B'$ is placed on AB; its face $A'B'$, which is in contact with AB, is semireflecting.

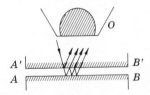

FIG. 16.13   Observation of the polishing defects of a surface.

The surface AB is observed under a microscope of small magnification; O is the objective, and the fringes shown in Fig. 16.14 can be observed in transmission or reflection. As we pass from one fringe to the next, the thickness changes by $\lambda/2$, but the fringes are very fine and the polishing defects are small irregularities which are easily visible. This method is employed in industry for the control of metal polishing.

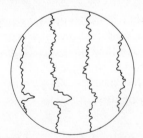

FIG. 16.14   Appearance of the fringes when the surface has polishing defects.

Sometimes we come across surfaces which are too rough to be studied by interference but with defects that are not large enough to be examined easily with a microscope. When examined by interference such surfaces show fringes whose deformations are so large that no interpretation can be made of them. The method of replicas can then be adopted. On the surface AB we deposit a transparent liquid substance $A'B'$ which is left to dry

FIG. 16.15   Method of replicas.

(Fig. 16.15). $A'B'$ is then stripped off. The face at $A'B'$, which is in contact with AB, has the same defects as the surface under test. The pellicle $A'B'$ is placed on a glass plate, $A''B''$ (Fig. 16.16) and care is taken to introduce

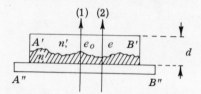

FIG. 16.16   Observation of the pellicle $A'B'$ which reproduces the polishing defects.

a liquid of known refractive index n between $A'B'$ and $A''B''$. Let n' be the refractive index of the pellicle. By transmission a ray, such as (1), traverses an optical path,

$$n(d - e_0) + n'e_0 = nd + (n' - n)e_0. \tag{16.3}$$

Another ray, such as (2), traverses a path $nd + (n' - n)e$. The path difference between (1) and (2) is

$$\delta = (n' - n)(e - e_0). \tag{16.4}$$

It is the path difference that is determined by interference measurements (e.g., with a Michelson or polarization interferometer). The variations of thickness $(e - e_0)$ are those of the object AB. If $(e - e_0)$ attains large values, δ can be kept low by choosing the index n close enough to n'. Thus δ can be brought to magnitudes measurable by interference. Two-beam or multiple-beam fringes can be used.

16.8   Study of a Spherical Surface

The surface under test is placed on a reference surface whose radius of curvature is approximately equal but of opposite sign; the fringes shown by the air film between the two surfaces are studied. If the radius of curvature of the reference surface and the number of fringes are known, the unknown radius can be calculated.

The centers of the two spheres are O_1 and O_2 and the radii of curvature are $R_1 = \overline{O_1 M_1}$, $R_2 = \overline{O_2 M_2}$ (Fig. 16.17). Suppose that the two spheres are

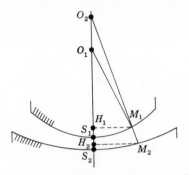

FIG. 16.17 Examination of a spherical surface.

not exactly in contact at S_1 and S_2 and a very thin film of air of thickness $e = \overline{S_1 S_2}$ remains. If we drop two perpendiculars $\overline{M_1 H_1}$ and $\overline{M_2 H_2}$ from M_1 and M_2, we get

$$\overline{H_1 S_1} = \frac{x^2}{2R_1}, \qquad \overline{H_2 S_2} = \frac{x^2}{2R_2}, \tag{16.5}$$

x being the distance to the axis from the points M_1 and M_2, whence

$$\overline{M_1 M_2} = \overline{H_1 S_1} + \overline{S_1 S_2} + \overline{S_2 H_2},$$

$$\overline{M_1 M_2} = e + \frac{x^2}{2}\left(\frac{1}{R_1} - \frac{1}{R_2}\right). \tag{16.6}$$

We know that the thickness of air increases by $\lambda/2$ when we pass from one ring to the next. Therefore, if K designates the number of fringes (K may be integral or fractional) between M_1 and M_2, we have

$$e + \frac{x^2}{2}\left(\frac{1}{R_1} - \frac{1}{R_2}\right) = K\frac{\lambda}{2}. \tag{16.7}$$

If

$$e = K_0 \frac{\lambda}{2}, \tag{16.8}$$

we obtain

$$\frac{1}{R_1} = \frac{1}{R_2} + \frac{(K - K_0)\lambda}{x^2}; \tag{16.9}$$

$K - K_0$ represents the number of fringes between the center and the circle of radius $M_1 H_1$. If R_2 is known, R_1 can be measured. Therefore the only thing necessary is to determine the number of fringes $K - K_0$ for a circle of radius x. If P is the unknown order of interference corresponding to the first ring, the order of interference at the center will be

$$K_0 = p - \varepsilon, \tag{16.10}$$

and the order of interference K which corresponds to the Nth ring from the center will be

$$K = p + N - 1, \tag{16.11}$$

whence

$$K - K_0 = N - 1 + \varepsilon. \tag{16.12}$$

We can then write

$$\frac{1}{R_1} - \frac{1}{R_2} = \frac{(N - 1 + \varepsilon)\lambda}{x^2} \tag{16.13}$$

or

$$x^2 = \frac{2}{1/R_1 - 1/R_2}N + \frac{\lambda(\varepsilon - 1)}{1/R_1 - 1/R_2}. \tag{16.14}$$

We measure the radii of the rings $N = 1$, $N = 2$, $N = 3, \ldots$, with a comparator and plot as abscissas the number N of these rings and as ordinates

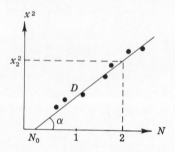

FIG. 16.18   Curve giving the squares of the radii of the rings as a function of their number N.

the square of their radii (Fig. 16.18). According to (16.14), we should obtain a straight line D whose slope

$$\frac{\lambda}{1/R_1 - 1/R_2} = \tan \alpha \tag{16.15}$$

gives the required radius of curvature R_1; straight line D represents the mean of the experimental points traced. We see that the value N_0 of N at the center of the rings $(x = 0)$ is given by (16.12)

$$N_0 - 1 + \varepsilon = 0, \tag{16.16}$$

whence
$$\varepsilon = 1 - N_0. \tag{16.17}$$

The distance between the point of intersection of the line D with the x-axis and the point corresponding to $N = 1$ represents the fractional part of the order of interference at the center of the rings. Let us study the accuracy of the method. Two errors are possible:

1. An error dN is made in the order of interference because the exact center of the fringe has not been intersected. Thus a number N has been attributed to the ring, whereas the exact number is $N + dN$.

2. The comparator shows an error dx in the measurement of the length x.

Considering $(N + 1)th$ ring, we can write (16.9)

$$\frac{1}{R_1} = \frac{1}{R_2} = \frac{N\lambda}{x^2}, \tag{16.18}$$

for

$$K - K_0 \simeq N; \tag{16.19}$$

by differentiating (16.18)

$$\frac{dR_1}{R_1} = \frac{\lambda R_1\, dN}{x^2} - \frac{2R_1 N\lambda}{x^2}\frac{dx}{x}. \tag{16.20}$$

According to (16.9), we have

$$1 - \frac{R_1}{R_2} = \frac{R_1 N\lambda}{x^2}, \tag{16.21}$$

whence

$$\frac{dR_1}{R_1} = \frac{\lambda R_1\, dN}{x^2} - 2\left(1 - \frac{R_1}{R_2}\right)\frac{dx}{x}, \tag{16.22}$$

and, on taking the sum of relative errors,

$$\frac{dR_1}{R_1} = \frac{\lambda R_1\, dN}{x^2} + 2\left(1 - \frac{R_1}{R_2}\right)\frac{dx}{x}. \tag{16.23}$$

We have the advantage of considering rings of large diameter and consequently of using a reference surface with a radius of curvature close to that of the surface under test; therefore (16.23) can be written

$$\frac{dR_1}{R_1} = \frac{\lambda R_1}{x^2}\, dN. \tag{16.24}$$

If we make

$$\Omega = \frac{2x}{R_1},$$

(16.25)

we have

$$dR_1 = \frac{4\lambda}{\Omega^2} dN.$$

(16.26)

For example, $\Omega = \frac{1}{5}$, $\lambda = 0.6\,\mu$, and we obtain $dR_1 = 0.06\,dN$ mm. If $dN = \frac{1}{2}$ (half a fringe), then $dR_1 = 0.03$ mm. It should be noted that the formula is applicable as long as the ratio Ω does not exceed values of the order of $\frac{1}{5}$.

The interferometric measurement of radii of curvature of spherical surfaces is very important in practice. In general, it is a question of working a surface to a definite radius of curvature. Two surfaces with opposite curvatures, AB and $A'B'$ (Fig. 16.19), are polished, and by placing one

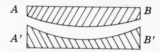

FIG. 16.19   Interferential caliber for measuring the radius of curvature.

surface over the other the existence of fringes is demonstrated. Radius of curvature of AB is measured (by comparison with a known surface), and by counting the fringes we easily derive the radius of curvature of $A'B'$ by the relation (16.9). We then calculate the number of fringes N that must exist between AB and $A'B'$ for $A'B'$ to have the required radius. This number is calculated according to (16.26):

$$N = \frac{\Omega}{4\lambda} dR.$$

(16.27)

The surface $A'B'$ is retouched (AB is kept for reference) until the calculated number of fringes is observed between AB and $A'B'$. The surface $A'B'$ has the desired radius of curvature, and the combination of AB and $A'B'$ constitutes an interferential caliber, which is utilized for controlling optical components of high precision.

16.9   Interference Microscopes

Transparent objects are numerous in biology, and microscopists are obliged to resort to coloring in order to perceive them. In living objects coloring has injurious effects, and an advantage of interference microscopes is that they permit the observation of such objects without coloration. The contrast produced is as good as that obtained by ordinary coloration methods. Another advantage of these instruments is that it is possible to measure the refractive index or the thickness of transparent details under examination. Their use is not limited to biology, for they have numerous applications in chemistry and physics and in different industrial techniques.

INTERFERENCE MICROSCOPES IN TRANSMITTED LIGHT

The principle of the two-beam interference microscope is the same as that of ordinary interferometers. A light ray SM coming from the condenser (Fig. 16.20) gives rise to two rays A and B at point M. The separation at M

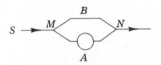

FIG. 16.20   Principle of two-beam interference microscope.

is brought about by one of the elements of the interferometer. The ray MAN traverses the dephasing object A, whereas the ray MBN passes by. Under the action of another element of the interferometer these two rays join at N to produce a single ray which then enters the microscope. The phenomenon is the same for all rays issuing from the condenser. Thus we have an incident wavefront Σ_0 (Fig. 16.21) which is doubled at M into two wavefronts Σ_1 and Σ_2. Wavefront Σ_2 is deformed after passing through the object A, whereas wavefront Σ_1 remains unaltered. After N, in the final image observed through the microscope, the two wavefronts take the forms shown in Fig. 16.21. The distance Δ between the two wavefronts, that is, their path difference, is regulated by means of the interferometer.

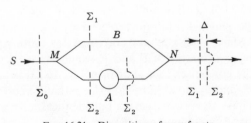

FIG. 16.21   Disposition of wavefronts.

If $\Delta = 0$, the two wavefronts are in phase, except in areas deformed by the object A, and the light intensity has the value of, say, I_0. If the object A introduces a path difference δ_1, the image of A will have an intensity $I = I_0 \cos^2(\pi\delta/\lambda)$. The intensity I is different from I_0, and the transparent object becomes visible. When $\delta = \lambda/2$, the object appears dark on a white background. In general, if Δ is different from zero, we have an intensity $I = I_0 \cos^2(\pi\Delta/\lambda)$ outside the image of the object and an intensity $I = I_0 \cos^2[\pi(\Delta \pm \delta)/\lambda]$ inside. If Δ and δ are small, the interference colors of Newton's scale will be observed in white light. The image of the object will appear in a color different from that of the rest of the field.

Figure 16.22 outlines the principle of the Leitz interference microscope. The light coming from the source S is separated into two beams (1) and (2) by the semireflecting plate L_1. Beam (1) passes through L_1, is reflected by the mirror M_1, passes through the object P, the objective O_1 of the

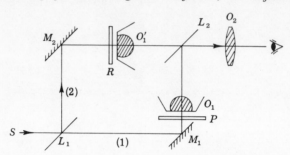

FIG. 16.22   Principle of the Leitz interference microscope.

microscope, is reflected by the semireflecting plate L_1, and enters the ocular O_2. Beam (2) is reflected by L_1 and M_2, passes through a reference preparation R, which contains nothing, then objective O_1' and L_2, and enters the ocular O_2. The interference between (1) and (2) permits the observation of dephasing details of the preparation. This is an adaptation of the principle of the Mach-Zehnder interferometer to microscopy. Of course, the two optical paths must be equal if we wish to observe the phenomenon in white light. Figure 16.23 is a diagram of the actual instrument; the mirrors M_1, M_2 and the plates L_1, L_2 are replaced by a combination of prisms Q_1, Q_1', Q_2, Q_2'. The objectives are corrected for infinity, and the lens l gives two superposed images of P and R which are observed through the eyepiece O_2. The condenser (not shown in Fig. 16.23) is at C. The plane-parallel plates d_1 and d_2 are used to vary the path difference between beams (1) and (2). We have thus two separate but identical microscopes, one containing the preparation under study (P) and the other (2) containing nothing (the glass supports at P and R are also identical). Microscope (1) produces an image that interferes with a reference plane wavefront furnished by microscope (2).

Figure 16.24 shows another type of interference microscope conceived by Dyson. A ray S coming from a condenser (not shown in the diagram)

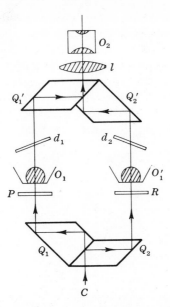

FIG. 16.23   Diagram of the Leitz interference microscope.

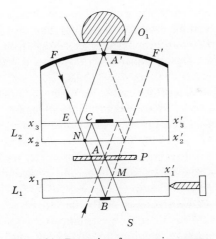

FIG. 16.24   Dyson interference microscope.

passes through a plane-parallel glass plate L_1 whose upper face $x_1 x_1'$ is semireflecting. At M on this face the ray is divided in two; one part follows the direction of the incident ray and the other is reflected by M toward the lower part of the instrument. The first ray passes through the preparation P at A, where the object is located, and then through another plate L_2, of the same thickness as L_1 and with semireflecting faces x_2x_2', x_3x_3'. This ray, reflected by C toward the lower face of L_2 and then by N toward the upper face, follows the path NEF. The second ray, reflected at M toward the lower part of the instrument, is reflected by B toward the upper face of L_1. In this region L_1 is covered with a small perfectly reflecting disk. After B, the ray follows the direction BN parallel to MC. The two rays are joined at N and are merged along the path NEF. In Fig. 16.25 these paths

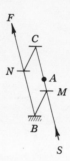

FIG. 16.25   Path of rays in the Dyson microscope.

have been shown separately. Figure 16.24 also represents another ray, symmetrical to the preceding with respect to the axis of the instrument. The object is illuminated by an infinite number of rays forming a cone issuing from the condenser. Dyson's instrument is thus a variation of Jamin's interferometer.

Because the preparation P is located between L_1 and L_2, it is impossible to reach it with a powerful objective of short focal length. The light emerging from L_2 is therefore taken up by a hemisphere. The ray NEF continues on its way in a glass block of the same refractive index as L_1 and L_2, limited by a reflecting spherical surface FAF' with its center at B. NEF is reflected back from this concave spherical mirror and retraces its path to be reflected again on the semireflecting surface x_3, x_3'. It arrives, in the end, at A', symmetrical to B with respect to the surface x_3x_3'. The cone of rays that converges toward A on the object, converges again toward A' in a region where the reflecting metallic film has been removed.

We have therefore a good image of A in A', as if A were in B, the center of sphere $FA'F'$, which we know is stigmatic at its center. The image A' is an interference image in which all transparent details are visible. It is observed by an ordinary microscope with O_1 as its objective. In fact, for problems of adjustment the faces of L_1 and L_2 are not exactly plane-parallel; rather, they form small-angled wedges.

INTERFERENCE MICROSCOPE IN REFLECTED LIGHT

We now describe Linnik's device (Fig. 16.26), which is based on the principle of the Michelson interferometer. The light beam coming from the vertical illuminator of the microscope (represented schematically by S and C) is divided into two parts by a separator inclined at 45°. Part of the light, reflected toward the lower part of the instrument, passes through the objective O_1 and then illuminates the reflecting object P under study. It returns, passes through O_1 and the separator G and is directed toward the eyepiece O_2. The light transmitted by G passes through objective O_1',

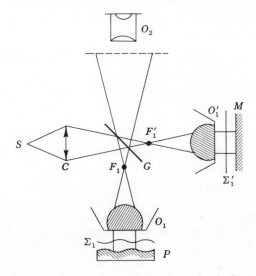

FIG. 16.26   Linnik interference microscope for the study of reflecting objects.

identical to O_1, is reflected by the plane reference mirror M, returns, passes through O_1', is reflected by G and then proceeds toward the eyepiece O_2. The images F_1 and F_1' of the source S are formed at the focii of the two objectives O_1 and O_1'.

The wavefront Σ_1 deformed by the irregularities of the surface of the object P and the reference wavefront Σ_2 interfere in the image P' observed by eyepiece O_2. If the image of the mirror M after reflection at G is parallel to P, the field is uniform. The irregularities of thickness produce variations in light intensity. If M is inclined slightly, its image by reflection at G no longer remains parallel to P, and straight-line fringes appear. The irregularities of thickness can now be measured by the displacements of the fringes. The displacement $\delta = 2e$ results due to a variation of thickness e.

16.10   Optical Holography

It was in 1948 that D. Gabor described for the first time a method of reconstructing an object by using the diffraction figure produced by the object. This operation is carried out in two steps:

1. The Fresnel diffraction pattern produced by the object is photographed. This is the hologram, which does not resemble the object but contains a large amount of information necessary to reconstruct the object.

2. The hologram is illuminated in a parallel beam of monochromatic light. There is diffraction caused by density variations in the plate which registered the hologram. This phenomenon of diffraction can be used to reconstruct the object.

It should be noted that the plate which registers the hologram is sensitive only to amplitude, and therefore the phase is lost. Loss of phase is a serious loss of information, for it renders the reconstruction of the object impossible, except for very simple objects as, for example, opaque letters on a transparent background.

Methods are known, however, which permit the registration of phase. In the phase-contrast method of Zernike the variations of phase are transformed into variations of amplitude which can thus be registered by the plate. The interferometers, too, allow the registration of phase on a photographic plate. Let us place a dephasing object in front of one of the mirrors of a Michelson interferometer. The object, for example, can be a glass plate with parallel faces that contain irregularities of refractive index. Thanks to the reference-plane wavefront, which is reflected by the second mirror, the interference transforms the variations in phase φ of the object into variations of intensity according to the classical formula $I = \cos^2 \varphi/2$.

Thus it is the addition of a uniform and coherent background to Gabor's hologram that produces registration of phase and consequently the necessary information for reconstructing a correct image of the object. The idea of adding a coherent background is due to Leith and Upatnieks. Their method is as follows:

1. A Fresnel diffraction pattern on which a uniform and coherent background is superposed is photographed. The hologram so obtained contains nearly all of the necessary information for reconstructing the image of the object.

2. The hologram is illuminated in a parallel beam of monochromatic light. We shall see that, thanks to the coherent background, the hologram gives a direct beam and two diffracted beams as in a $\cos^2 x$ sinusoidal grating. One of the two diffracted beams forms a real image which reconstructs the initial object.

Figure 16.27 is a diagram of the experiment for obtaining a hologram. The object, for example, a photographic plate representing a landscape, is at A. By its side is a prism P, and both A and P are illuminated by a parallel beam of wavelength λ. An unexposed photographic plate OH is

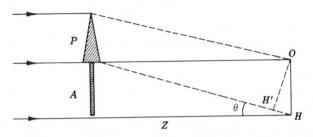

FIG. 16.27   Obtaining a hologram in which the reference wavefront OH' establishes the phase.

placed at a distance Z. A Fresnel diffraction pattern produced by the density variations of A is formed on this plate, but the prism P has been calculated to turn the beam aside to cover OH. This uniform beam produces the coherent background.

At a point (x, y) on OH (Oy is perpendicular to the plane of the figure) the complex amplitude due to the phenomenon of Fresnel diffraction can be written

$$U(x, y) = A(x, y) \exp[j\Phi(x, y)]. \qquad (16.28)$$

$A(x, y)$ is the amplitude and $\Phi(x, y)$ is the phase. But the plane wavefront of reference OH' at this point adds an amplitude

$$A_0 \exp(jK\theta x), \qquad (16.29)$$

where $K = 2\pi/\lambda$, A_0 is the constant amplitude of the wavefront, and θ is the deviation of the beam which passes through the prism p. Let us suppose, to start with, that the plate is perfectly uniform in amplitude and in phase. At the point considered, the complex amplitude is

$$A_0 \exp(jK\theta x) + A, \qquad (16.30)$$

from which the intensity received by the plate is

$$I = (A_0 e^{jK\theta x} + A)(A_0 e^{-jK\theta x} + A) = A_0{}^2 + A^2 + 2A_0 A \cos K\theta x. \qquad (16.31)$$

The hologram is a photograph of interference fringes produced by the two plane wavefronts inclined at an angle θ. The hologram is a true grating. Let us illuminate it with a parallel beam of light always of the same wavelength λ (Fig. 16.28). We obtain the direct beam (1) and the diffracted

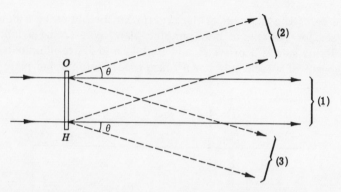

FIG. 16.28   Beams diffracted by the plate OH on which the hologram had been photographed.

beams (2) and (3) (spectra). This is important for an understanding of what follows. Let us now consider an object A formed by a small hole made in an opaque screen (Fig. 16.29). At a point situated at a distance ρ from the center C the complex amplitude is

$$A_0 \exp(jK\theta x) + A \exp\left(jK \frac{\rho^2}{2Z}\right). \tag{16.32}$$

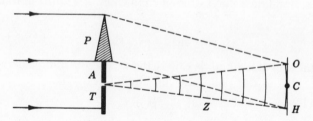

FIG. 16.29   Hologram produced when the object is a small hole T.

Z is the distance from T to C, and it is assumed that the point considered is near C. A is therefore almost constant. The intensity received by the photographic plate is

$$I = A_0{}^2 + A^2 + A_0 A \exp\left[jK\left(\frac{\rho^2}{2Z} - \theta x\right)\right] + A_0 A \exp\left[-jK\left(\frac{\rho^2}{2Z} - \theta x\right)\right]. \tag{16.33}$$

We know that the density of a photographic plate is proportional to the logarithm of intensity:

$$d = \gamma \log_{10} I, \tag{16.34}$$

where γ characterizes the plate. After it has been developed, the photographic plate constitutes the hologram (Fig. 16.30). The density is

$$d = \log_{10} \frac{1}{T} = \log_{10} \frac{1}{t^2},\tag{16.35}$$

where T is the intensity transmission factor and t, the amplitude transmission factor. According to (16.34) and (16.35), we have

$$t = I^{-\gamma/2}.\tag{16.36}$$

Let us illuminate the hologram with a parallel beam of light (Fig. 16.30). To find the amplitude transmitted by the hologram it is necessary to replace

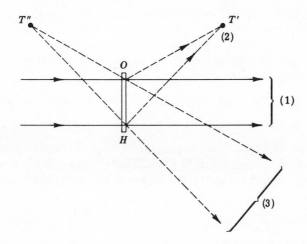

FIG. 16.30   Diffracted images formed by the plate on which the hologram of the small hole T had been photographed.

I in (16.36) with (16.33). If the amplitude A of the reference wave is very large compared with the amplitude transmitted by the object, t can be developed as under

$$t = -2A_0{}^2 + \gamma A^2 + \gamma A_0 A \exp\left[jK\left(\frac{\rho^2}{2Z} - \theta x\right)\right]$$

$$+ \gamma A_0 A \exp\left[-jK\left(\frac{\rho^2}{2Z} - \theta x\right)\right].\tag{16.37}$$

The constant terms $-2A_0{}^2$ and γA^2 correspond to the direct beam (1). Let us consider the third term:

$$\gamma A_0 A \exp\!\left(jK\frac{\rho^2}{2Z}\right) \exp(-jK\theta x) \qquad (16.38)$$

If we admit that the factor $\exp[jK(\rho^2/2Z)]$ alone is effective, the hologram will act as a true diverging lens, for the phase varies as the square of the distance ρ at the center. This term therefore, corresponds to a divergent beam (3) which appears to come from a virtual point source T''. The beam (3) is deviated because of the presence of the factor $\exp(-jK\theta x)$ as explained earlier. As for the fourth term,

$$\gamma A_0 A \exp\!\left[-jK\!\left(\frac{\rho^2}{2Z} - \theta x\right)\right], \qquad (16.39)$$

it acts as a converging lens which forms a real image at T' and which is nothing but the image of the hole T reconstructed from the hologram OH. This reasoning can now be generalized for any object A (Fig. 16.27). In accordance with (16.28) and (16.29), the amplitude transmitted by a point (x, y) of the hologram OH is

$$t = -2A_0{}^2 + \gamma A^2 + \gamma A_0 A \exp[jK(\Phi - \theta x)] + \gamma A_0 A \exp[-jK(\Phi - \theta x)].$$
$$(16.40)$$

Once again we find four terms analogous to those of (16.37), but Φ can be anything and is no longer equal to $K(\rho^2/2Z)$. If the hologram is illuminated by a parallel beam (Fig. 16.31), the first two terms of (16.40) provide an

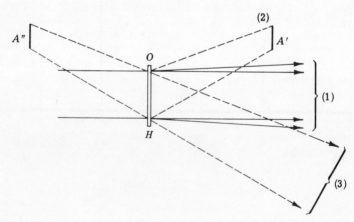

FIG. 16.31   Diffracted images formed by the plate on which the hologram of some object had been photographed.

almost undeviated beam (1). In fact, the term A^2 is not constant, but its variations correspond to frequencies that are low, compared with those of the grating produced by the reference beam. Under these conditions the rays deviate very slightly from the incident beam. The third term of (16.40) corresponds to the divergent beam (3), and the fourth term at A' provides a real image which reconstructs the object A.

Remark 1 In order that the development (16.37) may be valid, it is necessary that the ratio A_0/A be large. Because the illumination is coherent, the source has to be small. A laser must therefore be used so that $A(x, y)$ will not be too small.

Remark 2 The object A (Fig. 16.27) can be of any thickness. If it is opaque, it is illuminated by reflection (or diffusion). In Fig. 16.27 the object A is plane, but the hologram gathers information from all planes, such as A, in the case of a three dimensional object. When we reconstruct the image A' of the object with the hologram OH (Fig. 16.31), we find the images of all these planes. Thus we have an image in three dimensions that is thrilling to observe.

STROKE INTERFEROMETER BY SUCCESSIVE RECORDING OF INTENSITIES IN A SINGLE HOLOGRAM

In the classic interferometers, the deformed wavefront which has traversed a dephasing object is superposed on a reference wavefront. The recording of the two wavefronts is done simultaneously in order that the reference wavefront be coherent with the deformed wavefront to be studied. The technique of holography enables this recording to be done at two different instants of time. In the first operation (Fig. 16.32) a plane wavefront Σ is

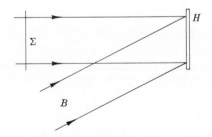

FIG. 16.32   Coherent background produced by Σ.

recorded in the hologram H in conjunction with a coherent reference beam B. The photographic plate so obtained is not developed. Let A_R be the amplitude in H due to the wavefront Σ and $A_0 e^{jk\theta x}$ be the amplitude in H due to the reference beam B. The intensity in the latent image is

$$I_1 = A_0{}^2 + A_R{}^2 + A_0 A_R e^{jk\theta x} + A_0 A_R e^{-jk\theta x}. \qquad (16.41)$$

Let us now place a dephasing object A (Fig. 16.33) without displacing the photographic plate placed at H. The amplitude in H is $A_R e^{j\Phi}$ where Φ is due

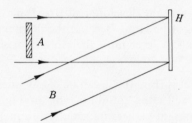

FIG. 16.33   Recording of the phases due to the object.

to the object A. The intensity in the latent image produced by this second recording is

$$I_2 = A_0{}^2 + A_R{}^2 + A_0 A_R e^{j(\phi + k\theta x)} + A_0 A_R e^{-j(\phi + k\theta x)}, \qquad (16.42)$$

whence the total recorded intensity is

$$I = I_1 + I_2 \qquad (16.43)$$

After developing, the amplitude transmitted by the hologram will consist of some terms independent of Φ and θ and the two terms

$$\gamma A_0 A_R e^{jk\theta x}(1 + e^{j\phi}) \qquad (16.44)$$

and

$$\gamma A_0 A_R e^{-jk\theta x}(1 + e^{-j\phi}). \qquad (16.45)$$

Thus, when the hologram is illuminated we obtain two images corresponding to these two terms. We know that the first term gives an image which shows interference between the object and reference wavefront Σ. We have thus obtained an interferometer by recording two wavefronts successively.

HOLOGRAM IN COLOR

Stroke and Labeyrie have developed a method, proposed by Denisyuk, which consists of recording the holograms in the Lippmann emulsions. In the procedure followed by Stroke and Labeyrie, the reference wavefront supplying the usual coherent background arrives at the back of the photographic plate (Fig. 16.34). In the emulsion a system of stationary waves (see

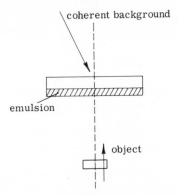

FIG. 16.34   Holography by stationary waves.

Chapter V) is obtained which produces a stratification. After developing, we observe the hologram by reflection and the only wavelength reflected is the one which was used for recording the hologram. We can, thus, illuminate the hologram in white light. Now, if the hologram is made with three wavelengths we shall obtain an image reconstructing the colors of the object. We can thus obtain by holography an image of an object in color and in three dimensions.

BIBLIOGRAPHY

Abeles, F., Thesis, *Ann. Phys.* (Paris) **5**, 596–640, 706–781 (1950).

Alpert, N. L., Infrared filter grating spectrophotometers—design and properties, *Appl. Opt.* **1**, No. 4, 437 (July 1962).

Arsac, J., *La transformation de Fourier et la théorie des distributions.* Paris: Dunod, 1961.

Babcock, H. W., Control of a ruling engine by a modulated interferometer, *Appl. Opt.* **1**, No. 4, 415 (July 1962).

Baker, L. R., The effect of source size in the coherence of an illuminating wave, *Proc. Phys. Soc. (London)* **B66**, 975 (1953).

Barber, N. F., *Experimental Correlograms and Fourier Transforms.* New York: Pergamon Press, 1961.

Bates, W. J., A wavefront shearing interferometer, *Proc. Phys. Soc. (London)* **59**, 940 (1947).

Baumeister, P. W., and F. A. Jenkins, *J. Opt. Soc. Am.* **47**, No. 1, 57 (1957).

Bendat, J. S., *Principles and Applications of Random Noise Theory.* New York: Wiley, 1958.

Benoit, J. R., C. Fabry, and A. Perot, *Nouvelle détermination du rapport des longueurs d'onde fondamentales avec l'unité métrique, Trav. mem. Bur. Int. Poids Mesures,* **15**, 1 (1913).

Beran, M., and J. Parrent, Jr., The mutual coherence of incoherent radiation, *Nuovo Cimento* **27**, 1049 (1963).

Beran, M. J., and G. B. Parrent, *Theory of Partial Coherence.* Prentice-Hall International Series in Physics. Englewood Cliffs, N.J.: Prentice-Hall, 1964.

Bernard, M. Y., *Masers et lasers.* Paris: Presses Universitaires de France, 1964.

Blanc-Lapierre, A., and P. Dumontet, La notion de cohérence en optique, *Revue d'Optique* **34**, 1, (1955).

Blum, E. J., and M. Cagnet, Interférométrie en présence de scintillations, *Compt. Rend.* **253**, 2657–2658 (Dec. 4, 1961).

Born, M., and E. Wolf, *Principles of Optics*, New York: Pergamon Press, 1964.

Brossel, J., Multiple-beam localized fringes: Part I, Intensity distribution and localization, *Proc. Phys. Soc. (London)* **59**, 224 (1947).

Bruhat, G., *Optique*, Sixième édition revue et complétée par A. Kastler. Paris: Masson, 1965.

Bryngdahl, O., Applications of shearing interferometry, *Progr. Opt.* **4**, 39 (1965).

Burch, J. M., The possibilities of moire fringe interferometry. *Interferometry*. London: Her Majesty's Stationery Office, 179 (1960).

Cagnet, M., M. Françon, and J. C. Thrierr, *Atlas de phénomènes d'optique*. Berlin: Springer–Verlag, 1963.
Revue d'Optique **40**, 154 (1961).

Campbell, G. A., and R. M. Foster, *Fourier integrals for practical applications*. Princeton, N.J.: Van Nostrand, 1948.

Chen, I., Measurement of microcurrent by the Michelson interferometer. *Appl. Opt.* **1** No. 4, 536 (July 1962). Letters to the editor.

Van Cittert, P. H., Die Wahrscheinliche Schwingungsver teilung in einer von einer Lichtquelle direkt order mittels einer linse beleuchteten Ebene, *Physica* **1**, 201 (1934).

Connes, J., Recherches sur la spectroscopic par transformation de Fourier, *Revue d'Optique* **40**, 45, 116, 171, 231 (1961).

Connes, P., Principe et réalisation d'un nouveau type de spectromètre interférentiel, *Reeue d'Optique*, No. 4, 157 (1959); No. 9–10, 416 (1959); No. 9, 402 (1060).

Connes, P., Principle and first applications of a new interferometric method of spectroscopy. *Interferometry*. London: Her Majesty's Stationery Office, 407 (1960).

Connes, P., L'étalon de Fabry–Perot spherique, *J. Phys. Radium* **19**, 262 (1958).

Cutrona, L. J., E. N. Leith, C. J. Palermo, and L. J. Porcello, Optical data processing and

Denisyuk, Yu. N., On the reproduction of the optical properties of an object by the wave field of its scattered radiation. *Opt. Spectry. (USSR)(English transl.)* **15**, 279 (1963).

Ditchburn, R. W., *Light*. London, Glasgow: Blackie, 1963.

Duffieux, P. M., *L'intégrale de Fourier et ses applications à l'optique*. Faculté des Sciences de Besançon, 1946.

Duffieux, P. M., La cohérence partielle et les fonctions de transmission, *Revue d'Optique* **32**, 129 (1953).

Dyson, J., An interference microscope, *Proc. Roy. Soc. (London)* **A204**, 170 (1950).

Dyson, J., Common-path interferometer for testing purposes, *J. Opt. Soc. Am.* **47**, No. 5, 386 (1957).

Dyson, J., *Interferometers—Concepts of Classical Optics*, Appendix B. San Francisco and London: Freeman, 1958, p. 377.

Elias, P., D. S. Grey, and D. Z. Robinson, Fourier treatment of optical processes, *J. Opt. Soc. Am.* **42**, 127 (1952).

Engelhard, E., and J. Terrien, Determination of the wavelengths of the radiation from Krypton-86 for nonperturbed atoms, *Revue d'Optique* **39**, No. 1, 11 (1960).

Fabry, C., *Les applications des interférences lumineuses*. Paris: *Revue d'Optique*, (1923).

Fabry, C., and A. Perot, Théorie et applications d'une nouvelle méthode de spectroscopie interférentielle, *Ann. Chim. Phys.* **7**, 16, 115 (1899).

Fellgett, P., Thesis, Cambridge Univ., 1951.

Fellgett, P., *J. Phys.* **19**, 187, 237 (1958).
P. 187: à propos de la théorie du spectromètre interférentiel multiplex. P. 237: spectromètre interférentiel multiplex pour mesures infrarouges sur les étoiles.

Fleury, P., and J. P. Mathieu, *Images optiques—Interférences*. Paris: Eyrolles, 1956.

Forrester, A. T., R. A. Gudmunsen, and P. O. Johnson, Photoelectric mixing of incoherent light, *Phys. Rev.* **99**, 1961 (1955).

Fox, A. G., and T. Li, Resonant modes in a maser interferometer, *Bell System Tech. J.* **40**, 453 (1961).

Françon, M., Interférences, diffraction, polarisation. *Handbuch der Physik*, Vol. XXIV. Berlin: Springer-Verlag, 1956.

Françon, M., *Modern Applications of Physical Optics*. New York: Wiley, 1963.

Fujita, S., H. Yoshinaga, K. Chiba, K. Nakano, S. S. Yoshida, and H. Sugimori, A new computing method for interference spectroscopy. Tokyo meeting on photographic and spectroscopic optics. 1964, 53.

Gabor, D., Microscopy by reconstructed wavefronts, *Proc. Roy. Soc. (London)* **A197**, 454 (1949); *Proc. Roy. Soc. (London)* **B64**, 449 (1951).

Gamo, H., Intensity matrix and degree of coherence, *J. Opt. Soc. Am.* **47**, 976 (1957).

Gamo, H., On the intensity interferometer with coherent background. *Advances in Quantum Electronics*. New York: Columbia University Press, 1961, p. 253.

Gamo, H., Matrix treatment of partial coherence, *Prog. Opt.* **3**, 189 (1964).

Gebbie, H. A., Two beam interferometry and numerical Fourier transformation. *Interferometry*. London: Her Majesty's Stationery Office, 423 (1960).

Gehrcke, E., and O. Lummer, Über die Anwendung der Interferenzen an planparallelen Platten zur Analyse geinster Spektrallinien, *Ann. Physik* **4**, 10, 457 (1903).

Genzel, K., and K. F. Renk, Interference filters and Fabry–Perot interferometer for the far infrared, *Appl. Opt.* **1**, No. 5, 643 (September 1962).

Glauber, R. J., *Optical Coherence and Photon Statistics*. Optique et électronique quantique, Les Houches. New York, London, Paris: Gordon and Breach, 1964, p. 63.

Gould, G., S. Jacobs, P. Rabinowitz, and T. Shultz, Crossed roof prism interferometer. *Appl. Opt.*, **1**, No. 4, 533 (July 1962).

Greenler, R. G., *Optical Filters—Concepts of Classical Optics*: Appendix O. San Francisco and London: Freeman, 1958, p. 580.

Gürs, K., Beats and modulation in optical ruby-masers, *Proc. Third Quantum Electronics Conf.* Paris: Dunod, 1963, p. 1114.

Hall, A. C., A technique for evaluating half-wave and quarter-wave plates, *Appl. Opt.* **2**, 864 (1963).

Hanbury-Brown, R., A stellar interferometer based on the principle of intensity interferometry. *Interferometry*. London: Her Majesty's Stationery Office, 355 (1960).

Hanbury-Brown, R., and R. Q. Twiss, Interferometry of the intensity fluctuations in light. I: Basic theory: the correlation between photons in coherent beams of radiation, *Proc. Roy. Soc. (London)* **A242**, 300 (1957). II: An experimental test of the theory for partially coherent light, **A243**, 291 (1957). III: Applications to astronomy, **248**, 199 (1958).

Hariharan, P., and D. Sen, Double-passed two-beam interferometers, *J. Opt. Soc. Am.* **50**, No. 4, 357–361 (1960).

Hariharan, P., and D. Sen, A simple interferometric arrangement for the measurement of optical frequency response characteristics. *Proc. Phys. Soc. (London)* **75**, 434 (1960).

Hariharan, P., and D. Sen, Fringes of equal inclination in the double-passed Michelson interferometer, *J. Opt. Soc. Am.* **51**, No. 6, 617–619 (June 1961).

Heavens, O. S., *Optical Properties of Thin Solid Films*. London: Butterworths, 1955.

Heavens, O. S., *Optical Masers*. London: Methuen, 1964.

Van Heel, A. C. S., *Interferometry with Savart's Plate—Concepts of Classical Optics*, Appendix D. San Francisco and London: Freeman, 1958, p. 400.

Hellerstein, D., Application of the Senarmont polariscope to analysis of optical maser light, *Appl. Opt.* **2**, 801 (1963).

Hercher, M., Relationship between the near field characteristics of a ruby laser and its optical quality. *Appl. Opt.* **1**, No. 5, 655 (September 1962).

Herriott, D. R., Spherical-mirror oscillating interferometer. *Appl. Opt.* **2**, 865 (1963).

Hopkins, H. H., The concept of partial coherence in optics, *Proc. Roy. Soc. (London)* **A208** 263 (1951).

Hopkins, H. H., The frequency response of a defocused optical system, *Proc. Roy. Soc.* **A231**, 91 (1955).

Hopkins, H. H., Applications of coherence theory in microscopy and interferometry, *J. Opt. Soc. Am.* **47**, 508 (1957).

Hopkins, H. H., Applications of two-beam interference to the study of optical images, *Interferometry*. London: Her Majesty's Stationery Office, 165 (1960).

Hopkins, H. H., The application of frequency response techniques in optics. *Proc. Conf. Optical Instruments and Techniques in Optics*. London: Chapman and Hall, 1961, p. 480.

Horman, M. H., An application of wavefront reconstruction to interferometry, *Appl. Opt.*, **4**, 333 (1965).

Jacobs, S. F., and P. J. Rabinowitz, Optical heterodyning with a CW gaseous laser. *Proc. Third Quantum Electronics Conf.* Paris: Dunod, 1963, p. 481.

Jacquinot, P., New development in interference spectroscopy. *Rept. Progr. Phys.* **23**, 267 (1960).

Jamin, J., Description d'un nouvel appareil de recherches fondé sur les interférences. *Compt. Rend.* **42**, 482 (1856).

Jaseja, T. S., A. Javan, and C. H. Townes, Frequency stability of He–Ne masers and measurements of length, *Phys. Rev. Letters* **10**, No. 5, 165 (1963).

Jenkins, F. A., and H. A. White, *Fundamentals of Optics*. New York: McGraw-Hill, 1957.

Jennison, R. C., *Fourier Transforms and Convolutions for the Experimentalist*. New York: Pergamon Press, 1961.

Jurek, B., La visibilité des franges d'interférences pour les petites différences de marche, *Opt. Acta*, **9**, No. 4, 383 (1962).

Kastler, A., Atomes à l'intérieur d'un interféromètre Perot–Fabry. *Appl. Opt., Suppl. Optical Masers*, 67 (1962).

Kelly, D. H., Spatial frequency, bandwith, and resolution. *Appl. Opt.*, **4**, 435 (1965).

Kislink, P., and D. J. Walsh, The interference between beams from the opposite ends of a ruby optical maser, *Appl. Opt.*, **1**, 45 (1962).

Kösters, W., *Handbuch der Physikaliwhen Optik*. Vol. I. Leipzig: Gehrcke, 1927, p. 484.

Krug, W., J. Rienitz, and G. Schulz, *Contribution to Interference Microscopy*. London: Hilger and Watts, 1964. Translated from *Beiträge zur Interferenzmikroskopie*. Berlin: Akademie-Verlag, 1961.

Kubota, H., Interference color, *Progr. Opt.*, **1**, 213 (1961).

Kubota, H., Measuring instruments for optical transfer function. Tokyo meeting on photographic and spectroscopic optics. 1964, p. 3.

Kubota, H., and T. Ose, On the interference color of chromatic polarization, *J. Appl. Phys.* **24**, 63 (1955).

Ladenburg, R., and D. Bershader, Interferometry in High-Speed Aerodynamics and Jet Propulsion, Vol. IX. *Physical Measurements in Gas Dynamics and Combustion*. London: Oxford University Press, 1955, article A.3.

Leith, E. N., and J. Upatnieks, Reconstructed wavefront and communication theory, *J. Opt. Soc. Am.* **52**, No. 10, 1123 (1962).

Lengyel, B. A., Lasers. *Generation of Light by Stimulated Emission*. New York: Wiley, 1962.

Linfoot, E. H., *Recent Advances in Optics*. Oxford: Clarendon Press, 1955.

Linfoot, E. H., *Optical Image Evaluation*. London: Focal Press, 1960.

Lippmann, G., La photographie de couleurs, *Compt. Rend.* **112**, 274 (1891).

Lipsett, M. S., and L. Mandel, Temporal coherence between superposed light beams from two ruby optical masers, *Proc. Third Quantum Electronics Conf.* Paris: Dunod, 1963, p. 1271.

Lohmann, A., Grating diffraction spectra as coherent light sources for two- or three-beam interferometry, *Opt. Acta*, 9, 1 (1962).

Mach, L., Über einen Interferenzrefraktor, *Z. Instrumentenk.* 12, 89 (1892).

McMurtry, B. J., and A. E. Siegman, Photomixing experiments with a ruby optical maser and a traveling-wave microwave phototube, *Appl. Opt.* 1, 51 (1962).

Magyar, G., and L. Mandel, An interference experiment with two independent beams of ruby maser light. *Proc. Third Quantum Electronics Conf.* Paris: Dunod, 1963, p. 1247.

Magyar, G., and L. Mandel, Interference fringes produced by superposition of two independent maser light beams, *Nature*, Vol. No. 198, No. 4877, 255 (1963).

Mandel, L., Photon degeneracy in light from optical maser and other sources, *J. Opt. Soc. Am.* 51, 787 (1961).

Mandel, L., Concept of cross-spectral purity in coherence theory, *J. Opt. Soc. Am.* 51, 1342 (1961).

Mandel, L., Fluctuations of light beams. *Progr. Opt.* 2, 183 (1963).

Mandel, L., and E. Wolf, Some properties of coherent light, *J. Opt. Soc. Am.* 51, 815, (1961).

Mandel, L., and E. Wolf, Coherence properties of optical fields. *Rev. Mod. Phys.* 37, No. 2, 231 (1965).

Marechal, A., and M. Françon, *Diffraction, structure des images.* Paris: Revue d'Optique, 1960.

Michelson, A. A., Interference phenomena in a new form of refractometer *Phil. Mag.* 5, 13, 236 (1882).

Michelson, A. A., On the application of interference methods to astronomical measurements, *Phil. Mag.* 5, 30, 1 (1890).

Michelson, A. A., Détermination expérimentale de la valeur du mètre en longueurs d'ondes lumineuses, *Trav. mem. Bur. Int. Poids Mes.* 11, 1 (1895).

Michelson, A. A., Measurement of the diameter of *Orionis* with the interferometer, *Astrophys. J.*, 53, 249 (1921).

Miyamoto, K., Propagation of laser light, *J. Opt. Soc. Am.* 54, No. 8, 989 (1964).

Moos, H. W., G. F. Imbusch, L. F. Mollenauer, and A. L. Schawlow, Tilted-plate interferometry with large plate separations, *Appl. Opt.* 2, 817 (1963).

Murty, M. V. R. K., Multiple-pinhole, multiple-beam interferometric observation of flat surfaces, *Appl. Opt.* 1, No. 3, 364 (May 1962). Letters to the editor.

O'Neill, E. L., The modulation function in optics. Tech. Note 110, B.U.P.R.L. (January 1954).

O'Neill, E. L., *Introduction to Statistical Optics.* Reading, Mass.: Addison-Wesley, 1963.

Nelson, D. F., and R. J. Collins, Spatial coherence in the output of an optical maser, *J. Appl. Phys.* 32, No. 4, 739 (1961).

Neugebauer, E. J. Coherence time of a maser, *Appl. Opt., Suppl. Optical Masers.* 90 (1962).

Nisida, M., and H. Saito, A new interferometric method of two-dimensional stress analysis, *Sci. Papers Inst. Phys. Chem. Res. (Tokyo)* 59, No. 1, 5–20 (1965).

Nomarski, G., Microinterférométrie interférentiel à ondes polarisées, *J. Phys. Radium* 16, 9(S) (1955).

Parrent, G. B., Studies in the theory of partial coherence, *Opt. Acta* 6, 285 (1959).

Parrent, G. B., On the propagation of mutual coherence, *J. Opt. Soc. Am.* 49, 787 (1959).

Ramsay, J. V., A rapid-scanning Fabry–Perot interferometer with automatic parallelism control, *Appl. Opt.* 1, No. 4, 411 (July 1962).

Ramsay, J. V., and E. G. V. Mugridge, A distortionless interferometer plate-mount, *Appl. Opt.* 1, No. 4, 538 (July 1962). Letters to the editor.

Rayleigh, Lord, On some physical properties of argon and helium, *Proc. Roy. Soc. (London)* 59, 198 (1896).

Richards, P. L., High-resolution Fourier transform spectroscopy in the far-infrared, *J. Opt. Soc. Am.* **54**, 1474 (1964).

Rundle, H. N., Construction of a Michelson interferometer for Fourier spectroscopy, *J. Res. Nat. Bur. Stand.* **69 C**, No. 1, 5 (1965).

Sirks, J. A., *Hd. Ned. Nat. en Geneesk. Congr. Groningen*, 1893, p. 92.

Skinner, T. J., Incoherent source with an arbitrarily narrow power spectrum, *J. Opt. Soc. Am.* **51**, 909 (1961).

Smith, E. H., *Modern Methods of Microscopy*. London: Butterworths, 1956, p. 76.

Steel, W. H., Scalar diffraction in terms of coherence, *Proc. Roy. Soc. (London)* **A249**, 574 (1959).

Steel, W. H., The compensation of a Williams interferometer, *Opt. Acta* **10**, No. 3, 205 (July 1963).

Steel, W. H., Interferometers without collimation for Fourier spectroscopy. *J. Opt. Soc. Am.* **54**, No. 2. 151–156 (February 1964).

Steel, W. H., A polarization interferometer for the measurement of transfer functions, *Opt. Acta.* **11**, No. 1, 1 (1964).

Stoicheff, B. P., and A. Szabo, Interference rings in ruby maser beams, *Appl. Opt.* **2**, 811 (1963).

Stone, J. M., *Radiation and Optics*. New York: McGraw-Hill, 1963.

Stroke, G. W., An introduction to optics of coherent and noncoherent electromagnetic radiations, University of Michigan. Ann Arbor, 1965.

Stroke, G. W., and D. G. Falconer, Attainment of high resolutions in wavefront-reconstruction imaging, *Physics Letters* **13**, 306 (1964).

Stroke, G. W., and A. E. Labeyrie, Two-beam interferometry by successive recording of intensities in a single hologram. *Appl. Phys. Letters*, **8**, No. 2, 42 (1963).

Strong, J., *Concepts of Classical Optics*. San Francisco and London: Freeman, 1958, Ch. VIII, p. 173 and Ch. XI, p. 235.

Strong, J., and G. A. Vanasse, *Applications of Fourier Transformation in Optics: Interferometric Spectroscopy. Concepts of Classical Optics. Appendix.* San Francisco and London: Freeman, 1958, p. 419.

Thompson, B. J., and E. Wolf, Two-beam interference with partially coherent light, *J. Opt. Soc. Am.* **47**, 895 (1957).

Thompson, B. J., Illustration of the phase change in two-beam interference with partially coherent light, *J. Opt. Soc. Am.* **48**, 95 (1958).

Tinaut, D., Influence de la dispersion sur les phénomènes d'interférence, *Compt. Rend.* **258**, 6110–6111 (June 22, 1964), Section 5.

Tolansky, S., *Multiple-beam Interferometry of Surfaces and Films.* Oxford: Clarendon Press, 1948.

Tolansky, S., *An Introduction to Interferometry.* London: Longmans, Green, 1955.

Tolansky, S., Multiple-beam interferometry applied to oscillating systems. *Appl. Opt.* **4**, 727 (1965).

Toraldo di Francia, G., *Electromagnetic Waves.* London: Interscience, 1949.

Tsujiuchi, J., Corrections of optical images by compensation of aberrations and by spatial frequency filtering. *Progr. Opt.* **2**, 133 (1963).

Tsuruta, T., Measurement of transfer functions of photographic objectives by means of a polarizing shearing interferometer, *J. Opt. Soc. Am.* **53**, No. 10, 1156 (1963).

Tsuruta, T., A polarizing shearing interferometer for evaluating photographic optics. Tokyo meeting on photographic and spectroscopic optics, 1964, p. 31.

Twyman, F., *Prism and Lens Making.* London: Hilger and Watts, 1952.

Twyman, F., and A. Green, British Patent No. 103832, 1916.

De Vany, A. S., On using a Williams interferometer for making a divider plate, *Appl. Opt.* **4**, 365 (1965).

Vasicek, A., *Optics of Thin Films*. Amsterdam: North-Holland, 1960.

Wiener, O., Stehende Lichtwellen und die Schwingungsrichtung polarisirten Lichtes, *Ann. Physik* **40**, 203 (1890).

Williams, W. E., *Applications of Interferometry—Concepts of Classical Optics*. Appendix A. San Francisco and London: Freeman, 1958, 373.

Wolf, E., A macroscopic theory of interference and diffraction of light from finite sources, *Proc. Roy. Soc. (London)* **A225**, 96 (1954).

Wolf, E., Correlation between photons in partially polarized light beams, *Proc. Phys. Soc. (London)* **76**, 424 (1960).

Wolf, E., Basic concepts of optical coherence theory. Symposium on optical masers, Brooklyn Polytechnic Institute, 1963, p. 30.

Zehnder, L., Ein neuer Interferenzrefraktor, *Z. Instrumentenk.* **11**, 275 (1891).

Zernike, F., The concept of degree of coherence and its application to optical problems, *Physica* **5**, 785 (1938).

Zernike, F., Degré de coherence et méthode du fond cohérent, *Revue d'Optique* **27**, 713 (1948).

Subject Index

305